The
Rose
Annual
1967

THE ROYAL NATIONAL
ROSE SOCIETY

Hon. Editor

LEONARD HOLLIS

The Editorial Board (1967)

MAJ.-GEN. R.F.B.NAYLOR, C.B., C.B.E.

J.CLARKE

GORDON EDWARDS, C.B.E.

F.FAIRBROTHER, M.SC., F.R.I.C.

BERTRAM PARK, O.B.E., V.M.H., MÉRITE AGRI.

W.C.THORN

© Leonard Hollis 1967

THE ROYAL NATIONAL ROSE SOCIETY

Bone Hill, Chiswell Green Lane,
St. Albans, Hertfordshire

Telephone: St. Albans 50461   *Telegrams:* Natiorose, St. Albans

H M QUEEN ELIZABETH THE QUEEN MOTHER in the Society's Gardens at Bone Hill, St Albans, on 12 July 1966

Contents

3

4   CONTENTS

THE ROYAL NATIONAL ROSE SOCIETY

(founded 7th December, 1876)

PATRON
Her Majesty Queen Elizabeth The Queen Mother

VICE-PATRONS
The Duke and Duchess of Devonshire
The Marquess and Marchioness of Salisbury
The Earl and Countess of Derby

COUNCIL

PRESIDENT Maj.-Gen. R. F. B. Naylor, C.B., C.B.E., D.S.O., M.C.

DEPUTY PRESIDENT
J. Clarke

HON. TREASURER
Frank M. Bowen

PAST PRESIDENTS

E. J. Baldwin, O.B.E.
F. Fairbrother, M.SC., F.R.I.C.
D. L. Flexman
F. A. Gibson

E. Royalton Kisch, M.C.
Maj.-Gen. R. F. B. Naylor, C.B.,
C.B.E., D.S.O., M.C.
Herbert Oppenheimer

VICE-PRESIDENTS

Miss A. M. Aldous
E. F. Allen
L. A. Anstiss
Frank M. Bowen
H. G. Clacy
S. M. Gault, M.B.E., V.M.H.
C. W. Gregory
Leonard Hollis

E. B. Le Grice
J. W. Mattock
R. L. Pallett
Bertram Park, O.B.E., V.M.H.
W. J. W. Sanday
B. W. W. Sampson
W. C. Thorn
H. Wheatcroft

ELECTED MEMBERS

R. C. Balfour, M.B.E.
W. K. Bentley
Mrs H. G. Clacy
Dr T. M. Cullingworth
Gordon Edwards, C.B.E.
E. V. Elwes, F.R.I.C.
K. E. Fisk
Miss J. E. Fulford

A. N. Harding
Mrs E. Harkness
J. L. Harkness
W. A. James
C. Pawsey
Brig. C. E. Lucas Phillips,
O.B.E., M.C.
Sir Harry Pilkington
H. N. Raban

C. F. Roberts
J. Roscoe
K. W. Seaman
G. S. Thomas
W. E. Tysterman
Mrs C. Wheatcroft
H. Williamson
F. C. H. Witchell

REGIONAL REPRESENTATIVES

J. Clarke (*Wilmslow, Ches.*)
A. M. Cocker, S.M.H. (*Aberdeen*)
Dr A. Dick (*Glasgow*)
A. P. C. Dickson (*Newtownards*)
C. J. Dillon (*Newcastle-on-Tyne*)
J. W. Mattock (*Oxford*)

S. McGredy (*Portadown*)
E. B. Le Grice (*N. Walsham*)
W. J. W. Sanday (*Bristol*)
J. H. Shotter (*Stroud, Glos.*)
E. Shreeves (*Swanland, Yorks*)
H. Wheatcroft (*Nottingham*)

HON. SCIENTIFIC ADVISER
E. F. Allen, M.A., Dip. Agric. (*Cantab.*), A.I.C.T.A.

HON. VICE-PRESIDENTS

E. M. Allen, C.M.G.
Mrs M. G. N. Blyth
Alex. Dickson
J. E. Rayer

H. Robinson, M.B.E.
A. R. Treseder
Dr J. H. Wilding

BANKERS
Coutts & Co.

HON. EDITOR
Leonard Hollis

AUDITORS
Evers & Co., Chartered Accountants

SECRETARY
L. G. Turner

6

COMMITTEES FOR 1967

FINANCE AND GENERAL PURPOSES COMMITTEE
J. Clarke (CHAIRMAN) *ex-officio*

E. F. Allen
L. A. Anstiss
H. G. Clacy

C. W. Gregory
J. W. Mattock
R. L. Pallett
Bertram Park

B. W. W. Sampson
W. C. Thorn
H. Wheatcroft

The President, Deputy President, Hon. Treasurer, Past Presidents, Hon. Editor, The Chairman of the New Seedling Judging Committee, and of the Exhibitions Committee are ex-officio members of this Committee.

NEW SEEDLING JUDGING COMMITTEE
Maj.-Gen. R. F. B. Naylor (CHAIRMAN) *ex-officio*

E. F. Allen
L. A. Anstiss
W. K. Bentley
F. M. Bowen
J. Clarke (*ex-officio*)
A. M. Cocker

A. P. C. Dickson
F. Fairbrother
S. M. Gault
F. A. Gibson
C. W. Gregory
J. L. Harkness
E. B. Le Grice

J. W. Mattock
S. McGredy
C. F. Roberts
B. W. W. Sampson
W. E. Tysterman
H. Wheatcroft

EXHIBITIONS COMMITTEE
S. M. Gault (CHAIRMAN)

Miss A. M. Aldous
R. C. Balfour
F. M. Bowen (*ex-officio*)
Mrs H. G. Clacy
H. G. Clacy

J. Clarke (*ex-officio*)
Maj.-Gen. R. F. B. Naylor
(*ex-officio*)
Bertram Park
C. Pawsey

C. F. Roberts
W. C. Thorn
Mrs C. Wheatcroft

TRIAL GROUND MANAGEMENT COMMITTEE
J. L. Harkness (CHAIRMAN)

F. M. Bowen (*ex-officio*)
H. G. Clacy (*ex-officio*)
J. Clarke (*ex-officio*)

S. M. Gault
J. W. Mattock
Maj.-Gen. R. F. B. Naylor
(*ex-officio*)

Bertram Park
W. E. Tysterman

EDITORIAL BOARD
Leonard Hollis (CHAIRMAN)

J. Clarke (*ex-officio*
Gordon Edwards

F. Fairbrother
Maj.-Gen. R. F. B. Naylor
(*ex-officio*)

Bertram Park
W. C. Thorn

7

PRESIDENTS OF THE
ROYAL NATIONAL ROSE SOCIETY

1877–1904 The Very Rev. DEAN HOLE, v.m.h.

1905–06 CHARLES E. SHEA	1939–40 JOHN N. HART, c.b.e.
1907–08 E. B. LINDSELL	1941–42 CHARLES H. RIGG
1909–10 Rev. F. PAGE-ROBERTS	1943–44 HERBERT OPPENHEIMER
1911–12 Rev. J. H. PEMBERTON	1945–46 A. NORMAN ROGERS
1913–14 CHARLES E. SHEA	1947–48 A. E. GRIFFITH
1915–16 EDWARD MAWLEY, v.m.h.	1949–50 E. J. BALDWIN, o.b.e.
1917–18 Sir EDWARD HOLLAND	1951–52 D. L. FLEXMAN
1919–20 H. R. DARLINGTON, v.m.h.	1953–54 WILLIAM E. MOORE
1921–22 Sir EDWARD HOLLAND	1955–56 OLIVER MEE, o.b.e.
1923–24 SYDNEY F. JACKSON	1957–58 A. NORMAN
1925–26 C. C. WILLIAMSON	1959–60 F. FAIRBROTHER, m.sc., f.r.i.c.
1927–28 H. R. DARLINGTON, v.m.h.	1961–62 E. ROYALTON KISCH, m.c.
1929–30 ARTHUR JOHNSON	1963–64 Maj.-Gen. R. F. B. NAYLOR, c.b.,
1931–32 HERBERT OPPENHEIMER	c.b.e., d.s.o., m.c.
1933–34 Dr. A. H. WILLIAMS	1965–66 F. A. GIBSON
1935–36 Major A. D. G. SHELLEY, r.e.	1967 Maj.-Gen. R. F. B. NAYLOR, c.b.,
1937–38 HERBERT OPPENHEIMER	c.b.e., d.s.o., m.c.

THE QUEEN MARY COMMEMORATION
MEDAL AWARDS

1957 ALEX. DICKSON & SONS	1957 OLIVER MEE, o.b.e.
1957 SAMUEL McGREDY & SON	1957 A. NORMAN
1957 E. B. Le GRICE	1964 BERTRAM PARK, o.b.e., v.m.h.
1957 HERBERT ROBINSON, m.b.e.	

THE DEAN HOLE MEDAL AWARDS

1904 The Very Rev. DEAN HOLE, v.m.h.	1946 A. NORMAN ROGERS
1906 CHARLES E. SHEA	1948 A. E. GRIFFITH
1908 E. B. LINDSELL	1948 WILLIAM E. MOORE
1910 Rev. F. PAGE-ROBERTS	1948 Dr. G. E. DEACON
1912 Rev. J. H. PEMBERTON	1950 E. J. BALDWIN, o.b.e.
1912 GEORGE DICKSON, v.m.h.	1950 JOHN RAMSBOTTOM, o.b.e.,
1916 EDWARD MAWLEY, v.m.h.	m.a., dr.sc.
1918 Sir EDWARD HOLLAND	1951 F. S. HARVEY-CANT, m.b.e.
1919 GEORGE PAUL	1952 BERTRAM PARK, o.b.e., v.m.h.,
1920 H. R. DARLINGTON, v.m.h.	Mérite Agri.
1921 SAMUEL McGREDY	1952 D. L. FLEXMAN
1923 Miss E. WILLMOTT, f.l.s.	1952 Dr. A. S. THOMAS, o.b.e.
1924 SYDNEY F. JACKSON	1954 W. E. HARKNESS
1925 COURTNEY PAGE	1956 OLIVER MEE, o.b.e.
1926 C. C. WILLIAMSON	1958 A. NORMAN
1930 ARTHUR JOHNSON	1959 W. J. W. SANDAY
1930 Dr. J. CAMPBELL HALL	1960 F. FAIRBROTHER, m.sc., f.r.i.c.
1930 WILLIAM E. NICKERSON	1962 H. G. CLACY
1932 HERBERT OPPENHEIMER	1963 E. ROYALTON KISCH, m.c.
1934 Dr. A. H. WILLIAMS	1964 G. D. BURCH
1935 WALTER EASLEA	1965 Maj.-Gen. R. F. B. NAYLOR, c.b.
1936 Major A. D. G. SHELLEY, r.e.	c.b.e., d.s.o., m.c.
1936 ALISTER CLARK	1965 H. EDLAND
1940 JOHN N. HART, c.b.e.	1965 E. BAINES
1942 CHARLES H. RIGG	1966 F. A. GIBSON
1942 Dr. HORACE J. McFARLAND	1966 EDGAR M. ALLEN, c.m.g.
1945 Dr. H. V. TAYLOR, c.b.e.	

Arrangements 1967

Amateur Spring Competition 2 and 3 May

The Amateur Spring Competition for roses under glass is to be held in conjunction with the Flower Show at the Royal Horticultural Society's Halls, Westminster. By courtesy of the Royal Horticultural Society, members will be admitted to both Halls on presentation of their Membership Certificates. Payment for accompanying visitors may be made at the turnstiles.

Summer Show 30 June and 1 July

The Summer Show is to be held at the Alexandra Palace, London, N22 and will occupy the Great Hall and Palm Court for both days.

Northern Show 18 and 19 July

The Northern Show is to be held in conjunction with the Roundhay (Leeds) Horticultural Society at Roundhay Park, Leeds. Members will be admitted on presentation of their Certificate of Membership. Holders of the Guinea certificate may be accompanied by one other person. Extra tickets will be available at the turnstile.

Autumn Show 5 and 6 September

The Autumn Show is to be held in the Royal Horticultural Society's Halls, Westminster, and will occupy both New and Old Halls for the two days.

Schedules for these Shows are available on request to The Secretary, The Royal National Rose Society, Chiswell Green Lane, St Albans.

Admission Tickets

To conform with the Postal Regulations, the Membership Certificate and the separate admission tickets are again worded as "invitations" to the Shows. Each member is asked to sign the Membership Certificate where indicated.

One-Guinea Subscribers will receive a Certificate of Membership, which will admit the holder to all the Shows listed thereon, five transferable tickets for the Summer Show and three transferable tickets for the Autumn Show. *Half-Guinea Subscribers* will receive a Certificate of Membership, which will admit the holder to all the Shows listed thereon, one transferable ticket for the Summer Show and one transferable ticket for the Autumn Show.

Members may also purchase additional tickets for the Summer and Autumn Shows at half price. Applications accompanied by remittances must be received at the Society's Office not less than three days before the respective show.

No price reductions for adults are granted at the Northern Show, but children under thirteen years of age will be admitted at half price.

Prices of admission to the public will be:

Summer Show 30 June Noon to 5 p.m. 10*s.*, 5 p.m. to 8 p.m. 5*s.*
    1 July 10 a.m. to 5 p.m. 5*s.*
Autumn Show 5 September 11 a.m. to 7 p.m. 5*s.*
    6 September 10 a.m. to 5 p.m. 2*s.* 6*d.*
Northern Show 18 July 11 a.m. to 3 p.m. 10*s.*, 3 p.m. to 6 p.m. 6*s.* After 6 p.m. 4*s.*
    19 July 10 a.m. to 5 p.m. 2*s.* 6*d.*

R.N.R.S. Classes at Provincial Shows and Admission Arrangements

By the courtesy of the organisers of the following Shows, members of the Royal National Rose Society are offered special concessions in respect of exhibiting and free admission which the Council acknowledges with thanks. Unless indicated by an asterisk both concessions will apply. Details of the Shows offering free admission to R.N.R.S. members are given on the Membership Certificate:

Alderley Edge and Wilmslow Horticultural and Rose Society's Show on 8 July.
Ashington Rose Society's Show on 8 July.
Berwick-on-Tweed and District Rose Society's Show on 16 July.
Bramhall, Cheadle Hulme and Woodford Agricultural and Horticultural Society's Show on 19 August.
Bristol and District Group of R.N.R.S. Members Show on 5 July.
Caledonian (Royal) Horticultural Society's Show at the Waverley Market, Edinburgh on 13, 14 and 15 September. (Noon to 10 p.m., 10 a.m. to 10 p.m. and 10 a.m. to 6 p.m.) J. Turnbull, 44 Melville Street, Edinburgh 3. (No free admission to Show, but R.N.R.S. Classes exempt from entry fee.)
Canterbury Gardeners' Society's Summer Show on 18 and 19 August.
Cardiff and District Group of R.N.R.S. Members Show on 8 July.
Clontarf Horticultural Society's Show on 1 July.
Colchester Rose and Horticultural Society's Show on 8 July.
Congleton and District Horticultural Society's Show on 8 July.
Eastleigh and District Rose, Carnation and Sweet Pea Society's Show on 8 July.
Formby Horticultural and Agricultural Society's Show on 8 July.
Franche (Kidderminster) and District Rose Society's Show on 24 June.
Glamorgan (Vale of) Agricultural Society's Show on 16 August.
Hereford and West of England Rose Society's Show on 14 and 15 July.
Hitchin Horticultural Society's Show on 24 June. (No R.N.R.S Classes.)
Ipswich and East of England Horticultural Society's Show on 15 July.
Isle of Wight Rose, Carnation and Sweet Pea Association's Show on 24 June.
Lakeland Rose Show on 7 and 8 July.
Manx Rose Society's Show on 8 and 9 July.

North of England Rose, Carnation and Sweet Pea Society's Show on 18 and 19 August.

Nottingham Rose Society's Show on 8 and 9 July.

Reading Horticultural Federation's Show on 18 and 19 August.

Scottish National Sweet Pea, Rose and Carnation Society's Show on 2 and 3 August.

Southampton (Royal) Horticultural Society's Show on 14 and 15 July.

*Southport Flower Show at Victoria Park, Southport on 23, 24 and 25 August. (10 a.m. to 9 p.m., 9 a.m. to 9 p.m. and 9 a.m. to 5.30 p.m.) G. W. Nicholls, Flower Show Department, Lord Street, Southport, Lancs. (R.N.R.S. Classes but *not* free admission.)

West Cumberland Rose Society's Show on 15 July.

Please note that the Certificate of Membership does not admit to the Southport Flower Show or the Royal Caledonian Horticultural Society's Show nor any other Show not listed.

Display Gardens

Members and their friends are cordially invited to visit the displays of rose varieties that have received awards provided at Roath Park, Cardiff, the Northern Horticultural Society's Gardens at Harlow Car, Harrogate and at Saughton Park, Edinburgh.

At Harlow Car the rose displays occupy a small portion of the ground and it is hoped that visitors will each be willing to contribute a small donation of two shillings towards upkeep.

Library, Film, Film Strip, Lantern Slides

Full particulars will gladly be sent on application. Owing to the heavy demand it is regretted that it is not possible to loan lecturing equipment for private viewing.

Identification of Rose Blooms

Members seeking to identify varieties, the names of which are unknown to them, are asked to write to the expert nearest their locality, see undermentioned list. If possible, more than one bloom of each variety should be sent—the ideal number is three, showing the different stages of development: the bud, the half-open bloom and the three-quarters-open bloom. Some wood and foliage, together with a brief description of the habit and approximate age of the variety, would also help. If the blooms are placed in water for at least six hours before despatch, they are less likely to drop during transit.

A stamped addressed envelope for reply must be enclosed with the blooms.

W. K. BENTLEY, Walter Bentley & Sons, Rose Nurseries, Loughborough Road, Wanlip, Leics.

A. M. COCKER, James Cocker & Sons, Whitemyres, Lang Stracht, Aberdeen.

C. J. DILLON, Springfield, Woolsington, Newcastle-on-Tyne 3.

M. H. J. DREW, Henry Drew, Rose Grower, Longworth, Abingdon, Berks.

J. L. HARKNESS, R. Harkness & Co. Ltd, The Rose Gardens, Hitchin, Herts.

E. B. LE GRICE, E. B. Le Grice (Roses) Ltd, Roseland Nurseries, North Walsham, Norfolk.

C. PAWSEY, B. R. Cant & Sons Ltd, The Old Rose Gardens, Colchester, Essex.

R. V. ROGER, The Nurseries, Pickering, N. Yorks.

W. J. W. SANDAY, John Sanday (Roses) Ltd, Almondsbury, Bristol.

I. TRESEDER, Stephen Treseder & Son Ltd, Ely Nurseries, Ely, Cardiff.

Extra Copies of Publications

Members may purchase copies post free of *The Rose Annual* for 1967, price 8s. 6d.; the handbooks *Roses: A Selected List of Varieties*, price 5s., and *Roses: The Cultivation of the Rose*, price 5s., on application to the Secretary.

Society Tie

The Society tie, made in good quality terylene and bearing a single motif of the Tudor rose on a plain background, is available at 15s. 6d. each, three for 45s. Choice of maroon, navy blue, rifle green or medium grey background.

Badges

A membership Badge is available. Price 5s. each for Stud or Brooch fitting.

The American Rose Society

An arrangement has been made whereby members resident in Great Britain may join the American Rose Society by remitting their subscriptions of £3 2s. 6d. to The Secretary, The Royal National Rose Society, Chiswell Green Lane, St Albans, Herts.

Subscriptions and Resignations

Members are reminded that subscriptions are due and payable on 1 January each year. Any member wishing to resign must give notice to the Secretary on or before 1 February, after which date the member will be liable for the subscription for the current year.

The Society's Gardens

The Society's Gardens at Bone Hill, St Albans are under the control of the Council and its policy is to provide a rose garden where roses of all types may be seen.

Trials of new varieties are held annually and Gold Medal, Certificate of Merit and Trial Ground Certificate awards are made to those varieties reaching the required standard. In addition the President's Trophy is awarded to the best variety and the Henry Edland Memorial Medal to the most fragrant variety on trial.

How to Get to The Gardens

The Gardens are situated approximately four miles from St Albans Station and are off the main Watford Road (A412). Visitors using public transport may travel by the following routes:

British Railways to St Albans City Station—London terminus St Pancras

or

Underground (Bakerloo Line) to Watford, and then by No. 321 bus which runs between Watford Junction and St Peter's Street, St Albans.

Green Line coach No. 712 Luton—London (Victoria)—Dorking. No. 724 Romford—St Albans—High Wycombe.

The fare stage at which to alight from both bus and coach is "The Three Hammers" Inn, Chiswell Green, and the gardens are half a mile along Chiswell Green Lane which is adjacent to the inn.

Visiting Arrangements for 1967

The Gardens will be open from Saturday, 17 June to Saturday, 30 September, at the following times:

Monday to Friday	9 a.m. to 5 p.m.
Saturday	9 a.m. to 6 p.m.
Sunday	2 p.m. to 6 p.m.

The Gardens will be closed on Monday, 28 August. Members wishing to see the Gardens before the above date may do so from Monday to Friday only.

Terms of Admission

(Membership Certificates to be shown at turnstiles)

One-Guinea Membership Certificate will admit the holder and two guests free of charge and three additional persons on payment.

Half-Guinea Membership Certificate will admit the holder free of charge and five additional persons on payment.

Affiliated Society Certificate will admit two persons free of charge and four additional persons on payment.

Affiliated Societies may arrange for a party to visit the Gardens each year. Applications must be made in writing to the Secretary at least fourteen days beforehand, stating the number in the party and the proposed date and time of the visit. Holders of Certificates and accompanying guests as specified above will be admitted free of charge. Members of the party not covered by such certificates will be admitted on payment.

Price of admission to persons accompanied by a member or in the party of an affiliated society, but not covered by certificate, is 2*s*. each. Children under 15 years 1*s*.

The Gardens are not open to the public.

Refreshments

There is no restaurant within the Gardens. A Visitors Lounge is provided where cups of tea and biscuits may be obtained from 1 p.m. on Saturdays and on Sundays. Soft drinks are available at all times. Picnics are not allowed in any part of the Gardens.

Car Park

A car park is provided but the Council accepts no responsibility for loss or damage to property or vehicles.

It is regretted that coaches cannot be accommodated in the car park or Grounds.

Disabled or Invalid Members

A wheel chair (not self-propelled) is now available at the Gardens for the convenience of disabled members. This should be booked in advance of an intended visit.

Photography

Amateur photographers may use cameras in the Gardens but photographs or transparencies must not be used commercially. Professional photographers must obtain written authority from the Secretary.

General Regulations

Dogs must be kept on a leash at all times. Entry and exit shall be through the respective turnstiles.

Rose blooms, buds, trees or parts of trees must not in any circumstances be cut, removed or taken from the Grounds.

'FRED LOADS' (shrub)
'Dorothy Wheatcroft' × *'Orange Sensation'*
Raised by R. Holmes
CERTIFICATE OF MERIT 1966 & TORRIDGE SILVER SALVER
See page 181

'REDGOLD' (floribunda—H.T. type)
('*Karl Herbst*' × '*Masquerade*') × ('*Faust*' × '*Piccadilly*')
Raised by Alex. Dickson & Sons Ltd, N. Ireland
CERTIFICATE OF MERIT 1966
See page 181

Report of the Council

For the year ended 31st December 1966

In submitting this report the Council is pleased to record appreciation of the honour bestowed upon the Society by Her Majesty Queen Elizabeth, the Queen Mother on two occasions during the year. Her Majesty graciously attended the Summer Show at Alexandra Palace in June and made a private visit to the headquarters at St Albans a few days later. It was our Patron's first visit to Bone Hill and a memorable one for all who were privileged to be present.

Membership

During the year 15,150 new members were enrolled; this figure is lower than the record of 1965 but is nevertheless most encouraging. The total membership is now approximately 109,500 and the Council thanks all who have helped to recruit new members during the year. Members of the trade who so willingly allow the Society to include membership leaflets in their catalogues account for a high percentage. In addition, particular appreciation is recorded to the band of lecturers who often travel many miles during the winter months to speak at meetings.

The increases in postal charges have added considerably to what was already a heavy item of expenditure. Members are earnestly asked to help in reducing it by paying subscriptions when due, thus obviating the sending out of reminders.

Finance

It will be seen from the Accounts that the Society's financial position is sound, but with increases in the cost of publications, of shows and many other items there is no room for complacency. With this in mind an appeal is made to all members able to do so to pay the higher subscription of £1 1s. 0d.

Changes in Investments during the year include redemption of £500— 5% Defence Bonds 1965; £1,500—4½% Defence Bonds 1967; £2,000—3% Savings Bonds 1960/70; £3,486 1s. 6d.—2½% Savings Bonds 1964/7; 27— New England Electric System Common Shares. The proceeds from these together with £8,000 from income accrued over the past two years were reinvested in £10,500—7¾% Wokingham Borough Mortgage 1968 and £5,063 Charifund (Equities Investment Fund).

Publications

The many appreciative comments which have been received show that the high standard of previous editions of *The Rose Annual* was well maintained in 1966.

During the year much work has been done by the Hon. Editor and Editorial Board in revising the handbook *Roses—A Selected List of Varieties.* Copies will be available to members in April next.

The Trial Ground and Display Gardens

The Society's Trial Ground is recognised internationally as the leading trial ground for roses. Once again over two hundred varieties were received from all parts of the world. Unfortunately, of those eligible for awards no variety was considered by the judges to be worthy of a Gold Medal.

Development of the Display Gardens has been curtailed as it is intended that the area being used at present for trials should be incorporated. The trials are to be transferred to the recently acquired adjoining land. This will allow much of the eastern side to be replanned.

Many members and their friends visited the gardens and it is hoped that next season, with the extended hours of opening over the weekend, even more will be encouraged to do so.

Provincial Display Gardens

The popularity of the Provincial Display Gardens at Harlow Car, Harrogate, Roath Park, Cardiff and that opened recently at Saughton Park, Edinburgh for varieties that have received Trial Ground Awards, has encouraged the Council to consider the extension of the scheme. Arrangements have been initiated at Vivary Park, Taunton and negotiations are proceeding for similar displays in the Midlands and North-West of the country.

The Council is grateful to the authorities concerned for their co-operation in ensuring the success of these displays.

Shows

The Summer Show held at Alexandra Palace on 29 and 30 June was of the high standard that has become associated with it over the years. The Northern Show at Leeds on 19 and 20 July in conjunction with the Roundhay (Leeds) Horticultural Society was well supported by trade and amateur exhibitors. There has been a great improvement over the years in the quality of the exhibits staged by amateurs at this show and they compare favourably with those at any other major show. The finest show of the season was undoubtedly the Autumn Show on 9 and 10 September, at the Royal Horticultural Society's Halls, Westminster. The New Hall was completely filled with trade exhibits of an exceptionally high standard while the Old Hall accommodated the amateurs who staged with their usual care and attention to detail. Many visitors appreciated the new arrangement whereby the Amateur Section remained open on the second day.

The Spring Competition for roses under glass, held at the Royal Horticultural Society's Hall on 3 and 4 May, was supported by the usual group of exhibitors. It is hoped that more members will exhibit in this competition in future.

Bureaux, Library and Lecturing Material

Bureaux were again established at the shows of the Society and at Chelsea, Southport, Bristol and Cardiff. The bureaux serve a very useful purpose in maintaining contact with existing members in addition to recruiting new members. The Council is grateful to those who assist the staff by giving advice on rose cultivation, and imparting information about the Society.

The demands for library books and lecture materials were again heavy and in view of the increased postal charges it would be appreciated if borrowers bore the cost of carriage in both directions.

Dean Hole Memorial Medal

The Dean Hole Memorial Medal was awarded to Mr Edgar M. Allen, C.M.G., for his outstanding work in the service of the rose.

Henry Edland Memorial Medal

The Council is pleased to announce that the Henry Edland Memorial Medal has been instituted in memory of the late Secretary. The medal will be awarded annually to the most fragrant rose on trial irrespective of country of origin.

Conclusion

In conclusion the Council again expresses its thanks to all members of the Standing and Special Committees and sub-Committees, the Hon. Editor, the Secretary and the staff at Bone Hill for their work during the year.

By order of the Council,

31 December 1966   F. A. GIBSON, *President*

BALANCE SHEET, 30th SEPTEMBER, 1966

1965 £		£	£
	SURPLUS		
	Balance 1st October, 1965	66,974	
	Add Excess of Revenue over Expenditure for the year 30th September, 1966	3,847	
	Proceeds of Sale of 27 New England Electric System Common Shares (presented to the Society and not previously valued)	249	
		71,070	
66,974	*Less* Loss on Realisation of Investments ..	452	70,618
	SPECIAL FUNDS		
	P. P. Gaskill Prize Fund	100	
	L. Hewlett Prize Fund	100	
	A. E. Griffith Memorial Fund	100	
400	Gilbert Burch Memorial Fund	100	400
	RESERVE FOR DEVELOPMENT—TRIAL GROUND, DISPLAY GARDEN AND PROPERTIES		
	Balance 1st October, 1965	15,000	
15,000	*Add* Charge against Revenue Account ..	1,000	16,000
	RESERVE FOR NEW EDITIONS OF PUBLICATIONS, FILM AND CONFERENCE		
	Balance 1st October, 1965	6,135	
6,135	*Add* Charge against Revenue Account ..	6,865	13,000
	RESERVE FOR PENSIONS		
12,000	Balance 1st October, 1965		12,000
	CURRENT LIABILITIES		
	Sundry Creditors	4,987	
25,424	Subscriptions received in advance and one quarter of 1966 subscriptions (excluding Life Members)	21,510	26,497
125,933			138,515

AUDITORS' REPORT

To the Members,
The Royal National Rose Society.

We have audited the above Balance Sheet dated 30th September, 1966 and Revenue Account for the year ended on that date and have obtained all the information and explanations we have required. In our opinion such Balance Sheet and Revenue Account are properly drawn up so as to exhibit a true and correct view of the state of the Society's affairs according to the best of our information and explanations given us and as shewn by the books of the Society. We have verified the Securities representing the Investments of your Society at 30th September, 1966 and have found the same to be in order.

EVERS & CO., *Chartered Accountants, Auditors*
2, NORFOLK STREET, LONDON, W.C.2. 9th November, 1966

1965 £		£	£
	FIXED ASSETS		
30,950	Freehold Properties		37,000
	Alterations to Bone Hill:		
	Balance 1st October, 1965	4,000	
	Add Expenditure during year	1,153	
		5,153	
4,000	*Less* Amount written off	2,653	2,500
	Office Equipment, etc.:		
	Balance 1st October, 1965	2,200	
	Additions during year	716	
		2,916	
2,200	*Less* Amount written off	516	2,400
	Motor Van, Mower and Equipment:		
	Balance 1st October, 1965	400	
	Additions during year	618	
		1,018	
400	*Less* Amount written off	218	800
125	Library as valued by the Secretary		125
37,675			42,825
	INVESTMENTS AT COST		
	£4,000 6⅝% Winsford U.D.C. Deposit October 1966	4,000	
	£5,000 6⅝% Chelmsford Mortgage 1968 ..	5,000	
	£10,500 7¾% Wokingham Mortgage 1968	10,500	
	£5,000 6½% St. Albans Reg. Mortgage 1969	5,000	
	£5,000 5⅝% Norwich Mortgage 1970 ..	5,000	
	£10,000 5⅝% Tadcaster U.D.C. Mort. 1970	10,000	
	£1,500 3¼% Mersey Docks & Harbour Board Debenture Stock 1970/80	1,084	
	£5,000 6% Conversion Stock 1972 ..	4,988	
	£125 7¼% Imperial Chemical Industries Ltd. Unsecured Loan Stock 1986/91	123	
	29,660 Shares Charities Official Invest. Fund	28,979	
67,578	3,779 Shares Equities Investment Fund for Charities	5,063	79,737
(65,871)	(Market value 30th September, 1966 £75,290)		
	CURRENT ASSETS		
	Stock of Publications, Badges, etc. as valued by the Secretary	2,101	
	Loan to Member of Staff	188	
	Sundry Debtors for Advertisements, etc. ..	1,030	
	Cash at Bankers on Deposit and Current Account and in Hand	10,976	
20,680	Income Tax Recoverable	1,658	15,953
125,933			138,515

REVENUE ACCOUNT FOR THE YEAR ENDED 30th SEPTEMBER, 1966

1964/5 £	1964/5 £	1964/5 £	Particulars	£	£	£
			PUBLICATIONS			
22,487			Expenditure		22,412	
404	445		Less Sales	445		
2,716	3,532		Advertising Revenue	3,532	3,977	
		19,367				18,435
			SHOWS			
3,003			Prize Monies, Medals and Plate		4,044	
2,249			Expenses		3,310	
5,252					7,354	
652			Less Proceeds		562	
		4,600				6,792
		5,248	**TRIAL GROUND AND DISPLAY GARDEN**			5,362
			SECRETARIAL AND OFFICE EXPENSES			
9,180			Salaries and Assistance		9,436	
1,300			Non-recurring Disbursements			
1,033			Superannuation Contributions & Supplementary Pensions		1,360	
1,195			Rates, Lighting, Heating, etc.		1,032	
3,994			Printing and Stationery		2,149	
7,612			Postages		9,017	
2,281			General Expenses, Telephone, Hire of Rooms, etc.		2,515	
205			Repairs & Renewals—Office & Premises		307	
250			Auditors' Fee		250	
477			Bank Charges		725	
27,527					26,791	
3,110			ADVERTISING AND PUBLICITY		3,138	
211			PRESENTATION ROSES		238	
			RESERVE FOR NEW EDITIONS OF PUBLICATIONS, FILM & CONFERENCE		6,865	
—			RESERVE FOR DEVELOPMENT—TRIAL GROUND, DISPLAY GARDEN AND PROPERTIES		1,000	
5,000			RESERVE FOR PENSIONS		—	
2,630			ALTERATIONS TO BONE HILL—Amount written off		2,653	
212			MOTOR VAN, MOWER AND EQUIPMENT—Amount written off		218	
549			OFFICE EQUIPMENT—Amount written off		516	
68,454						72,008
2,003			BALANCE—Excess of Revenue over Expenditure for the year			3,847
70,457						75,855

1964/5 £	1964/5 £	Particulars	£	£
		SUBSCRIPTIONS AND AFFILIATION FEES		70,071
64,993		Subscriptions		907
879		Affiliation Fees		70,978
	65,872			
		INCOME FROM INVESTMENTS, ETC.		
4,585		Gross		4,877
	70,457			75,855

The President's Page

It is a very great honour for me to be invited to assume the duties of President for a second tour and it is one I greatly appreciate.

Before dealing with the future I must refer with gratitude to the fact that our Royal Patron, Her Majesty Queen Elizabeth, the Queen Mother, found time to honour the Society on two occasions during the past year, by attending the Summer Show at Alexandra Palace and later by visiting our headquarters and gardens at Bone Hill. The great interest shown by Her Majesty in all she saw was obvious to all those fortunate enough to be present on these occasions.

Although members joining in 1966 fell short of the record total of 1965 by some 12 per cent, this may be due to the greater financial stringency. There seems ample scope for increasing our total membership if satisfied members will bring to the notice of their friends the very low subscription and the substantial benefits which it secures.

Your Council is constantly seeking ways of furthering the objects of the Society. The following matters are to be dealt with in 1967:

(a) Research into the causes of various diseases of the rose is to be undertaken at Bath University and the Society plans to contribute financially to this work.

(b) Additional Display Gardens are to be sought in the Midlands and the North-west.

(c) A scheme is to be considered for the closer co-operation of selected Affiliated Societies with the Society.

(d) Plans for an International Rose Conference in 1968 are being formulated.

(e) A new edition of *A Selected List of Roses* will be issued.

(f) The Display Gardens at Bone Hill are to be extended and the lay-out altered as necessary.

(g) A new film with sound commentary, showing the cultivation of the rose and other features of interest, is to be prepared.

May 1967 prove to be favoured with fine weather, so that the lovely roses now available may be permitted to show to advantage. Meanwhile, will our hybridists please proceed in their search for more all-weather roses!

R. F. B. NAYLOR

MAJ.-GENERAL R. F. B. NAYLOR, C.B., C.B.E., D.S.O., M.C.
PRESIDENT 1967/68

Weatherproof Roses

C. E. LUCAS PHILLIPS

There will always be plenty of people whose love of the rose will compel them to a willing service in overcoming all the dangers that threaten its beauty. The ardent rosarian, whether an exhibitor or not, will aim at high standards and will go to infinite pains to achieve them. There are, however, some hazards that it is almost impossible for him to overcome and these are the elements of rain, wind and sun when delivered in excessive quantities.

High winds I take to be the harshest of all the elements. They dehydrate the foliage, damage the blossoms, loosen the roots and in spring the cold breath of a wind from the north or east will so "burn" the leaves as to make them appear to be attacked by a fungus or to be suffering from a soil deficiency. Standards are the most susceptible and I have had complete heads broken off below the union in a June gale.

Some roses, however, are notably resistant to the elements, particularly the Rugosas and the Burnet roses, which will not only stand up to wind, rain and hot sun but will even resist salt spray from the sea. The Rugosas, because of their height, are particularly useful as shelter hedges for more delicate plants, rivalling the *Olearia albida* which is grown so successfully at Scarborough.

Thus, wind is no good to hybrid tea, floribunda and many other roses. Rain and sun, on the other hand, are very necessary and plenty of roses will not mind how much they get of either, but many varieties, including several of the choicest exhibitors' sorts, are ruined by heavy rain, while a few others quickly flag under a hot sun. It is not surprising that several which hate rain revel in the hot sun, as exemplified by 'Karl Herbst'.

For those of us who have space enough for only a limited number of roses and for people whose lives are too busy to spare time for daily attention, it is important to concentrate on those varieties that will flower abundantly and resist both the attacks of disease and the assaults of the elements. For such gardeners, not being exhibitors, the aim must be to have the greatest possible pleasure over the longest possible period with the least possible fuss.

Hybrid Teas in Rain

Other things being equal, the varieties first to avoid are those that are rain-shy. Rain may damage roses in various ways, but the worst damage is "balling", in which the whole bud, when it is just about to uncoil, becomes a soggy, pulpy mess. Discolouration of the outer petals and spotting will also spoil a rose for exhibition or the vase at home, but do not as a rule seriously detract from its garden value.

Balling is particularly associated with those varieties that are of dense and multiple petalage, especially if the petals overlap at the top of the bloom. Thus, those that are worst affected unfortunately include many of the most beautiful exhibitors' sorts, such as 'Perfecta', 'Gavotte', 'Royal Highness', 'Anne Letts', 'Gordon Eddie', 'Premier Bal' and so on, all of which are ruined by heavy or persistent rain. Other popular examples are 'Montezuma' and 'Margaret'. This, however, is only a by-and-large pronouncement, for there are several exceptions and contradictions when we come to examine petalage.

Thus, the new lilac-mauve floribunda 'Africa Star', a highly decorative rose of distinctive character, is utterly rain-hardy in my garden, though it carries up to 50 petals, which is the same count as 'Royal Highness' and almost the same as 'Perfecta' (50–60). 'Gail Borden', with the same count of 50, is also quite rain-proof, and so is 'Eden Rose', with 40–50 (though it has other faults). 'Stella', also with 40–50 petals, is outstanding in its resistance to rain.

On the other hand, we find a few roses with quite light or moderate petalage that do not behave well, such as 'Josephine Bruce' (25–30) and 'Dorothy Peach' (35), both of which may become pitiful spectacles, and to a less extent, the floribunda 'Dearest' (30). 'Ena Harkness' is spoilt in a different way; she does not ball, but her weak neck causes her to hang her head as though in dejection.

Thus, petalage is only a rough guide, but certainly a point to which the intending purchaser of roses should pay particular attention. We can become very much more definite when we consider two colour groups. In the first instance, I know of no white hybrid tea rose that will withstand rain, with the exception of the old 'Frau Karl Druschki' (actually a hybrid perpetual), but it is a rose I do not care for, being in my eyes a cold, austere and aloof creature. All other whites or near-whites, such as 'McGredy's Ivory' (only 25–30 petals), 'Message' (35), 'Memoriam' (50), and the cream 'Burnaby' (55) become spoilt, and more's the pity, for they are very beautiful when conditions are right, 'Burnaby' being a flower of wonderful form and substance. 'Virgo' (25–30) often opens fairly satisfactorily in rain, but is apt to become badly spotted. I have not yet had experience of 'Pascali'.

The second colour group among the hybrid teas of which we can be fairly definite comprises the yellow shades. In this instance we have roses that are generally rain-hardy, but, by contrast, usually not hardy to much sun, which causes their pigment to fade. Typical yellow varieties are 'McGredy's Yellow', 'Peace', 'Sutter's Gold', 'Grand'mère Jenny', 'Isobel Harkness', 'Summer Sunshine', 'Lydia' and 'Buccaneer', all of which behave well in rain, though some are sun-shy, as we shall observe shortly. 'King's Ransom' is unfortunately an exception, its buds often going to pulp in a wet spell.

In general, we may say that, from the point of view of rain-hardiness, the most promising roses are those that carry some 25–30 petals. Fortunately this means a great many of the popular and gratifying roses of all colours, of the likes of 'Mischief', 'Ophelia' and her beautiful progeny, the tall and strapping 'Prima Ballerina', which is particularly good on this count, 'Picture' of classic form, 'Mme Louis Laperrière', perhaps the best of all dark reds for bedding, the new 'Fragrant Cloud', 'Sutter's Gold' and the charming little 'Michèle Meilland'.

Others of slightly fuller petalage that are sound bets are dear old 'Mrs Sam McGredy', the lusty 'Rose Gaujard', which will grow anywhere, 'My Choice' (particularly good), 'Wendy Cussons', 'Super Star' and, in spite of its bulk, 'Isabel de Ortiz'. It may be noted, incidentally, that most of these varieties are scented in some degree.

Hybrid Teas in Sun

So much for rain. The effects of strong sun are far less disfiguring, but nevertheless of importance to the gardener who aims at the maximum floral display from a small area. In some varieties the colour may become bleached and washed out; in others the rose, opening its petals in too great a hurry, is quickly "blown", reminding one of the French poet's classic lines on his mistress: "Herself a rose, she lived for but the life of a rose—the space of a morning."

Fading, as we have noted, is particularly associated with the yellow hybrid teas, but there are some marked exceptions in such instances as the gaunt 'Buccaneer' and 'Spek's Yellow' and in 'Golden

Masterpiece', in which hot weather actually enhances the full colour. In other varieties the fading is not altogether objectionable, as in 'Lady Belper' and the beautiful 'Golden Melody', which wane to a tolerable buff. Similarly the brilliant sunset colours of 'Violinista Costa', a rose so easy and willing that it will succeed even on chalk, fade to a quite acceptable cherry pink.

Apart from colour, thin or sparse petalage may also cause a rose to be quickly blown. This we see in the extreme form of single roses, especially in the large-flowered single hybrid teas, now so little grown but the joy of my early gardening days and of great charm to people who admire simplicity and perfection of form; of such are 'Dainty Bess', 'Mrs Oakley-Fisher', 'Irish Elegance' and 'Isobel'. Other roses that for one reason or another share the unhappy fate of the French poet's mistress include 'Piccadilly', 'Beauté', 'Isobel Harkness' and dear old 'Betty Uprichard'. This weakness can to some extent be mitigated by planting these varieties in a position where they will not be assailed with the full force of the sun when in the south.

Floribundas

When we turn to floribundas (one or two of which we have already noted), we find a much simpler picture. On the whole, the floribundas stand up well to all kinds of weather, though the increasing introduction of hybrid tea sap into their cells may foretell troubles similar to those we have found in the straightforward hybrid teas. 'Spartan' is a horrible warning, for, although it carries only 30 petals, it balls abominably. So may 'Sweet Repose', otherwise so winning a rose in the bud stage. 'Dearest' has been much impugned for rain-shyness in summer, but my own experience is that it takes quite a lot of rain to spoil it and it is beautiful in autumn. 'Ivory Fashion' is another that is not at its best in wet weather, becoming badly spotted. 'Elysium', a tall and elegant beauty with delightful, richly scented, pale salmon blooms of some 30 petals, also falls down badly, partly through balling and partly through the collapse of the pedicel.

Few floribundas are sun-shy, though 'Lilac Charm' turns grey too soon. 'Honeymoon' (a poor rose anyway) and the new 'Jan Spek' turn pale and wan and 'Firecracker' may become a poor squib. Perhaps the worst (in this regard), however, is 'Paddy McGredy', whose salmon-carmine hybrid tea type blooms, borne in such liberal profusion in the season, fade to a flat, insipid pink.

Thus the general run of floribundas are pretty weatherproof, but several are outstanding. Of these, we may particularly note 'Pink Parfait', one of those roses that is beautiful in all stages from the bud to the blown; 'Tivoli', a deeper pink similarly endowed; 'Orange Sensation' of popular fancy; 'Red Dandy', whose blooms are almost identical with those of 'Ena Harkness' but without the droop; 'Allgold', still unbeatable as a yellow floribunda; the poppy-like 'Paprika'; Mrs Olga West's 'Africa Star' from the Eastern Highlands of Rhodesia; 'Meteor', which absolutely revels in heat, 'Dickson's Flame', which I find a splendid companion for 'Allgold'; 'Red Favourite', defiant of all enemies; the robust 'Buisman's Triumph' (inevitably called "Busman's Holiday" in our home); and the much neglected pink 'Nathalie Nypels', which, behaving as all good floribundas should, is continuously massed with blooms from June to October.

Shrub and "Old" Roses

Among the shrub roses, there are plenty that stand up to all weathers —the Rugosas and their charming pink hybrid 'Sarah van Fleet', the flowerful "Hybrid Musks", the Bourbons as a whole, 'Nevada', the lusty 'Kathleen Ferrier', 'Iceberg' (which I firmly classify as a shrub, for all mine grow at least 5 ft high and wide), 'Kassel', 'Bonn' and nearly all the species roses. In hot sun the beautiful single flowers of 'Golden Wings' are fleeting, but are produced successively in such profusion that one feels little loss.

All these in their different ways are splendid and impressive plants that will give their owners little trouble, but some of them take up a great deal of space, as exemplified by 'Kathleen Ferrier', my plants of which grow 8 ft high and wide, with thick, lusty branches that get bowed down with the weight of their huge trusses and have to be strongly staked.

Some of the "old" roses are by no means able to withstand the onslaughts of rain, which, in addition to blossom damage, may beat them down to sprawl on the ground in a distressing manner. The Albas are usually good, however, especially the beautiful 'Celeste' and 'Mme Plantier'. The Centifolias are not generally reliable, but the sumptuous 'Fantin Latour' and 'Tour de Malakoff' seem to be exceptions.

The following tables of hybrid teas and floribundas may be useful as a guide in this matter. They are not exhaustive, being confined to varieties of which I have knowledge and omitting border-line cases.

Rainproof hybrid teas

Buccaneer	Grand'mère Jenny	Eden Rose
Michèle Meilland	Mischief	Mrs Sam McGredy
My Choice	Ophelia	Mme Butterfly
Lady Sylvia	Peace	Picture
Prima Ballerina	Stella	Super Star
Sutter's Gold	Wendy Cussons	Isabel de Ortiz
Fragrant Cloud	Rose Gaujard	Pink Favourite (usually)
Gail Borden	Hector Deane	Lady Eve Price

Rain-shy hybrid teas

Premier Bal	Josephine Bruce	Karl Herbst
Margaret	Montezuma	Dorothy Peach
Perfecta	Gavotte	Anne Letts
Red Ensign	Gordon Eddie	Royal Highness
Burnaby	Ethel Sanday	Tiffany
Silver Lining (partially)	Virtually all whites	

Rain-proof floribundas

Allgold	Orange Sensation	Highlight
Dickson's Flame	Pink Parfait	Red Dandy
Paprika	Sarabande	Nathalie Nypels
Red Favourite	Elizabeth of Glamis	Africa Star
Buisman's Triumph	Frensham	Shepherd's Delight
Evelyn Fison	Alamein	Anna Wheatcroft
August Seebauer	Jiminy Cricket (but spots)	Lilac Charm
Lilli Marlene	Masquerade	Queen Elizabeth (fairly)
Goldgleam	Tivoli (very good)	

Rain-shy floribundas

Spartan	Dearest (if rain heavy)	Ivory Fashion (spots)
Chanelle (spots)	Elysium	Europeana
Golden Jewel		Sweet Repose

Sun

As the majority of roses (apart from going over quickly) stand up pretty well to sun where exhibition quality is not the aim, and as examples have been quoted in the text above, it will be sufficient simply to summarize those that are noticeably not fully sun-proof:

Hybrid teas: 'Beauté', 'Betty Uprichard', 'Opera', 'Isobel Harkness', 'Lady Belper', 'Violinista Costa' (in part), 'Golden Melody', 'Chrysler Imperial', 'Montezuma' (goes a dull pink), 'Phyllis Gold', 'Gordon Eddie'.

Floribundas: 'Paddy McGredy', 'Firecracker', 'Honeymoon', 'Lilac Charm', 'Goldilocks', 'Jan Spek' and 'Arthur Bell'.

Rosa rugosa

An assessment of the garden value of its varieties and hybrids

GRAHAM THOMAS

Many people have an erroneous idea of *Rosa rugosa* because one of the understocks, still used extensively for the making of stems for "standard" roses, is known under this name. In reality it is probably a cross between *R. rugosa* and *R.* 'Manetti', another understock, and from a gardening point of view has very few of the excellent qualities of *R. rugosa* itself. This hybrid, *R. rugosa hollandica*, is a freely-suckering rose and when cuttings of it are made for stocks, all "eyes" which will be beneath the ground are removed in an effort to prevent the base of the plant from producing the unwanted suckers in the garden. Occasionally this operation is not quite successful and the resulting ever-increasing, far-questing, underground shoots are a constant nuisance. It is seldom that this plant is sold as a shrub on its own, and practically all the plants one finds in old gardens are the result of the stock outgrowing the scion. It is a tall, rank grower, reaching some 9 ft in height, of indefinite width, a prickly, pretty-leaved shrub, bearing clusters of single or nearly single mallow-pink flowers from early June until the autumn. As a boundary bush or as a coloniser in waste ground it has its merits.

How different is the genuine *R. rugosa*. It reveals, it is true, the suckering proclivities of its hybrid, but not in such a marked degree, and in any case the resulting thicket is not much more than 4–5 ft high, and indeed a spreading bush of this fine species can be enjoyed in all but the smallest of gardens. Space will not be grudged to a shrub which has so many attributes. Let us consider these. Its flowering period is longer than modern roses, as with pruning it can be made to flower continuously from late May until the frosts finally stop it, and its rich scent is free in the air. The single-flowered forms produce large, round, tomato-like heps concurrently with the later crops of bloom. The foliage is deeply veined (rugose), rather glossy, of rich deep green, dying off bright yellow in the autumn. The grey wood is covered with grey thorns—both a beautiful pale green when young—forming an impenetrable thicket or admirable hedge. It grows well in sun or part shade, in heavy or light soil, even on chalk, and is indeed established like a native on sand-dunes on the south coast, and in Suffolk. It does not suffer from pests or diseases.

On the debit side we must balance, I suppose, its habit of producing underground shoots when it is established on its own roots (and this it is most likely to do even if budded on *R. canina*), its masses of prickles and its rather limited colour range. Forms are available in white, pink and crimson-mauve, but no yellow, orange or flame. In fairness to *R. rugosa*, though, we must here remember that this is a range of colouring as great as, or greater than, all other species, and is only eclipsed by modern hybrid roses which owe these other colours to the contribution of but two species in the genus.

Among single varieties I place the white very high. It is not only a good pure white, but the flowers contrast very beautifully with the orange-red heps, and it is an excellent vigorous grower achieving 6–7 ft, with luxuriant foliage. I have this with a clematis 'Perle d'Azur' growing through it and the light lavender-blue flowers look well with the rose. As this clematis is one of those which are best cut down to 1 ft. every January, it does not become a tangle, in fact I recommend greater use of the Viticella types of clematises for providing colour in August among shrub roses. Equally vigorous as *R. rugosa alba* is the form known as 'Scabrosa', with the most handsome leaves and largest flowers and heps of the group. The flowers are 3 in. or more across, of bright mauve-crimson. It shares with *R. rugosa rubra* (*R. rugosa rugosa*, *R.r. typica*), whose flower colour is similar but varies to light or dark when raised from seed, the disadvantage of a sharp contrast with the orange-red heps. Not so the clearer pink variety 'Frau Dagmar Hastrup', whose heps are rich crimson-red, without a hint of orange when mature. This like *R.r. rubra* is compact, not normally exceeding 4–5 ft, and is the best variety for smaller gardens; the wide open blooms are exquisite and offset by the central creamy-yellow stamens, as in all of the above.

Doubles are headed by the well-known white 'Blanc Double de Coubert' (1892), the least bushy of all these varieties, and its extra double sport 'Souvenir de Philémon Cochet'. This occurred originally in 1899, but has repeated itself in recent years on several occasions on stock under my care; the densely packed petals, which have a pinkish flush in the centre on opening are surrounded with wider outer petals, in effect rather like some double hollyhocks. The most superlative of the doubles is 'Roseraie de l'Haÿ' (1901), reaching about 6 ft, with neater

Top: Rosa rugosa 'Scabrosa', a form of *R. rugosa* with particularly fine foliage and large flowers of magenta pink (*see page* 28)
Below: 'BELLE POITEVINE', one of the double forms or hybrids of *R. rugosa* (*see page* 29)

Top: Rosa paulii, a hybrid of *R. rugosa*, of valuable ground-covering habit (*see page* 31)
Below: At the official opening of the Rose Display Garden at Saughton Park, Edinburgh. On the right is senior Bailie Craig H. Richards and next to him is F. A. Gibson, President (*see page* 151)

foliage and good flowers 4 in. across emerging from long shapely buds, of a most gorgeous rich crimson-purple. Those who cannot stand this colour must turn the other way, but grouped in the garden with light blue or light yellow flowers it is superb. 'Hansa' (1905) is as vigorous and free flowering, but not as handsome in actual bloom. There are two good and very similar mallow-pinks, 'Souvenir de Christophe Cochet' and 'Belle Poitevine' (both 1894), and I prefer the latter for its better foliage and cooler tint. A still more pleasing variety is 'Delicata' (1898) but unfortunately I have yet to see a good bush, though it appears to do well in hot climates; it is of a particularly cool soft pinkish-lilac. These doubles rarely set seeds and seldom provide heps. They are probably all hybrids, but shew so little other influence than that of *R. rugosa* that they are best considered from a horticultural point of view as forms of the species; this will be the more apparent when we come to examine the mixed hybrids later.

These forms will all make good bushy plants, often as wide as high, if left unpruned, but to get the best from them they should be pruned hard every winter. For hedge-making they can be clipped with the shears, but will also need some old wood removing from the base. If left unpruned or unclipped they will produce the usual prodigal first crop and seldom be without a few flowers for the rest of the season. The pruning makes them throw out strong shoots, every one of which bears a big cluster of blooms, and the continuity is ensured. Though they will grow perfectly well on poor soils, it is obvious that a rich soil will enable them to give a greater quantity of growth and blossom.

Like many plants native to the Far East (North-eastern Asia, N. China, Korea and Japan) this rose was first introduced from Japan—in 1796, having been recorded by travellers in 1784. E. A. Bunyard records how the Chinese in particular portrayed this rose as far back as A.D. 1000. We may be sure it was a noted rose as its petals have been used for *pot pourri* and its bulky heps can provide nutriment. But it did not "catch on" as a novelty over here, which is scarcely surprising, as there was nothing spectacular about its colouring, and flowering shrubs were not a cult as they are today. It probably existed mainly in botanic gardens during the heyday of the old garden roses of Gallica derivation, and, when the China rose hybrids began to prove their worth as parents of repeat-flowering roses, we can imagine that *R. rugosa* was considered its potential equal. This is certainly suggested by the crop of hybrids dating from the 1880s. Fortunately or not, according to which way we look at it, *R. rugosa* is a prolific parent, and has produced a number of worthy garden hybrids of great vigour and size, but subsequent generations decline in vigour or are sterile, as a general rule. As a consequence *R. rugosa* never established a dynasty—for want of a better term—as did *R. chinensis*. Practically all of these early hybrids of *R. rugosa* inherit its hardiness, extreme prickliness, rich clove fragrance and repeat-, or even continuous-flowering habit, but are gaunt lanky shrubs for the back of the border, achieving anything from 6–9 ft in height.

'Mme Georges Bruant' (1887) and 'Sir Thomas Lipton' (1901) are two good white varieties still seen, both semi-double, of loose formation with two good crops of bloom; 'Sarah Van Fleet' (1926) in silvery-pink eclipses them in bushiness and floriferousness, seldom being without flowers. Possibly the most handsome in flower is 'Conrad Ferdinand Meyer' (1899) a hybrid of 'Gloire de Dijon' from which it derives its fully double magnificent blooms, of light silvery-pink, and rich fragrance. Its blush-white sport, 'Nova Zembla' (1907) is perhaps even more beautiful, and both of these must be counted as having two distinct crops, June and September, but are not continuous. 'Fimbriata' (1891) set a new style, with its pale pink petals fringed like those of a carnation; a later fringed hybrid, of different parentage, is the crimson 'F. J. Grootendorst' (1918) with its lighter sport 'Pink Grootendorst' (1923) and darker red variant 'Grootendorst Supreme' (1936). 'Fimbriata' is the most pleasing of these; of the Grootendorst varieties I find the original the most healthy, as the later sports are progressively poorer in foliage; all are reasonably bushy, reaching to 5 ft or more on good soils. 'Mrs Anthony Waterer' (1898) is a full, double, rich crimson, but repeats rather rarely, and is of wide arching growth. These all repay hard pruning in winter except the last which should be pruned after flowering only. There are many more; among these less worthy plants are 'New Century', 'Carmen' (poor foliage), 'Dr Eckener' (gaunt, yellow), 'Parfum de l'Haÿ' (only good in hot weather), 'Ruskin' (a gorgeous double crimson sometimes opening well, of large open growth), 'Calocarpa', 'George Will' and 'Dr E. M. Mills', an unsatisfactory hybrid with *R. hugonis*.

Some interesting and beautiful hybrids, individuals not conforming to the general characteristics of the bulk of the above, have been made or occurred with a wide variety of other species. Raised at Ottawa in

1922 'Agnes' is a cross between R. *rugosa* and R. *foetida persiana* and stands midway between the two. Its early crop of fully double, rich butter-yellow flowers, tinted with amber, makes a lovely contrast with the bright green leaves, and it has a sweet fragrance; it usually produces more flowers in September, and grows to some 6 ft high. I find this an excellent shrub, valuable for its early-flowering season, and a lovely contrast for R. *moyesii*. A first-rate plant, continuously in flower is 'Schneezwerg' (1912), a hybrid for which Peter Lambert claimed the parentage to be R. *rugosa* × R. *bracteata*. Doubts have been expressed about this but it has many characters which one might expect from these forbears. The neat leaves, beautiful white semi-double flowers opening flat with yellow stamens, fragrant and pure, and small scarlet heps maturing with the later crops all add up to a pretty shrub. It would make an excellent hedge, as with hard pruning a continuous succession of blooms would be enjoyed. Of equal interest is, I think, R. *micrugosa*, a union of R. *rugosa* × R. *roxburghii* (R. *microphylla*) raised prior to 1905. It forms a densely branched firm bush 7–8 ft high and wide; in fact on poor sandy soil at Sunningdale it has exceeded this and when its wide single light pink flowers mingle with the silvery-leaved trails of the weeping pear, *Pyrus salicifolia pendula*—which grows nearby and tends to overspread it—a picture of extreme beauty occurs. This would be an ideal shrub to exclude hooligans. In the 1920s Dr C. C. Hurst raised a second generation from this hybrid, almost identical except that it has white flowers, borne recurrently through the season. This I rank very highly.

We are left with several hybrids of sprawling habit and one season of flowering. These are all ideal for informal plantings, covering hedges and stumps, or steep banks, and of extreme beauty when bearing their single flowers in June. They would make ideal host plants for the types of clematises mentioned earlier. 'Lady Curzon' (1901) will mound itself up to 6–7 ft and has wide clear pink blooms. It is a hybrid of 'Macrantha', a garden hybrid of unknown parentage, and is of the same merit. There are two excellent whites: 'Schneelicht' (1896) and R. *paulii* (prior to 1903), both hybrids with white rambling species, forming large, low, arching bushes; the latter is the more vigorous, 4–5 ft high and 12–15 ft across, an impenetrable mass of overlapping shoots; weed-, dog-, and hooligan-proof, and ideal for covering banks. Its exquisitely fashioned pink sport R. *paulii rosea* is rather less vigorous.

Finally in this long list of useful hybrids is 'Max Graf' raised in 1919 from *R. rugosa* × *R. wichuraiana*. As might be expected from having one parent completely prostrate, this is the lowest, flattest, ground-covering rose hybrid that we have today. Its flowers are bright pink, borne at midsummer only, and it has fairly glossy bright green leaves, while those of all the above are dark green and inclined to be dull. It roots as it goes and is a first-rate weed-proof ground-cover. (In mentioning this unusual use for a rose, it should be borne in mind that before planting, all perennial weeds should be removed from the site, to enable the rose to make its dense permanent growth.)

I am unable to say how many of these valuable garden hybrids are sterile, but probably all are, like some other landmarks in rose breeding such as the noteworthy 'Mermaid' and 'Nevada'. Otherwise we might by now be enjoying further hybrids of wide appeal derived from them. But, as I mentioned earlier, *R. rugosa* has not been a good rose for breeding, with one exception, 'Max Graf'. This rose was sterile until the early 1940s when, under the care of Wilhelm Kordes, it spontaneously doubled its chromosomes and produced tetraploid seedlings. This in effect was a new species and is named *R. kordesii*, and from it Kordes was able at last to create a race of roses derived from *R. rugosa*. Many of his most spectacular climbing roses are the result and are repeat-flowering, though so far the continuous-flowering of *R. rugosa* has not been truly obtained. Even so, the hardiness of *R. rugosa* has been added to a race of climbing roses developed to withstand the rigours of north German winters. The resulting plants shew little of the influence of *R. rugosa*; we may still say, therefore, that this species has not yet provided a race of hybrids giving enough of its striking characters of fragrance, foliage and bushiness. More may yet be done, having once broken it in, so to speak, but, in spite of its masculine appearance, the continued dominance of the gentle, small *R. wichuraiana*, as in so many previous instances, seems to be assured.

The complete freedom from pests and diseases of the typical varieties of *R. rugosa* mark them out at once as the shrubs of today; ideal for the shrub border, the outskirts of the heather garden, hedges and for public park planting. Their many attributes are making them more popular year by year and so long as they are regarded as valuable shrubs in their own rights, rather than comparing them with their sophisticated highly bred sisters, they should have an assured future.

'SIR LANCELOT' (floribunda)
'Vera Dalton' × *'Woburn Abbey'*
Raised by R. Harkness & Co. Ltd
TRIAL GROUND CERTIFICATE 1966
See page 182

'KING ARTHUR' (floribunda—H.T. type)
'Pink Parfait' × *'Highlight'*
Raised by R. Harkness & Co. Ltd
CERTIFICATE OF MERIT 1966
See page 181

Beginners' Luck

J. L. HARKNESS

Somewhere in Kai Lung it is said that he who fails the public examinations three times becomes a teacher. This was a great comfort to me in my school days. But what is to be said about one like me, who sees the results of his first year at breeding roses, and promptly writes?

My excuse is this, that as a beginner I need have no shame in owning the mistakes I made; and there may surely be some interest in recording the intentions, methods and results of the first year in a breeding programme. But I have in addition to the excuse a justification, which is better. It is to convey the excitement and joy that I found in breeding roses.

I shall never forget May and June of 1963, when our first seedlings came successively into flower; each day there was at the least interest, at the most enthralment. It was very much like being eight years old again, with Santa Claus coming every day.

The daily round is never dull, for permutations of parentage arise in the mind unbidden; the number plate of the car in front reminds you of a seedling number, and the hymn board in church declares that we shall shortly sing 'Vera Dalton' × 'Paprika'.

I made up my mind to breed roses long ago and in 1938 we built a lean-to glasshouse against the packing shed. We planted a number of varieties imported from Meilland, Max Krause and other hybridists. I never saw the seed from these for instead of sowing it, I was being taught how to be a soldier by an efficient drill sergeant, a man of great intensity of purpose.

When I returned to roses six years later, the urgent business on hand was to bring our rose crop back to its pre-war glory. Some of our stock was growing in the hedges; our foreman used to bud on to the briars there to relieve the monotony, I suppose, of growing cabbages and onions. Moreover, we had less need to breed new roses, for Mr Norman had sent us his wonderful seedlings. I well remember my first sight of 'Ena Harkness'.

The years go quickly, and opportunities vanish with them. But late in 1961 I determined to try again. I had little knowledge of growing under glass and less of hybridising. To amend these deficiencies, I hired a greenhouse upon a friend's nursery, and went off to Ireland to ask two expert breeders how to go to work.

I am happy to record in *The Rose Annual* the help and encouragement I received from Pat Dickson and Sam McGredy. They put me up in their homes, showed me what they were doing and, short of revealing their breeding lines, gave me all the information I had the wit to ask for. Indeed, subsequently, when we were about to sow our first crop of seed, I asked Sam McGredy about a little point when I met him in London. He answered it and said, "If you like to send one of your staff over to Portadown, he can see exactly how we do it."

We planted the greenhouse in December 1961, choosing the healthiest hybrid teas and floribundas we could think of. We then awaited the first set-back, which duly arrived. It is common in long-used greenhouses that a residue of fertiliser salts may sting the roots. We found this out when our roses stopped growing. After we had the sense to flood them they recovered, but the number of flowers on the hybrid teas was disappointing. We hybridised them, and our appetite thus aroused, tackled the floribundas. In point of quantity, we naturally had more floribunda seed than hybrid tea and this, unintentional at first, has dominated our breeding programme ever since.

We never troubled to buy paint brushes for pollinating, but used the flowers themselves; with the petals held back, the stamens are Nature's paintbrush. Perhaps this is a prodigal use of pollen, but in our climate we usually have pollen in plenty. We prefer to use it fresh, although other breeders say they like to store it awhile. I think the intensity of light in Hitchin, and our long hours of sunshine, ripen the pollen more quickly than in many districts.

It was fiendishly hot, Whitsun 1962, and we worked like slaves at the job. The greenhouse was six miles away, which added to our burdens. But at the finish we made over 2,000 crosses, which fell to 1,500 in the following months due to incomplete fertilisation and botrytis, the mould which robs every raiser of some of his work.

While we wait for the seed to ripen, let me tell you of our objectives. First, to breed healthy hybrid teas. For this purpose the seed parents we planted were 'Buccaneer', 'Karl Herbst', 'La Jolla', 'Montezuma', 'Peace', 'Pink Peace', 'Rendez-vous', 'Rose Gaujard', 'Summer Sunshine', 'Super Star' and 'Wendy Cussons'. Unable to resist reds we also had 'Chrysler Imperial' and 'Josephine Bruce', not so healthy as the others.

Secondly, to breed improved floribundas, we planted 'Ann Elizabeth', 'Iceberg', 'Orange Sensation', 'Pink Parfait', 'Red Dandy' and 'Vera Dalton'.

Thirdly, to breed neat roses of low height, we planted 'Baby Faurax' and 'Baby Masquerade'.

Fourthly, to breed tall roses for hedges and shrubs, we used 'Buccaneer' and 'Queen Elizabeth'.

Fifthly, to have a ticket in the "blue rose" sweepstake, we relied on 'Baby Faurax' and 'Lilac Charm'.

We had in each case a number of other varieties for use as pollen parents. These are the other side of the story, and equally important; but to save giving a long list, I will later mention those which proved successful.

While our seed was ripening, I learned that a nurseryman in Hitchin was retiring, and to cut a long story short, we became the owners in November 1962 of a few assorted greenhouses, some quite venerable. This seemed an economic way of advancing our breeding. We wanted something to learn on, before we went building ourselves. I have been told that there has been a nursery on that same site for 200 years.

We harvested the seed, stored it, and began making seed benches. I had the compost ready; it was Arthur Bower's Seed and Potting Mixture. This was a stroke of luck, for I knew Arthur Bower personally; and knowing both his skill and himself, I took his compost at his word, and it proved just marvellous for us.

You may remember January and February 1963, when vehicles were disappearing under snow, and the thermometer never got its mercury above its ankle. Innocently we lit the boiler to get ready for sowing; but like many faithful old servants given six months' rest after years of work, it could not return to duty. It leaked. It was hopeless. All right, we said, we don't really need this big boiler to warm all the houses—we will get a small one and heat only the seed house. We can cut the pipes about, sink a boiler house and it will cost less in fuel.

This pleased our nursery manager, who had long since passed his wits' end to find work for the staff in the snow. He organised the laying of the pipes and the digging of the hole. I went about the simple task of buying a boiler. I pictured myself choosing from serried ranks of boilers, dog-like salesmen in hopeful attendance. But it was not so. Apparently at that time, even if you went to the factory, you would have to camp out for two or three weeks before a boiler came out for you.

We declined to wait, and began searching the district for a second-hand one. I inspected some interesting boilers, in various stages of demolition. Some looked big enough to turn the Albert Hall into a gigantic oven. At last somebody heard of one, which we bought for a "fiver", and transported with as much sweat as the climate would permit.

The boiler house was dug out, and needed concreting. Everybody except the nursery manager saw no alternative but to pray for a thaw. He made his own thaw, by unfreezing the ballast on corrugated iron sheets over a fire. The boiler house floor was concreted, and a lorry load of sacks thrown in. It set. Then we put the boiler in, connected it —and lit it. That kept the frost out while we concreted the walls.

The seed was sown, a few days later than intended, but still in time. Great was the sense of satisfaction in the greenhouse. One pod from 'Queen Elizabeth' proved to contain just over 100 seeds.

When the seeds grew, I was not really satisfied with the germination, but greater experience now shows me we did reasonably well. The seedlings grew like mad; the first one in flower was 'Ann Elizabeth' × 'Red Dandy' on 24 April, about ten weeks from the time of sowing. We still have it, under the code 16A. Altogether we selected about 650 varieties, and in some cases were able to bud twenty good eyes from a seedling plant. The benefit of this proved to be a saving of twelve months in sending the best to the Trial Ground. I have always thanked Arthur Bower's compost for that.

The results of our first year may be assessed as follows, the figures being nurseryman's round numbers:

2,000 crosses made summer 1962
1,500 pods harvested autumn 1962
40,000 seeds sown early 1963
20,000 seedlings grown by summer 1963
650 seedlings budded for trial 1963
107 seedlings for further trial 1964–66.

Of the 107 seedlings, we are still looking at 90; and 17 have so far been selected as possibly good enough to introduce.

In each of our five objectives there were both failure and success to report.

Hybrid Teas. We had only one success, a pink seedling from 'Red Dandy' × 'Peace', which is now named 'Guinevere'. We banished from the seed house 'Chrysler Imperial', 'Josephine Bruce', 'Karl Herbst', 'Montezuma', 'Pink Peace', 'Rendez-vous' and 'Rose Gaujard' as being unlikely to be of any use.

Low Growers. We had one partial success, a dwarf variety from 'Iceberg' × 'Baby Faurax'. It has hard narrow leaves and very double flowers of pretty shape. The colour is white to blush, with an icy touch. No commercial acquisition, this, but I can imagine it looking nice in conjunction with water and warm stone. It is named 'Little Lady'.

The two seed parents we had for this objective were quite useless. We made a high class bloomer in planting 'Baby Masquerade', which sets no seed; 'Baby Faurax' proved very difficult to work with, and although it set a few seeds they were worthless.

Floribundas. We were quite amazed by the wealth of beautiful varieties we received. The seedlings in full flower were spectacular, and it will not be easy to summarise them in a few words.

'Ann Elizabeth' produced several good-looking varieties, usually spoilt by a tendency to grow too tall and wave about. The best is 'Ann Elizabeth' × 'Paprika', coded 12B, a brilliant scarlet, chiefly notable for the clean form of the young blooms.

I had a feeling when pollinating it that 'Pink Parfait' might prove a good parent, and so it proved. (But I wonder why 'Pink Parfait' could do no wrong for us in 1962, and little right ever since?) 'Pink Parfait' × 'Circus' gave us the multi-coloured 'Merlin'; also a stately buttermilk-coloured floribunda (178AA) for the future.

'Pink Parfait' × 'Highlight' yielded scarcely a bad seedling. From this cross came 'King Arthur', salmon-pink; 'Sir Galahad', wine-red; and a vigorous cream variety named 'Moonraker'.

On the contrary, 'Pink Parfait' × 'Ivory Fashion' was unreliable, most of the seedlings growing in an untidy way. One exception is a charming misty pink variety, known at present as 181E. From 'Pink Parfait' × 'Masquerade' we have 186C, an improvement on 'Masquerade' I feel sure, but there is now little interest in this type. 'Pink Parfait' × 'Red Dandy' produced a fragrant pink floribunda of 'Mme Caroline Testout' colour which we call 'Dandy Dick'.

The other outstanding floribunda parent was 'Vera Dalton'. With 'Masquerade' pollen it produced a most unusual variety, something like orange shaded by tea in the young flowers, opening yellow, and blessed with a quite exotic scent. This variety is being named 'Glory of Ceylon', to mark the centenary of the tea industry there. 'Vera Dalton' × 'Paprika' bore 311R, a scarlet floribunda notable for its colour fastness. 'Vera Dalton' × 'Woburn Abbey' produced both 'Sir Lancelot' and 'Excalibur', the one a pleasing apricot yellow, the other a somewhat savage scarlet fading to blood red, appropriate to the name, I suppose, and fit to be seen a long way off on a dull day. We kept all our floribunda seed parents, for there was promise from each one.

Hedges and Shrubs. No varieties were found to be immediately fit for introduction, though several are still on trial. 'Buccaneer' was thrown out of the seed house and 'Queen Elizabeth' kept for the future.

"Blue" Roses. Two possible introductions turned up, though neither of them is very blue. From 'Pink Parfait' × 'Baby Faurax' came a semi-double seedling, magenta rose in colour with a light centre (174F). The gaiety of this variety arises in part from the carriage of the flowers on the plant. Probably it will not be widely grown, for semi-double roses are not popular today, but it has given me much pleasure. The other "possible" is from 'Vera Dalton' × 'Sterling Silver' (316B), a strong-growing rosy-mauve, with scent and vigour.

The mathematical may have observed that thirteen combinations proved successful; and in all we crossed 342 different sets of parents.

Before I end this report, I should add two significant factors which have not yet appeared. The first is that in each of our objectives, except hybrid teas, we obtained seedlings which appear valuable for future breeding. The story of these obviously belongs to the next instalment.

The second factor was that well-known Aberdonian, Alexander Cocker. He, too, was interested to start breeding, and we two agreed to pool our knowledge, exchange our seedlings and work together. This has made the task twice as interesting and the progress, we trust, will be twice as fast. There is even a pollen supply service operating between Aberdeen and Hitchin.

It has been difficult to write this report without being carried away by the well-known optimism of plant breeders. Obviously there was no sense in describing the failures, only the successes. On a sober note, we can reflect as we close, out of forty thousand—only seventeen!

Back to My Land

LESLIE SNOOK

> *Breathes there the man, with soul so dead,*
> *Who never to himself hath said,*
> *This is my own, my native land!*

So exclaimed our now neglected old friend Sir Walter Scott. He goes on to imply that if a man's heart fails to burn on returning to his "native strand" he is a poor fellow.

Six years ago my heart started to glow like a bed of 'Orangeade' at dusk. It was then that I returned from forty years of wandering in my personal wilderness to make a rose garden in the New Forest. Sad to think it will be the last of a lovely succession. Anyhow, it is the largest of the line and the first one in which I have had all day to roam.

Only once a week am I ordered away from my Paradise. Then accoutred with basket and my wife's shopping list, I make for the bus which will take me to the ancient city ten miles distant. In our village, elderly retired gentlemen do not lose caste because briefcases have been exchanged for baskets of fancy design. My basket is only a cover story, anyway, hiding another intention. So, last Tuesday, I set off.

On reaching my destination, the items on the list were demolished in a series of frantic bursts and all deposited in the parcels office at the coach station. Then I pirouetted and jumped my way across traffic-bound streets where fifty years ago I would dawdle—and reached my objective.

The second-hand bookshop dreams in a sequestered approach to the Cathedral Close under the shadow of the great spire. I now have two whole hours before the bus returns, to browse—and search for books on roses. I enter and scan the shelves, puffed up with anticipation over my recent capture, an almost mint copy of *A Book about Roses* by dear old Dean Hole, and at a price which shows that even booksellers some-times nap. I can see nothing by, say, Pemberton, William Paul or Rivers, nor, of course, by Redouté or Ellen Willmott. No doubt these two would be entered for the Sotheby Stakes anyway.

Suddenly, my eyes alight on a book which for me has even more significance—a National Rose Society *Annual* for 1934. It was the year I started to make my first rose garden.

A quick purchase and I am soon sitting on a seat in the quiet Close. The years fall away with the turn of the pages and I am back in that suburban garden of thirty-two years ago. I look at a black and white illustration of a hedge of 'Else Poulsen' (labelled hy. poly.) flanking a stately mansion. I had a hedge of this rose pink miss in my 1934 garden. I still have one now, cunningly alternated with her red sister 'Kirsten'. The stately mansion has been absent in both cases.

I turn to an attractive coloured plate of still another sister, the intense scarlet 'Karen'. I saw her blooming in a friend's garden a week ago. The Poulsen girls certainly seem to have discovered the secret of perpetual youth. I recently planted a bed of their distant relation, the deep crimson-maroon 'Dusky Maiden'. This luscious brunette puts scent behind her ears.

A photograph of 'Mermaid' sweeping up the side of a house I find depressing. I planted one three years ago. Pruning instructions to cut out dead wood and keep within its allotted space have so far proved redundant. At present mine is two feet high with never a primrose yellow sausage. Take warning! Don't plant her in a wind tunnel. She's a slow starter at the best of times. What memories of lovely rose beds arise as I scan the pages. Fortunately some varieties are still with us, and I know that their beauty is more than nostalgic imaginings. The still unsurpassed 'Mrs Sam McGredy' has carried her copper and scarlet blooms up and over the rustic work in my present garden, and so has white 'Mrs Herbert Stevens' of shapely form. Yet when the latter was a standard in my 1934 garden, her few blooms hung their heads on stems like ill-fed worms. What a re-birth!

Now I read an article by an Indian gentleman from Lucknow. It seems that when his bushes arrive, they are planted into pots and syringed eight to ten times a day. That makes my fortnightly spraying look bone lazy. I read on to discover that he owns a ground staff and head gardener who is detailed for the tricky chores. I muse. I am lying on a couch, guarding against Black Spot by a clap of the hands and a spit of an order. Reality returns. What would happen if I turned on this routine at home? A ticking off for frightening the cat.

I glance at my watch and close the *Annual* with a snap. The bus leaves in ten minutes. I am well off my mark, but the driver is about to let in his gear as I pull myself aboard.

When I reach the village, I walk down the lane to my hundred-and-fifty-foot frontage of happiness. Before entering, I pause and lean over the five-bar gate. What a lovely vista; created by the sweat of my joyful brow and several attacks of lumbago, bravely borne.

My eyes rove along the row of floribunda standards. Dark crimson, brooding 'Lilli Marlene'; peach and rose complexioned 'Circus'; 'Rumba' showing her yellow, pink and red frillies—and 'Honeymoon', her bright yellow blooms clear with confident hope. Bless the man who first wedded floribunda bud to standard briar.

Across the lawn I see a hedge of 'Nevada'. She has been completely plastered with creamy-white, semi-double blooms as large as coffee saucers. In her third season she already arches gracefully five feet from the ground. Even in winter her dark brown stems seem to herald the spring. A real promise, for she is the first rose to open in my garden.

Then I gaze at one of my showpieces which flanks the drive. A thirty-foot line of cream and peach 'Chanelle', backed by the surprisingly little known 'Ulster Queen', a blend of deep salmon and pale silvery salmon. These two floribundas mingle their hybrid tea type blooms in perfect harmony all summer. This combination was my wife's choice but I preen nevertheless.

My feathers contract quickly as I glimpse a line of rustic work over by the orchard. I planned the delightful symmetry of a line of climbing 'Mrs Sam McGredy' alternating with the pale pink, sedate rambler 'New Dawn'. Ambition made me add more poles after my rose order had been placed. So, when I was called away on business I left two untenanted.

During my absence my wife bought two 'American Pillar' ramblers "off the peg" at a supermarket and happily completed the planting. I must own that their bright rose, white-eyed blooms make a beautiful picture in July. Unfortunately, after three seasons they have swamped each other and covered everything in sight, including their adjacent companions. In the autumn they will be moved to a place where their exuberance can screen the compost-heap-cum-rubbish-dump. It's a pity, but I suppose we cannot expect our womenfolk to be so practical and far-sighted as us men.

Great Scott! I've just remembered! I left the shopping basket at the coach station.

What is a Rose Sport?

ROGER WHEATCROFT

Do you believe in miracles? Do you ever consider when you prune your rose trees how it is that the hard, dormant wood can grow and give you the same enchanting beauty of a rose as it did the year before? Surely a miracle has taken place! Taking this one stage further, have you ever wondered how a nurseryman can be sure that the wood he is using to propagate a variety will grow true to type?

It is evident that the processes taking place inside the plants as they grow are very rigidly controlled. There is a regime working to implement conformity—conformity which gives us the same plant, the same flowers year after year. By his skill the nurseryman can propagate this same regime to produce another plant.

The main controllers and executives of the regime in a plant are called genes—they hold council on the chromosomes. Different genes are responsible for the colour, the perfume, the habit of the rose, indeed all the processes taking place in the plant. The genes are subject as individuals to the laws they enact as a body. One law governs their own reproduction, and because they themselves can be reproduced accurately, so also can the perfume, the colour, the habit and the very nature of the rose.

Those who wish to find a new variety must find another regime. It may not incorporate entirely new genes. By hybridisation the genes may be re-assorted, and in their new positions may do a new job. Consider, for example, your own family—brothers are often alike, but by paradox, they are always different. In the rose world these different varieties are said to have the same parents—'Sutters Gold' and 'Mojave', also 'Marella' and 'Jolie Madame' and two new ones, 'Papa Meilland' and 'Mister Lincoln'. The same genes have been re-assorted, or, to put it another way, a new executive has been elected from existing candidates.

Sometimes, however, a fundamental innovation can take place. This usually happens by accident. Some accidents involve the genes themselves. For example, one might be destroyed—compare a member dropping out of the executive. The old regime will be changed—if it manages to survive to the point when we can recognise that a change has taken place, we call the change a mutation. Mutations are accidents, and accidents can happen—even in the best households!

If the mutation occurs in the growing tip of a rose shoot, a new type of shoot might result. We call such shoots sports. Imagine going into your garden one day and finding a bright red rose on your plant of 'Peace'. You will have found a sport—and perhaps a fortune.

But do not think that different coloured flowers are the only sports. Very important are those which differ in vigour, for from these we get climbing varieties; but other types undoubtedly occur—thorny to thornless stems, variegation in stem and leaves, for example, and, most interesting, normal flowers to moss flowers or to frilled or waved petals.

However it is not altogether certain that we will be able to propagate the new-found sport. If we are able to do so, it is said to be "fixed" or stable.

All varieties differ in their stability—just like some people seem to have more accidents than others, so do roses. For example, 'Orléans Rose' is definitely accident-prone! More than twenty different sports have been recorded from this one variety. Of course one must consider the number of trees being grown to decide if one variety is more stable than another. There are many sports of 'Peace'—'Chicago Peace' and 'Lucky Piece' are examples—but consider the many millions of plants of this variety which are grown throughout the world.

Newly found sports are themselves amongst the most unstable varieties, but this is not altogether surprising. There are usually repercussions after every accident, and notorious indeed are the climbing sports. A nurseryman who introduces a climbing sport is very careful to test it for many years to ensure that it will continue to climb in your garden, but it is still possible to receive a plant which will refuse to climb. Please don't blame the nurseryman.

To different degrees the climbing sports show a tendency to revert to the bush form. 'Clg. Tzigane' does it often, whereas 'Clg. Mrs Sam McGredy' does not. In a similar way, flower colour sports revert too— 'Chicago Peace', which is pink, sometimes produces ordinary 'Peace' flowers.

At first sight it may seem odd that the mutation, which we have stressed all along has been a freak occurrence, should quite often be exactly reversed in this way. In some cases, the reason for this can be shown by experiment. Root cuttings of the rose 'Better Times' will grow into plants of 'Briarcliff'! This could be termed reversion, as 'Briarcliff' was the original parent. In fact the tissue of 'Briarcliff' had never been replaced altogether—it had only been submerged by the new tissue of the sport. Root cuttings reveal this fact as they develop from the internal tissue exclusively. This same internal tissue gives rise to the flower parts which are important in producing seed. We might therefore expect that the children of this sort of sport will be identifiable with the parent; in the case of some climbing roses this has been demonstrated.

It is interesting that very stable climbing sports have been shown to give rise to many seedlings of the climbing habit. Unstable ones do not. This tallies with our expectation that, in the stable varieties, the change from the parent type to sport has been almost complete, or at least sufficient to include the flower parts important in this respect, whereas the unstable varieties, which are always giving trouble by reverting, have only a superficial layer of the sport tissue and the parent underneath is always breaking through and still gives rise to the seed.

So we see that sports play an important part in the quest for new roses. We know that a small change in a variety that has stood the test of time is more likely to be a success itself than many a new seedling. We also know that mutations can be artificially induced these days. But radiation . . .? Do you think we should try it?

(With acknowledgements to Professor C. D. Darlington.)

Pruning and Other Problems Following the Wet Season of 1965

LEONARD HOLLIS

Short papers were invited from a number of experienced rose growers resident in different parts of the country, with a view to ascertaining whether die back and stem cankers were generally extensive, following the wet season of 1965 and the severe frosts early in November of that year. Our contributors were asked to refer to the relative damage as affecting the various main groups of roses, and to mention individual varieties which were seriously affected or, on the other hand, which come through virtually unscathed. They were also asked, where possible, to indicate whether there was any significant difference in the incidence of damage according to the type of rootstock used, or according to whether a particular variety was grown in bush, standard or climbing form. Contributors were also invited to mention any special features of their own gardens which might have a bearing on the incidence of damage, such as an exposed position, a low-lying "frost pocket", or the proximity of shelter from hedges, large trees or outbuildings.

Our contributors, four in number, seem to be agreed that 1965 was a really wet season, although Dr Dick, resident in the west of Scotland, did not think that the summer rainfall was more than average, and attributed the troubles in his area more to the excessively cold spring of 1965, which caused late and sometimes stunted growth. It seems to me that it is not so much the comparative rainfall for the year which is important in this discussion, as its distribution over the year and, in particular, during the vital growing season. In the following Table, based on statistics provided by the Meteorological Office, I have inserted sub-totals to indicate the periods approximating to the intervals between pruning and maturity of the first growth, and the period of development of the secondary growth, respectively. For this purpose I have assumed that pruning takes place during March, although it is conceded that many amateurs now prune in February or even earlier.

ENGLAND AND WALES

(Rainfall in inches)

	Average 1916/50	1964	1965	1966
January	3·6	1·0	3·8	2·2
February	2·6	1·2	0·7	4·8
March	2·2	3·8	2·8	1·3
	8·4	6·0	7·3	8·3
April	2·3	2·6	2·5	4·1
May	2·5	2·4	2·5	2·7
June	2·2	3·1	2·8	3·3
	7·0	8·1	7·8	10·1
July	3·1	2·0	3·8	3·1
August	3·2	2·0	2·8	4·1
September	3·0	1·3	5·6	2·2
	9·3	5·3	12·2	9·4
October	3·6	2·4	1·2	5·1
November	3·8	2·2	4·3	
December	3·5	3·8	6·3	
	10·9	8·4	11·8	
Total for year	35·6	27·8	39·1	

It will be evident from the foregoing figures that there was nothing abnormal about the rainfall during the first two quarters of 1965 except that during February it was well below the average for that month. But in 1966 rainfall was exceptionally heavy in February, April and August and well above the average for the month in June. The heaviest rainfall in 1965 occurred in September and December, with the total for each of these months nearly double the corresponding averages over the period 1916/50. With a total of 12·2 in. in July/ September 1965, approximately 3 in. more than the average of 9·3 in., over the period when the new basal shoots were growing, it is not surprising that the early November frosts of that year seriously damaged much of this resultant sappy wood, developing as it did during a period when hours of sunshine per day and temperatures were below average.

In general our contributors had comparatively few losses among their roses, although damage to the wood was severe and die back persisted until June or even later. It was found necessary to prune severely to remove the frost-damaged growth. General Naylor mentions that he found unsound wood as the summer progressed, and this was my own experience in rural Surrey. A difficulty arises in pure air districts troubled with Black Spot and Rust in distinguishing between die back caused by these diseases and that due to frosting of the tissue. While the recognition of typical Rust-damaged wood is fairly easy, the after-effects of Black Spot are not always quite so obvious.

Only Dr Dick of our contributors deals specifically with the effect on consignments of new plants. He does not mention any losses among these, but refers to severe die back in some cases. Out of one consignment of 21 plants of new varieties which I received shortly before the November 1965 frosts, I had 21 losses. The whole of the top growth turned black right to the budding point and not one of these plants showed any sign of life thereafter. I have had no comparable experience in over forty years of ordering roses, and as every plant survived from nine other consignments, comprising 111 plants, which were given identical treatment, it seems reasonable to conclude that the plants in the first-mentioned consignment were particularly soft wooded. I certainly had nothing like this experience during the winter of 1962/63, which is generally acknowledged to have been the most severe in living memory.

The evidence produced concerning stem cankers was not clear cut. General Naylor refers to older wood having a considerable number of buds which were black and dead, either from frost or stem canker. He also attributes some of the canker on the old wood to the after effects of the very severe winter of 1962/63. Mr Pallett mentions that many shoots developed dead patches round the growth breaks, but he does not identify these with canker. Mr Woolley refers to freezing rain and snow lodging in the angle between leaf stalk and stem, damaging the immature bud and setting up canker.

As an additional affliction, a heavy fall of snow on 14 April caused much damage in rural Surrey and presumably elsewhere, too. In my garden the weight of snow (a fall of between 4 and 5 in.) was such that most of the new growths were stripped from the plants and littered the surface of some beds near the house, which were very advanced, with new growths about 5 in. long at that time. As was to be expected, these beds were slow to recover from this setback. Mr Pallett also refers to this heavy snowfall and mentions that his trees then looked in a bad way.

It is unfortunate that little reference was made to the incidence of damage according to the rootstock on which the trees were budded. Mr Pallett, with all his bush roses budded on Canina stocks, did not suffer a single fatality among them. On the other hand, Dr Dick, growing his roses in what is recognised as a less favourable climate, had nine losses, all of them budded on Multiflora stocks. This accords with my own experience over the years that roses budded on Multiflora seem to be less hardy than those on Canina. I also had many dormant buds killed on cutting Multiflora stocks which were perfectly healthy late in October 1965, having been budded early in August. The severe frosts in November of that year were no doubt responsible.

Dr Dick draws attention to the fact that seven of his nine losses were of 'Perfecta' and its descendants. The trouble with 'Perfecta' seems to be an unusually high ratio of pith to hard wood in the growths, even those produced early in the season. This means, of course, that there is usually frosted wood on this variety in the average winter. As compensation it habitually throws up plenty of new basal shoots.

SUMMARY OF FINDINGS

Hybrid teas:

(a) Frost-damaged wood was much in evidence. Varieties mentioned specifically as suffering losses or severe damage include 'Super Star', 'Peace', 'Buccaneer', 'Isabel de Ortiz', 'Liberty Bell', 'Colour Wonder', 'Perfecta', 'Uncle Walter', 'Golden Melody', 'King's Ransom', 'Chrysler Imperial' and 'McGredy's Ivory'.

(b) Those mentioned as showing little damage include 'Eden Rose', 'Mischief', 'Pink Favourite' and 'Rose Gaujard'.

(c) Despite damage to the wood, losses were few, but in one instance they were confined to plants budded on Multiflora rootstock.

(d) The best treatment after extensive damage of this nature appears to be hard pruning followed by liberal but balanced feeding.

Floribundas:

(a) Frost-damaged wood was less in evidence than among the hybrid teas, even in the north. Certain varieties, however, suffered severe

'RED DEVIL' (H.T.)
'Silver Lining' × *'Prima Ballerina'*
Raised by Alex. Dickson & Sons Ltd, N. Ireland
CERTIFICATE OF MERIT 1965

'FOLIE D'ESPAGNE' (floribunda)
Raised by O. Sonderhousen, Denmark
TRIAL GROUND CERTIFICATE 1965

damage, and these include 'Dorothy Wheatcroft', 'Elizabeth of Glamis', 'Woburn Abbey', 'Chinatown', 'Heidelberg', 'Circus', 'Alison Wheatcroft', 'Lilac Charm', 'Moulin Rouge', 'Dainty Maid' and 'Paprika'.

(b) Those referred to specifically as suffering little damage include 'Queen Elizabeth' and 'Iceberg'.

Despite considerable damage to the wood of both of the above groups, the plants in general made a good recovery and produced adequate new growth from the base. Evidence regarding the incidence of stem cankers was inconclusive.

Other groups:

There was insufficient evidence produced in respect of standards and half-standards, climbers of various types and miniature roses to draw any reliable conclusions, but the Wichuraiana ramblers, as was to be expected, proved absolutely hardy.

R. L. PALLETT,
Dawes Green, Leigh, Nr Reigate, Surrey

The summer of 1965, in mid Surrey, was not a good one. The rainfall was not excessive but the frequency of wet weather produced heavy growth on the trees. Sunshine was well below average and in November an exceptionally cold spell for that time of year, lasting three days, was experienced. Fourteen degrees of frost (Fahrenheit) was recorded on one night and for twenty-four hours there was continuous frost.

My garden is on heavy soil with Wealden clay a foot below the surface, low lying, and subject to heavy radiation frost but fairly sheltered from cold winds. The beds are raised 6 to 12 in. to assist drainage. All my bush trees are on Canina stock.

Pruning was done, as usual, after leaf fall (in November in 1965) and, as for many years, a heavy mulch of cow manure applied immediately after. Supplementary feeding consisted of 4 oz. Tonks' manure at the start of spring growth and 2 oz. Tonks' at mid-July, also with some foliar feeding in July.

In February 1966 growth was normal and promised well but shortly after die back began to show itself, and this continued relentlessly, the dead wood being removed from time to time. Cold winds and a heavy snow fall occurred in mid-April and the trees then looked in a bad way, the early foliage appearing to have been burnt back.

Strong stems which had started into growth died back, some to the ground, while many shoots developed dead patches round growth breaks, which died. While the trouble was not confined to any particular variety, being common throughout the garden, two of the worst hit were 'Peace' and 'Super Star'. These had made particularly strong growth, up to $\frac{3}{4}$ in. thick, and some of these growths turned black and died to the ground.

It appears that the trouble was due to a combination of several things, first the soft growth due to the wet season and lack of sunshine, in 1965, followed very suddenly by the exceptionally cold weather of November. The damage appears to have been done at that point and showed itself when growth began and the affected stems were unable to pass the sap.

Friends who saw the roses in early May commented on their poor appearance and a bad season was anticipated. Although cutting away of dead and diseased wood continued into May, a spell of warm weather produced some rapid growth on the unaffected wood (not a single tree was killed). The improvement continued and although somewhat dwarfer than normal the trees gave a magnificent show by late June. Basal shoots in abundance have followed and, provided ripening is better this year, most of the trees will be restored to full vigour by the autumn.

Floribundas were not affected, due probably to their greater hardiness. Standards (on briar and rugosa stocks) escaped much damage, probably due to better wood-ripening and being above the most intense frost at ground level. Climbers on walls were also unaffected, doubtless due to the additional protection.

Living in a Black Spot area my trees are always affected somewhat by that disease, but it never gets the upper hand and I do not think that Black Spot was in any way the cause of the die back.

I have not, in the past, applied additional potash to my roses but shall give a late summer dressing this year to assist ripening.

Disastrous though the situation appeared at one time, I have had one more example of the strength and vigour of the rose and its ability to overcome extremely adverse conditions. As I look out over the garden on the 2 August, 1966, I see every prospect of a good autumn display and plenty of strong wood for next year.

MAJ.-GEN. R. F. B. NAYLOR,
Barnet, Herts.

Writing this on 28 August when my garden is ablaze with lovely roses and looking back over a summer in which, weather permitting, they have given me great satisfaction, I wonder why I am worrying about the winter of 1965/66! Then I remember the great quantity of frosted wood and die back I had to cut out after its depredation. So let's go back to the beginning.

The summer of 1965 was very wet and there was much unripened growth when the first frosts occurred early in November, with twelve degrees of frost recorded on several nights. From then on it was a case of "stop and go"—mild until Christmas, then a few days when twenty degrees of frost was recorded; then mild again until mid-January, followed by a bitter spell of cold east winds and the thermometer again recording twenty degrees of frost.

February was mild and by the 24th I had completed my pruning—or thought I had. I found a considerable amount of frosted wood and die back—mostly on the older wood, the younger growth appearing surprisingly sound. Early in March I gave the beds a dressing of 3 oz. per square yard of John Innes Base Fertiliser followed by a mulch of leaf mould and cow manure early in May. In late March there was another cold spell when up to fourteen degrees of frost were recorded.

Early in April I went over my roses again and found more frost damage and die back. In some varieties the older wood (two years and older) was very discoloured—from black to purple and pink and a considerable number of buds were black and dead, either from frost or stem canker. Some of the discoloured wood proved on being cut into to have been frosted, but some was quite sound. Where necessary I carried out a severe second pruning and hoped I had left only sound healthy wood. However, as the summer progressed I continued to find wood that had been affected, which I at once cut out.

The most affected varieties were: *Hybrid teas:* 'Super Star', 'Golden Melody', 'McGredy's Ivory', 'Chrysler Imperial', maiden bushes of 'King's Ransom'. *Floribundas:* 'Lilac Charm', 'Circus', 'Alison Wheatcroft', 'Moulin Rouge', 'Paprika', 'Dainty Maid'.

My climbers got off lightly, except 'Meg', which was killed—it was not very strong anyhow.

I lost few bushes and those that were killed were, like 'Meg', poor specimens. The worst affected of the lot was 'Super Star' of which I have two beds separated by the house. They were very vigorous plants.

Thinking that the soil must be deficient in potash following the persistent rain I gave the beds a dressing of sulphate of potash (2 oz. per square yard) in July.

The result of all this was that my roses have done very well, throwing up a quantity of new basal shoots and providing a fine show of bloom. One or two further casualties have occurred but in general the discoloured shoots to which I referred earlier bloomed well.

Comparison with the very severe winter of 1962/63 is difficult. On looking back through my records the roses seemed to have suffered more in the winter of 1962/63, the after effects of which can still be blamed for some of the canker in what is now old wood—though then it was young.

I have been an advocate of moderate pruning, but following a hard winter I shall certainly prune correspondingly severely.

BOB WOOLLEY,
Newcastle-upon-Tyne

To me the most striking outcome of the autumn, winter and spring of 1965/66 was that experienced southern rose growers I met seemed filled with dismay and near despair at being faced with rose damage that we in the north-east have learned to expect from time to time and to take in our stride. But I understood their concern well enough—after coming from Somerset to settle on Tyneside I had felt the same way myself the first time I pruned my roses after a really hard winter.

However, let me admit that our problems were greater than usual last year. A cold start to the growing season had delayed the first flush of roses until the end of July and then, encouraged by heavy rainfall during August and September, growth was soft and lush right through autumn. Hard frost struck at the beginning of November and we were rarely without frost or snow until well into March 1966. These hard conditions were in themselves sufficient to cause widespread damage to the unripe, autumnal, basal growth, but an additional hazard made matters worse. When winter set in there had been very little of the usual, natural, end-of-season defoliation; freezing rain and snow lodged in the angle between leaf stalk and stem, damaging the immature bud and setting up canker.

The best time for pruning in this area is accepted as being the beginning of April and is adhered to by all the top growers I know. They also believe in hard pruning of hybrid teas in particular. In the spring of 1966, hard pruning became severe pruning for hybrid teas and also for many floribundas. There simply was no alternative. All wood with brown damaged pith had to be removed and that meant most of the wood above ground level. There is a standing joke among our exhibitors that when rose beds are mucked in spring following pruning, you shouldn't be able to find the rose bushes. This time it wasn't a joke, it was reality.

Of the hybrid teas, only one variety, 'Pink Favourite', really stood out in my garden as having a pronounced degree of frost resistance. In general, we expect the floribundas to be of a tougher constitution, but for the first time in my eighteen years' experience on Tyneside, they too suffered considerable damage; that is, all except 'Queen Elizabeth'. For some years I have had a 6-ft tall hedge of 'Queen Elizabeth' interplanted with 'Buccaneer'; 'Queen Elizabeth' came through the 1965/66 winter practically unharmed; 'Buccaneer' was killed outright.

Two of my favourite varieties, 'Dorothy Wheatcroft' and 'Woburn Abbey', both lusty growers, suffered very badly indeed and continued to die back after pruning, but were saved by a second severe pruning in early June.

I have never been very happy about climbing sports of hybrid teas in this area; flowering is late to start and after the first flush blooms are sparse. One, however, that does well, flowering early, is 'Clg. Mme

Edouard Herriot' and surprisingly it was not affected much at all by the frosts. On the other hand, there was a lot of dead wood on 'Clg. Mrs Sam McGredy' and 'Clg. Crimson Glory' in particular.

'New Dawn', 'Albertine', 'Emily Gray' and 'Crimson Conquest' have always been hardy in my garden, as also have the ramblers 'American Pillar', 'Dorothy Perkins' and 'Excelsa'. Again they came through the winter unscathed.

My old-fashioned roses showed no sign whatsoever that the winter had been more arduous than usual, but they would not have retained their popularity if they didn't have such tough constitutions, would they?

We grow and have considerable affection for miniature roses, in particular the varieties 'Pour Toi', 'Rosina', 'Baby Masquerade', 'Baby Gold Star' and 'Perla De Alcanada'. They needed no more pruning than usual in spring.

Our situation is too windy for full standards, so we have to be satisfied with half-standards. Of these, the floribunda 'Meteor' and the hybrid tea 'Barbara Richards' did not survive the winter. The floribunda 'Dickson's Flame' only just struggled through and, as it hasn't improved much during the summer, it will be scrapped. On the other hand, both 'Iceberg' and 'Masquerade' proved to be completely hardy.

Among ordinary week-end gardeners, who probably outnumber the enthusiasts by something like ten thousand to one, pruning is, in my opinion, the least understood part of rose growing. But experience is a grand teacher and a lot of gardeners who previously were unable to recognise damaged wood will now know what it looks like and that it always needs to be cut right out.

In recent years autumn and early winter pruning has become something of a vogue. I remained unconvinced. One local acquaintance, fairly new to rose growing, started to practise autumn pruning a couple of years or so ago. By the end of 1965 he had come to believe that autumn pruning was the answer and that spring pruning was a thing of the past. The old hands in the north-east just smiled and bided their time. Surely enough it came. During the spring of 1966, die back had really set in and he was a very worried man indeed. Unfortunately he has since kept very quiet, so I am unable to tell you whether there was a happy ending.

But, in general throughout the north-east the roses have risen, renewed and triumphant, from their stumps. The first flush was magnificent, and rich in colour. There were very few pests—at least the winter had given *them* a hard pruning. Mildew, really the only disease problem in this area, was less than usual up to the end of July, although it has developed on the second growth of August.

At the moment of writing, there is, however, one disconcerting thought. It has been the wettest August for very many years. Are we in for a repeat of last year or even more so? I sincerely hope not, particularly for the sake of the nurserymen.

DR A. DICK,
Glasgow

Situation. My relatively small rose garden of ¼ acre is situated in Clarkston just outside the Glasgow City boundary. I grow about 1,500 rose bushes, 350 floribundas in my front garden and mainly hybrid teas in my back garden. The front garden faces due north and is very exposed; the back garden, which is terraced, is partially surrounded by a hedge almost 6 ft high and is somewhat protected from high winds and frost.

Soil. The soil is a heavy clay loam varying from 12 in. to 18 in. in depth with a blue clay sub-soil. Drainage is adequate but is assisted by land drains. The gradient is 1:7 sloping from S to N.

Feeding. Organic material in the form of farmyard manure or peat is applied in April after pruning and is lightly forked under the surface without disturbing the roots. A first dressing of rose fertiliser is then applied evenly at the rate of approx. 2 oz. to each square yard. Further dressings are given about every three weeks until the end of July, not later. A final dressing of sulphate of potash is applied before the end of August.

Weather experienced in 1965. We are concerned with any adverse effects which might be associated with the "wet season of 1965". I will not deny it was an excessively wet season in the south because on two of four visits to judge rose seedlings at Bone Hill I was well and truly soaked! However, in the west of Scotland, while we had our share of the rain, the summer rainfall was average and the hours of sunshine only slightly below average.

I consider that as far as Scotland is concerned, great significance must be placed on the lateness of the rose season in 1965. This was not due primarily to the high annual rainfall but rather to an excessively cold spring, especially during the months of April and May, which caused late and sometimes stunted growth. This cold spring was reflected in the lateness of the onset of roses coming into bloom. From the open I was able to cut only three blooms by the end of June and the first flush of hybrid teas was not at its best until 21 July. I cannot recollect such a late season during the past thirty years.

The second main flush was inevitably late. Partly because of abundant rain and lack of sunshine in the autumn months, certain varieties including 'Uncle Walter', 'Perfecta', 'Liberty Bell' and 'Isabel de Ortiz' made lush basal growth, but it was mid-October before the garden was really colourful, although blooms were unfortunately somewhat weather-marked. The rain continued until the end of the year, apart from two cold snaps in mid-November and late December when the temperature dropped below 20° F.

Diseases encountered in 1965. Serious rose disease was not encountered in my garden during 1965. Black Spot affected only a few notoriously susceptible hybrid teas but was not really troublesome, while Rust was not experienced. Mildew was seen from mid-August onwards and was rather prevalent throughout the west of Scotland. In my own garden, in spite of preventive spraying, 'Brilliant' and 'Christian Dior' were two varieties most affected. In a wet season (or should I say in Scotland!) I doubt if Karathane, used at the strength recommended by the manufacturer, is of much value in preventing the onset of Mildew. Once it is established, as I have stated previously in *The Rose Annual*, I have still to find a remedial spray which is superior to the white oil emulsion "Volck".

The Aftermath—1966. A good time to assess the health of a rose tree is when it is pruned, so let us now proceed to assess what damage, if any, can be attributed to the season 1965. The early months of 1966 were relatively mild; owing to illness I was confined to home and was somewhat perturbed to watch the sap rising and the buds growing, almost daily, during February. Pruning commenced during the last week in February and was completed by mid-March. As the result of pruning I should like to comment briefly on frost damage, stem canker and total loss.

1. *Frost damage.* I prefer to remove all wood damaged by frost but I have found that in the presence of only superficial damage, provided the bud at the pruning site is not involved, then reasonable growth and blooms can be expected.

It was at once apparent that frost damage was exceptionally severe among all hybrid teas, although some varieties obviously suffered more than others. The abundant autumnal basal growths on 'Uncle Walter' and on 'Perfecta' and some of its offspring were frosted, almost to ground level. Also the tall growths on the floribunda shrubs 'Heidelberg', 'Chinatown' and 'Dorothy Wheatcroft' were similarly affected. Certain other varieties such as 'Eden Rose', 'Rose Gaujard' and 'Mischief', to mention a few, tended more to have superficial damage to the bark, while the inner pith was healthy.

Damage among floribundas, generally, was less severe but 'Elizabeth of Glamis' suffered badly; virtually no damage was sustained by 'Iceberg' and 'Queen Elizabeth'.

I have only 24 standard roses, budded between 2 ft and 3 ft from ground level, and the frost damage to these trees was no different from that found in the bush form of the same variety.

2. *Stem canker.* Stem cankers were encountered in the following varieties:

Number of bushes	Variety	Rootstock
2	'Isabel de Ortiz'	Multiflora
2	'Intermezzo'	"
1	'King's Ransom'	"
1	'Elizabeth of Glamis'	"
2	'Eden Rose'	Canina
1	'Peace'	"
3	'Wendy Cussons'	Laxa

I rarely encounter stem canker, so its incidence in twelve bushes must be considered high in 1966; the numbers, however, are too small to comment on its incidence in relation to different rootstocks.

3. *Total loss.* I have found previously when pruning that bushes seemingly dead eventually made late new growth; all plants which appeared to have died were left *in situ* and in no instance did revival take place. The following losses were sustained:

Number of bushes	Variety	Rootstock
2	'Isabel de Ortiz'	Multiflora
2	'Liberty Bell'	„
2	'Colour Wonder'	„
1	'Perfecta'	„
1	'Uncle Walter'	„
1	'Elizabeth of Glamis'	„

It is worth noting that all were budded on Multiflora, but is it coincidental that seven of my losses involved 'Perfecta' and seedlings therefrom?

New Rose Trees. I received several consignments of new roses during November 1965 from nurseries in Scotland, Ireland and England. Planting was delayed by wet weather and by illness, so the new bushes were of necessity heeled in at the foot of a hedge to await spring planting. Pruning was accordingly performed at the time of planting and it was found that plants grown in a latitude north of Glasgow suffered severe die back and had to be cut to within one inch of the union, while bushes grown in the south suffered no such damage. However, all bushes which were drastically pruned, as a result of severe die back, had made excellent growth by the end of July, confirming the benefit of hard pruning all newly planted bushes.

Summary of Findings. The rose season in 1965 was exceptionally late in Scotland, largely due to an excessively cold spring followed by wet summer and autumn months which lacked sunshine. Lush basal growth was late in developing, and in spite of a dressing of sulphate of potash in August was frosted almost to ground level. Stem canker was encountered but did not appear to be related to the understock.

There were nine losses, all of which were budded on Multiflora; seven of these comprised 'Perfecta' and its descendants. In a late season such as 1965 there are obvious disadvantages and difficulties experienced in rose growing in the north, because insufficiently ripened wood on both cutbacks and maidens suffers considerable winter damage.

The Minoan Roses

RONA HURST

Many have agreed with my late husband (Dr C. C. Hurst) that the frescoes from the great Minoan Palace of Knossos in Crete show the earliest depictions of roses known at present. But owing to muddles over the colour and other points due to faulty reproductions and mis-statements, the later descriptions seem to have wandered considerably from the real facts. Recently I have been able to see the original Blue Bird fresco which was described and depicted by Sir Arthur Evans in his book, *The Palace of Minos*, Vol. II, in the famous Museum at Heraklion in Crete, where the treasures of these great excavations are exhibited. I was really startled at how much the facts of the real picture have been distorted and it seems important to put the story straight about this most interesting painting before more discrepancies arise.

First and foremost, a word about the frescoes themselves. It is now fairly widely believed that the great Minoan civilisation came to an abrupt end by the devastating earthquakes, blown ash and tidal waves caused by the terrific volcanic explosion of the peak in the island of Santorini, some distance to the north of Crete, around 1450 B.C. This is believed to have been of even greater violence than the comparable one at Krakatoa last century which affected places over huge distances for a considerable time. Sir Arthur Evans, the great British archaeologist, who excavated Knossos at his own expense at the beginning of this century, also believed that the Palace had been ruined by earthquakes from the very collapsed condition of the buildings of this extremely advanced civilisation. During the excavation of these, many remains of frescoes were found, both within the Palace and in other excavated buildings, showing how delightfully decorated their inner walls had been.

These broken fragments of thin slabs of plaster, with the remains of paintings showing on one side, constituted a major jigsaw puzzle for those who so painstakingly attempted to build them up into their original form. Pieces found together were not necessarily belonging to the same picture or pattern, since not only were different designs occurring on the same wall, but in some cases one on top of another

—having become tired of one decoration the room had been "re-decorated" by another being placed on top, as may be seen in the Queen's Megaron. The plaster was not only broken into pieces of different sizes but much of it was smashed beyond recognition so that, though the remains of the frescoes as a whole give a most lively picture of the beauty and charm of the interiors, there is no complete fresco remaining and much imagination had to be exercised by the artist who was responsible for their restoration, the placing of the pieces, and the necessary additions to unite these and to build them up into a complete picture. Many people are shocked to see the liberties that have been taken in the process, though if one examines other frescoes in the "picture gallery" they now form in the Museum, one can see that it is possible to build up unified pictures by the close study of similar ones, though one feels that the results are usually more highly stylised than the originals, judged from the remaining parts of these.

Some of the greatest liberties, however, have been taken in produc-ing the various freehand copies which have been made to give the idea of a fresco as a whole without the confusion of the originals, in which the remaining pieces of painted plaster are stuck on to a background and joined together by painting in additional bits, as the artist thought it might have been judging from the remaining parts of the design. If one imagines a large and intricate jigsaw puzzle with at least half its pieces lost from various parts of it, often in huge chunks, and the vacant places painted in by someone who has never seen the completed picture, one gets a pretty good idea of most of the fresco pictures as one sees them today. The freehand reproductions follow these fairly closely in outline but leave out as a rule the joins, so obvious in the restored fres-coes, between the real parts and the additions, so that one has no idea which is which. They are also more stylised than the originals and, working on the basis that frescoes painted some three and a half millenia ago must have faded, the colours are often made extraordin-arily brilliant with little relation to those remaining on the frescoes. Since these were securely buried in relatively dry conditions it is not very probable that they would have lost much of their pristine colours if one compares them with the still unfaded colours of the paintings in the Egyptian tombs, many of which are much older.

As Hurst describes in his *Notes on the Origin and Evolution of Our Garden Roses*, R.H.S. Journ. XLVII, 1941 (reprinted by Graham

Thomas in his *Old Shrub Roses*, 1955, p. 66) he first saw one of these reproductions at Sir Arthur Evans' house at Oxford in 1926, during our visit there for the British Association Meeting. This was not of the famous Blue Bird fresco previously mentioned, but I think probably the one described by R. W. Hutchinson in Chapter 10 of his *Prehistoric Crete*, in which two blue monkeys are seen among rocks, with various flowers around. In the reproduction we saw, the rose flowers were of the deep terracotta pink favoured in these copies, but Hutchinson describes the ones he saw as yellow and names them as *Rosa foetida*, the so-called Austrian Briar. I have not seen the fresco but it seems rather unlikely that there would be a yellow rose in this area at that time. *R. foetida* was originally a wild rose of western Asia which seems to have been unknown in Europe and North Africa until the coming of the people from western Asia in the first millennium A.D. This species also has a very different leaf shape.

In view of the blue monkeys, Hurst was not unduly perturbed at the colour of the flowers, which were also unusual in having six petals, but most artists, even today, care little as to botanical details when they are building up a stylised picture. The leaves were all trifoliate but this again is not unusual, several *Rosa* species having mostly three leaflets and many more show this character in the upper leaves of their flowering stems.

When visiting the Heraklion Museum in 1964, I was delighted to find the Blue Bird fresco "in the flesh"—and even more delighted to find the roses neither terracotta, nor yellow, but definitely pink. Hurst had tentatively identified these Minoan roses as *Rosa sancta*, the Holy Rose of Abyssinia and Egypt. This is a type of single Gallica, probably a cross with *R. phoenicia*, which was found growing in Christian sanctuaries in Abyssinia by two French travellers of the last century, who brought it back to Europe. In England, however, although plants have been flowered at times, it is not really hardy. During the 'eighties Sir Flinders Petrie found a wreath in one of the tombs he was excavating in Egypt, of between the second and fifth centuries A.D. Among other flowers were nine roses which were sent to the great Belgian botanist and rosarian, François Crépin, who identified them as *Rosa sancta*, which had been so named from its connection with the Abyssinian holy places. Crépin did not believe the rose to be indigenous to these African countries but more probably an introduction from Italy, Greece or

Asia Minor in Roman times when roses were widely cultivated in Egypt for the Roman market. The great seafaring civilisation of Minoan Crete was in close contact with these three areas where the wild *R. gallica* grows and its descendants were cultivated from the earliest known times.

If we look up *R. sancta* in Miss Willmott's *The Genus Rosa* (Part XVII, 1912 and p. 337, Vol. II, 1914) we find a fine picture of this rose by the artist, Alfred Parsons, which curiously corroborates the Minoan story since, though it is pictured with five petals, there is a small extra petal inside in what is usually called the "semi-single" manner—presumably *R. sancta*, like all Gallicas, has a propensity for increasing its petals. The colour of the flowers is normal rose colour slightly tinged with yellow, and is described in the text as pink. Moreover the leaves below the flowers have three leaflets, though there are five to seven on the lower leaves.

It was not till after I had first seen the Blue Bird fresco that I discovered that the Minoan roses were being widely described as yellow, and that Sir Arthur Evans himself had described them as a golden rose colour. E. A. Bunyard had seen what was presumably a reproduction of the Blue Bird fresco at an Exhibition at Burlington House in 1936, and wrote a note on this for the 1937 *Rose Annual* (p. 160) with a colour illustration in which the roses have certainly come out yellow, whether really so in the reproduction used, or through a fault of the printing, one cannot say. Actually the whole thing is rather out of gear, since only a small section of the whole picture has been taken and not only put sideways but also in reverse, so that one gets a mirror image of the real thing. But it does show with splendid clarity the outlines of the actual pieces of the fresco itself, as distinct from the modern additions, which brings into sharp relief the fact that *only one rose flower* survives of the original fresco; the others are modern additions. But most fortunately this one flower comes in the middle of quite a large piece of genuine fresco and though obviously not appearing as clear-cut as the modern additions or the reproductions of it, it has a more natural appearance and although not outlined as in the modern ones, it appears to have five petals (see p. 64). In fact with its pale pink colour it looks a perfectly normal single rose. It is in the two which have been added by the modern artist that we find six boldly outlined petals, and although he has used the pink shade of the original he has added a slight hint of yellow which is probably what caused Sir Arthur to call it a golden rose colour, meaning of course rose pink with a touch of gold and not the colour of a golden rose. In the rather garish reproductions that one can buy as postcards in the Museum, they are again shown as the deep terracotta pink, though not quite so deep as the ones we saw at Oxford. The Blue Bird itself had lost its head in the original fresco and the one added also seems somewhat imaginative.

During this spring (1966), I was again visiting the Heraklion Museum and having by this time realised its importance I took a colour photograph of the fresco which happily, on Kodachrome II film, did come out the real colour, in spite of the fact that the painting is hanging in rather a dark corner and, having glass over it, reflects rather badly. The modern additions are far more stylised than the original bits. The flower buds in particular have been criticised as most un-roselike, but the few remaining on the original part are not unlike those of R. sancta which has curiously foliaceous sepals. These are just above the flower and show three buds with rather long pedicels coming from nearly the same point, another agreement with Parsons' painting. The cluster of rose leaves and stems at the top of the fresco is largely imaginary, since there are only three single pieces of plaster left showing leaves and stems which might be in any position with regard to one another or to the rest of the picture. The restoring artist has joined them with curving stems, adding more leaves, a flower and the unlikely buds. One cannot help feeling that these pieces might be better located at the bottom below the other rose section and the other way up, with less curving stems.

An interesting point about the leaves in the original, and also copied in the additions, is the strong simple veining which is such a characteristic appearance in the Gallica roses. This is left out in the Bunyard reproduction in which the leaves as a whole are different from those on the fresco. Incidentally the upper leaves of the flowering branches of my own bush of R. gallica officinalis have three leaflets, the paired ones almost sessile and at right angles to the upper leaflet exactly as depicted in the original fresco, though not always in reproductions.

It would really seem that the Minoan Rose, on the Blue Bird fresco at all events, if not R. sancta itself, was probably some other form of R. gallica which, as a wild-growing species, extends from France to Persia. It appears to have been one of the earliest roses to be cultivated,

M. Gravereaux identifying it with the roses used in the religious ceremonies of the Median Fire Worshippers as far back as the twelfth century B.C., which is only some three hundred years subsequent to the
end of Minoan Crete. It has also early connections with various
Mediterranean civilisations, either as a religious symbol or as a garden
ornament, while in its darker forms it comes into our own history as
the Red Rose of Lancaster.

A is the rose flower of the original fresco, with five petals.

B & C are two roses added by the modern artist, with six petals.

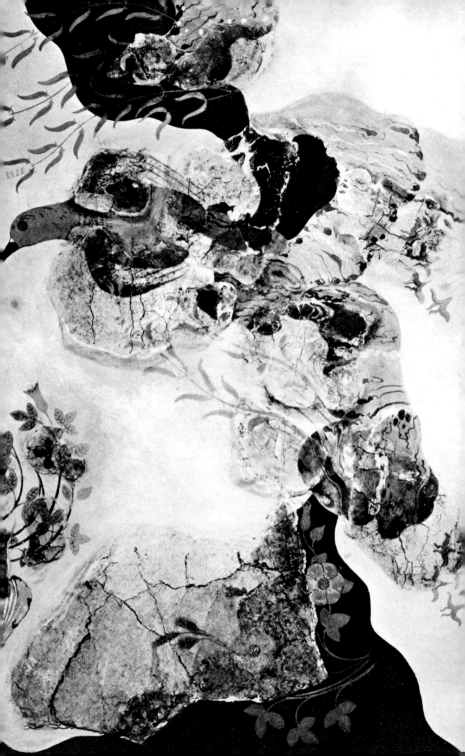

A fine specimen weeping standard of 'Excelsa' (Wichuraiana rambler)
(*see page* 66)

Weeping Standard Roses and Kindred Types

C. PAWSEY

I have often stood looking in admiration at a weeping standard rose in full flower, and wondered why so few people make use of these specimens in their gardens. Standing in their own individual bed on a lawn, on their tall stems, with cascades of rich crimson, pink, yellow or white flowers, they are, indeed, a handsome sight. Is it because the Wichuraiana ramblers, with their naturally trailing growth, have been the main type of rose used for this purpose and, with only three weeks of prodigal flower, are for so long a period in the year lacking in colourful appeal, although still graceful specimens in the garden? If so, with the advent of the repeat-flowering Kordesii types now available such as 'Leverkusen' and 'Ritter von Barmstede', the future for weeping standards may look more promising.

The ideal setting for such a specimen is in a small round bed, some 2 ft 6 in. in diameter, cut in a lawn—the greensward accentuating the beauty of the display and the grace and symmetry of outline. Used as a centrepiece or feature in a rose bed, these plants are not displayed to their best advantage, and the trailing growth may well damage the surrounding bushes in high winds.

As with all the good things in life, the best results are not obtained without understanding, patience and effort, and I will try in my limited way to give advice on how perfection may be achieved.

These trees are supplied on stems varying in height from 4 ft 6 in. to 5 ft, usually on Rugosa understock, although cultivated briar stems are available. This height is reasonable to give dominance to a position, although in the old days of the hedgerow briars plants as tall as 7 ft were on offer. It has been recognised that these were too tall to be conveniently managed, and were liable to damage in exposed positions.

The preparation of the ground and planting is most important. The soil should be double dug, with a good application of well rotted manure and/or garden compost well mixed into both top and sub-soil. Bonemeal should be added to the soil when planting so as to come into reasonably close contact with the roots to enable the plant to make quick use of this fertiliser. A stout hard wooden stake, some 1½ to 2 in. square, to reach well into the head, should be driven into position prior to, or at the time of, planting, and the plant securely tied. When supplied from the nursery, for tidiness and ease of packing, the top growth will be tied up straight to a cane; released from these ties, the varieties with drooping growth will fall into position in a natural manner.

Here is where we come to a division of types, between the varieties of natural trailing habit and those of stiffer growth necessitating the use of a trainer, and I will first detail the procedure with the former, taking as an example the Wichuraiana 'Excelsa'.

In the first season following planting no pruning is necessary, other than cutting away any die back of the shoots which may occur. A well-balanced fertiliser may be given to advantage in late May, to encourage healthy growth, and a reasonable flowering display can be expected in July. Remove any wild growth that may appear on the stem, or from below ground level, making sure that both are cut away cleanly. When pruning in succeeding years, bear in mind that the wood to be retained, and which will produce the best flower sprays, comprises the young rods that develop from the head of the plant, the number of which will determine the amount of old wood that can be removed. Some six of these rods will furnish the plant, and I would not recommend at any time leaving more than nine, as it is surprising the amount of coverage the flowering sprays produced will effect. Sufficient rods may not be obtained in the first year or two to allow dispensing with all the old wood, so where some of this wood has to be retained, the laterals which have flowered should be spurred back to within three or four eyes of the main shoot. However, avoid retaining this old wood for a further year.

It may be wiser to effect the pruning in two stages. In the autumn, remove the surplus old wood and tie down the new shoots without tipping them. Partially spur back on the old wood, so reducing the top growth to a minimum, to help withstand the winter gales, completing the operation in the spring. I firmly believe that pruning as outlined above is best—one must not think of the amount of wood that is being cut away, but rather of the strong growth which will result if one hardens one's heart. Too light pruning will mean a matted head which will carry few sprays of high quality and lead to a much earlier replacement of the tree than would otherwise be necessary.

Without doubt, it is the Wichuraiana types which are most naturally suited for weeping standards, but the use of Kordesii type climbers, with their repetition of flower, provides a tree with full attraction for the greater part of the summer. Their growth varies from stiff to trailing, and the latter can be treated in exactly the same way as Wichuraianas.

The stiff growers—for example, 'Danse du Feu'—require different treatment in the initial stages, and with these a trainer is a necessity. This is an umbrella-shaped metal cage of galvanised or plastic-coated wire, easily attached to the head of the stake, and it can be obtained in two forms—in one piece for maiden trees, or in halves for attaching to established specimens, where it would be impracticable to fix in position in one piece.

Because it will be impossible to pull down the shoots of the stiff growers when supplied from the nurseryman without breakage, these should be left tied as received. In the spring, sacrificing any thought of early flowers, cut the shoots down to within two or three eyes of the head, securing the resultant growth to the trainer when in a pliable state before it has really ripened. These shoots will flower in late August and September, and subsequent pruning will be on the lines earlier described, remembering to tie down the young rods as they are growing in the summer.

I have not touched upon the old favourites such as 'Albertine', 'Albéric Barbier' and 'Paul's Scarlet Climber', but for these the type of treatment depends upon the nature of the growth, and one or other of the methods already described should be used as appropriate.

Thus, when selecting the variety to add grace to the garden, there are three distinct types to consider. The true Wichuraiana rambler, with its mass of trailing flower sprays has, undoubtedly, the greatest elegance and beauty. The Wichuraiana climbing variety of the 'Albertine' type, with its stiffer growth, but larger flowers, can be a picture if correctly pruned and trained, and, finally, the repeat flowering varieties. The great disadvantage of the two former types is the limited period of flowering, and it is to be hoped that many more of the Kordesii varieties, with a natural trailing habit of growth, and other repeat flowering types will become available for this purpose in future.

Below will be found a Schedule of varieties of the various types commonly, or formerly, grown in weeping standard form. Some of these are available through the trade today—in the case of those that are not, the enthusiastic amateur may well propagate the variety of his choice, using the techniques explained in the admirable article on Standard Roses by Mr Pallett in the 1966 *Rose Annual*.

Schedule
Varieties of the various types

	(1) *Summer flowering*	(2) *Repeat flowering—*
(a) *True Wichuraiana weepers*	(b) *Those of stiffer growth*	*Kordesii and others*
*'Crimson Shower'	*'Albéric Barbier'	*'Danse du Feu'
*'Dorothy Perkins'	*'Albertine'	*'Dortmund'
*'Excelsa'	*'American Pillar'	*'Golden Showers'
*'François Juranville'	'Chaplin's Pink Climber'	*'Hamburger Phoenix'
'Jersey Beauty'	'Chaplin's Pink Companion'	*'Leverkusen'
'Lady Gay'	*'Crimson Conquest'	*'New Dawn'
*'Lady Godiva'	'Dr W. Van Fleet'	'Parkdirektor Riggers'
'Léontine Gervais'	*'Easlea's Golden Rambler'	*'Ritter von Barmstede'
*'Minnehaha'	*'Emily Gray'	'Soldier Boy'
*'Sanders' White'	'Mary Wallace'	
*'Snowflake'	*'Paul's Scarlet Climber'	
'Veilchenblau'	'Purity'	
*'White Dorothy'	'Thelma'	

Editor's Note: It is, unfortunately, true that some of the varieties included in the above Schedule are not available in weeping standard form today. Those which are offered in at least one well-known rose specialist's catalogue for 1966/67 are indicated with an asterisk (*). In addition, some of the smaller rose specialists may be prepared to bud with a variety not normally listed, against a firm order.

> For if I wait, said she
> Till time for roses be,
> For the moss-rose and the musk-rose
> Maiden blush and royal-dusk rose,
> What glory this for me
> In such a company?
>
> —Elizabeth Barrett Browning

This Rose is Alive

W. J. W. SANDAY

It is true to say I discuss the growing of roses with hundreds of rose friends each year. Some have vast experience, but by far the greater number are needing helpful advice, anxious to do everything well, but with some sense of fear—possibly looking upon the rose as some special branch of horticulture needing precise treatment, failing which success is most unlikely. If these few pages help to dispel such views and prove to our less experienced friends that the title of this article is the basis of good growing then I am well rewarded.

It may serve a useful purpose if in the first instance I talk of these very doubts that we all have faced over the years, growing this glorious flower, for no one was born with knowledge: all had to be learned by experience, enthusiasm and experiment out of which developed an ever growing affection for the rose.

More queries and doubts are raised concerning pruning than anything else and so often the advice of the experienced grower to prune newly planted bush hybrid teas and floribundas to within a few inches of the soil is difficult to accept. I understand full well that it requires a little pluck to cut down a strong healthy young plant in this way, but believe me it must be done and if it provides a little courage, I assure you that when I am planting a new bed the trees are reduced to two or three inches from the soil without the slightest anxiety. It is in this first year that the work of pruning is so utterly important in preventing basal eyes going to sleep and providing a well-developed plant free from those ugly bare stems that we see so often as the result of inadequate pruning.

To emphasise Nature's work and with the Editor's permission, I quote from an article I wrote in the 1961 *Annual*:

"I get a lot of joy just marvelling at the protection Nature provides in an effort to sustain plant life. The safety-valves represented by basal dormant eyes, more cautious than the frivolous eyes that break into growth at the first approach of spring. A sharp frost—Nature's only pruning—and these young shoots are cut off, following which the stronger and more capable basal eyes come into growth, making further attempt to flower and form a seed-pod. It's an untidy way of doing things as you can see if you study briars growing in the hedgerows, but the object is not tidiness. Then again a season without damaging frost and so many of those basal eyes on the briar stems remain dormant, leaving ugly, leggy stems, useful no doubt to those of us wanting to bud up standards. When this cycle of events is studied and understood our own practised pruning becomes much more simple in the effort to avoid untidy plants in our own garden.

Hard pruning will never kill a healthy tree but bad drainage and starvation certainly will."

Let me add one thing to what I have already written—see that you work with sharp secateurs—to "make do" can only lead to trouble.

Climbers and shrubs are of course rather a different matter and need to be treated according to their classification, so clearly defined in R.N.R.S. publications. In any event they do not seem to create anxiety, largely, I assume, because the treatment is not so drastic.

It is essential to emphasise that all the pruning in the world will not compensate for lack of food. If you fail to feed adequately how can you expect the trees to thrive? Do humans and animals make sturdy subjects if starved? However, this does not mean you should plaster with artificials, hoping the young plant will catch up with others planted years before.

It really is so simple if you consider that the new plant must make new root in its new home. It must be given time to like you and to feed gently into the depth of the soil in the bed you have prepared well before planting time, taking nourishment meanwhile from the slow-acting bone meal and the peat used at planting time which assists the formation of fibrous roots.

Following first year pruning disappointment is often caused by shoots failing to produce a flower bud, referred to as "blind" shoots. Most varieties are subject and in the case of some very strong growers such as 'Peace' and 'Queen Elizabeth' it is not unusual to find it happening each year. The cause is basically three-fold. In the first place the young plant is trying to do too much work before the roots are sufficiently established to sustain all shoots to fertility. Late frost arresting the flow of sap at a vital period of development can be a factor, particularly with older trees, and lastly, following a severe winter, the mistake of pruning to frosted wood is bound to restrict the flow of sap. From the blind shoots we are talking about lateral growth will eventually appear from which come flower buds, but the process can be quickened by reducing the blind shoots an inch or two when first observed. In any case it is nothing to cause anxiety.

I might mention one further thing before passing to another subject. It is essential following a severe winter, when evidence of frost damage exists, to hard prune established plants, even if you prefer to join the school of less severe pruners of which I am certainly *not* a member. I believe that reasonably hard pruning (with a few exceptions) is a long-term necessity resulting in healthy eyes producing strong basal shoots and a uniform and healthy plant. With this warning—pruning and good food are inseparable and go hand in hand.

How often do we hear the complaint of heavy flowers balling or rotting in wet weather or, conversely, lighter petalled flowers opening too quickly in heat. Poor rose! What it is expected to suffer without showing any sign of distress. What do we look like in a thunderstorm without a mackintosh or umbrella, or how do we feel in abnormal heat? Why should the rose function perfectly and last for ever under all conditions, when nothing else does? Rotting of blooms is normally the result of heavy, wet flowers being unable to get rid of water and afterwards becoming sun baked. Certainly petal texture is very much a factor affecting one variety more than another, yet 'Karl Herbst', with very tough petallage, is one of the worst offenders. If you love your roses you must forgive the bad days and appreciate to the full the good ones. Don't blame the rose or listen to reams of nonsense on what the breeder should or should not do, to avoid it. Of course it's a fault if you expect absolute perfection always, but, thinking of Nature generally, are you justified in such an outlook?

Insect pests of one form or another attack all flowers and whilst green fly and caterpillar are largely understood and easily seen, the tiny insect, thrips, is often overlooked until too late to prevent damage. In a dry, hot summer, or early autumn, the winged female is at its worst and eggs are deposited among the closely knit petals as the green sepals slowly unfold. The minute reddish brown nymphs can be seen among the petals moving very quickly and the general action causes bruising and discoloration on the edges of the bloom, so obvious when the flower is fully open, particularly the pastel-shaded varieties. Make a point of dusting with DDT in the full green bud stage.

This leads me to disease, and so much has already been written concerning treatment for such as Black Spot that little, fortunately, need be added, apart from the reminder that even kids get measles. But we might for a moment look at possible causes of rose disease generally, because I am sure that good gardening can minimise so much trouble.

It is an accepted fact that in heavy industrial areas roses are virtually free, whereas in pure air districts they are more vulnerable. It is again accepted that bad drainage (possibly the worst enemy of the rose) prevents good growth, and poor plants are sick plants, much more likely to contract disease. You may say that well-grown plants contract Black Spot and Rust, and this is true. Therefore, let us look for the reasons. A high pH, i.e. the presence of too much lime, is I am sure a contributory factor, in which case liberal dressings of peat in and above the soil give much help. Lastly—and again I am reasonably satisfied—the feeding of artificial manures with too high a ratio of nitrogen is thoroughly bad for roses, resulting in soft growth at a time of year when disease is likely to be most troublesome, weakening the structure of the plant and laying it open not only to disease but also to frost damage and die back. Nature, you see, will not be hurried.

As with everything alive, some varieties are of course more resistant than others. Consequently, whilst I have listed the above suggestions as an aid to good growing, the efforts of the hybridist in producing new seedlings from disease-resistant parents must continue to be the all-important factor in this our world of roses.

I conclude these few pages as I began—"This Rose is Alive". This incomparable flower that brings us joy and friendships, demands your understanding and kindness and surely of all the virtues of the true gardener, patience is the greatest.

> Then wherefore waste the rose's bloom
> Upon the cold insensate tomb? . . .
> But now, while every pulse is glowing,
> Now let me breathe the balsam flowing.
>   Thomas Moore—Odes of Anacréon, Ode 32 (1806)

The Iconoclasts

J. H. WILDING

A feature of the large Flower Shows, Southport and Chelsea, is the Rock and Water Gardens. They have fascinated me for many years. The sight and sound of running water in association with alpine plants attracts me like a panda to bamboo shoots. The upkeep must demand intricacies of attention if not as minute as a watch repair then as complicated as carving a jig-saw puzzle. These rock gardens course through close-cut lawns where the grass licks its way like a cat lapping milk into the interstices between the outcrops of rock—highly delectable to look at while you pass by—but that grass grows and then how do you mow it?

The lawn mower has not yet been invented that can crop neatly and closely these tongues of turf. I would require a miniature mower designed for a teddy bear and even then I would have to kneel, praying to Allah, or squat like a toad on an oak leaf in order to cut the grass; unless the machine was furnished with outlength handles or radio control like toy boats or model aeroplanes. Perhaps they mean us to cut the grass with scissors or hedging shears, and that would be conducive only to sacro-iliac strain or acute indigestion.

Limestone looks the best and the more water-worn and weather-worn the rock the better it is, so that at least one face of a piece of rock should show contour lines like the mountainous area of an ordnance survey map. These contour lines on all pieces of rock, whether water-worn or weather-worn, should travel parallel to each other. We decided on limestone for the three best reasons possible. It looks the best. It is the natural rock around Morecambe Bay. Thirdly, because it was fairly readily available, transport costs would be lighter.

The main function of the rock garden was to provide colour in the spring season of the year. The whole of the front garden would also incorporate floribunda roses and they would take care of the summer and the autumn; although I imagined a plateau somewhere in my miniature mountain landscape devoted to dwarf roses; 'Rosina', buttercup yellow dewdrops in the form of hybrid teas; 'Pour Toi', tiny white edelweiss roses; 'Dwarf King', double red buttercups; 'Coralin', salmon-coloured threepenny-bit roses; '*R. roulettii*', the wild midget rose that grows naturally in Alpine meadows; 'Tinker Bell', pink fairy rosettes; and 'Cinderella', pale blush pink like a miniature 'Chanelle'.

We drew a plan—floribunda roses down each side of the drive and alongside the wall at the bottom of the garden; a lawn of sea-washed turf to serve as a setting for the roses and to the rock and water garden, where a mountain ghyll tumbled amongst the rocks to a mountain tarn. How artificial! But all formal gardening is artificial! You break your heart fighting a losing battle against Nature in the fond hope that you are creating a natural composition—signing your name on a constantly disappearing canvas—stamping your trade mark on a patch of all absorbent sedge moss. We sent the plan to a landscape gardener and he quoted a price. That, we thought, was that. How little I knew!

It was then September and the first disappointment turned up like a snail amongst the lettuces when he said he could not begin the construction for another twelve months. Fortunately that autumn we were able to plant the first half of the rose trees, already ordered, in a bed and a border away from the construction area. The following summer we ordered the second half of the roses. We had drawn the rose borders to be prepared by the landscape gardener. However, that summer we decided to prepare them ourselves lest the roses should arrive in the autumn before the garden was ready. Meadow grass, thistles, creeping buttercup, and other perennial growth had gained a tight hold over the garden, as it then stood, like leeches on succulent flesh and they were as averse to releasing their grasp.

The thistles and the buttercups were the worst. The roots of the one grew as deep as a plumbline set in an unfathomed sea, and the others ranged as far as the distant water holes on a prairie; and if you left behind a fragment of root they cropped up again like the serpents on a Medusa's head. I have read poetic accounts of purple-headed thistles on the Argentine pampas and meadows golden with buttercups. They might play a leading part in verse or prose but in a garden they cast only satanic spells.

September came round again and charmed the days away with roses dancing a front row chorus against a backdrop of blue fells at the head of the estuary, and beyond Holm Island, which sparkled like an emerald in a ring of the golden sands of the estuary. Beyond the nearer sands Meathop Crag stood sentinel above the toy railway before it crossed the viaduct over the estuary to Arnside.

A letter arrived to say that the firm of landscape gardeners was short-staffed and could not undertake garden construction for another month. Meanwhile the second half of the rose trees arrived and we planted them out. One month rolled away into another. The meadow grass and the weeds died down so that the top of the wall at the bottom of the garden leered above the lower rose border like carious dragon's teeth.

Winter passed away. We pruned the roses and they began to grow. So did the meadow grass, the thistles and the buttercups. Then one week in May the gardeners appeared, and positioned bamboo canes to map out the line of the river channel and the site of the pool. The bamboo canes were some of those we had ourselves used to indicate the edge of the rose borders so that they would not tread on the rose trees. However after re-positioning *our* bamboos they brewed a cup of tea and then went home again.

The next day they dug out the river channel and the tarn, and lined them with coarse concrete, topped by fine and waterproofed concrete. It was too late then for early spring alpines, but I began to have visions of sapphire blue trumpets of *Gentiana acaulis* mirrored in running water, dwarf daffodils, a hanging valley planted with threepenny-bit roses, dwarf cyclamen blooming on a moraine and primulas beside the tarn, dwarf campanulas in July and miniature star-shaped phlox in June. They had brought a long hose and attached it to the tap in the garage to mix the concrete and to wash the soil away from the river channel. That was the cause of the first of the mishaps. If someone knocks a growing shoot off a rose tree it is for me more than a mishap. It is a catastrophe. That hose coiled like a long snake across a rose bed and and when they jerked it roughly it attacked tender rose shoots like a hungry python and left them lying limp and helpless on the soil.

That was only one of a chapter of accidents that seemed to haunt us all the way through the preparations for this garden. After they had laid the concrete for the ghyll and the tarn they could not continue until they had obtained the rock.

There were outcrops of limestone locally on Hampsfell and Wart Barrow. I knew Hampsfell. There were lovely views from the crown of the fell to the Lakeland mountains and across Morecambe Bay to Ingleborough. I liked the idea of transferring pieces of rock from this delectable viewpoint to our own garden. If the stone could talk what tales it could tell of fell-top walks and mountain views. The trouble was they were not digging any more out for another week and the man responsible for its extraction had broken his arm.

The gardeners came back and reported, brewed another cup of tea and departed. They received my suggestion that they might start work on the back garden with stony silence. Then one of them turned sick and we could not entice them to return until the middle of June.

One day they appeared about lunch time and said that they had found a lorry to go to Hampsfell and transport a load of rock. They found that they could not drive on to the fell by the nearest route. The lane was too narrow and so they had to go a long way round by devious roads. They returned eventually the same day with a waggon load of good looking pieces of limestone, well weatherworn and well waterworn.

A month previously I had asked them to take good care of the roses. New shoots at that time were about 6 in. long. Now they had become loaded with buds and what previously was a calamity to break off a new shoot had turned for me into a disaster. They had brought two railway sleepers to bridge the rose border from the side of the lorry and they intended to roll the bigger pieces of rock down these. I knew that more shoots would break and I found myself wondering, by a process of mental elimination, which I would mind the least seeing sacrificed, 'Evelyn Fison' and 'Melba', 'Faust' and 'Celebration', or 'Orange Sensation' and 'Celebration'. I settled for 'Faust' and 'Celebration' and could do nothing but sit and wait for the slaughter of the innocents.

The lorry arrived and trouble began when the driver started to reverse it up the drive. It was a ten-ton lorry and there was scarcely enough room to turn from the road and reverse half way up the incline of the drive. He missed the stone gatepost literally by an inch and my heart flew into my mouth. It was a magnificent piece of driving but my heart had taken wings and would not return to its thoracic nest for another hour.

They began to position the railway sleepers bridging the rose border at an angle over 'Faust' and 'Celebration', laden with plump buds like bunches of grapes. Then a sleeper slipped and fell across the roses, snapping off a strong shoot from each variety. Plump buds rolled like heads beneath the guillotine at the French Revolution.

"Pity I dropped that sleeper," said one gardener, "it was a pure accident." I thought to myself, "We haven't finished yet."

It was then that they began to hurl the rocks from the lorry across the rose border. The smaller ones they tossed over fairly easily but to the half-hundredweight boulders they could not give enough impetus to sail over the farther row of 'Celebration'. Each time a shoot snapped I could imagine a flow of sap like my own blood. It felt like an abdominal incision without anaesthetic. The crowning moment of despair came when the lorry driver, who was only sparsely built and looked in his early twenties, lifted an outsize boulder and then heaved. Unfortunately he hurled himself with it. They both fell with a dull thud on to two trees of 'Faust' and I felt as though my intestines were writhing across the floor.

"Oh well, we're only re-pruning," said one of the gardeners!

As the last piece of rock rolled down the sleepers, followed by the rapid departure of the lorry, with my gateposts still intact, I breathed a sigh of relief. I might even have forgiven them if the gardeners had gone home and not appeared again all summer.

However they stayed and began to lay the rock and said they would try to return after the weekend. But I had learned not to trust anything but definite promises and those had been conspicuous by their absence. I did not expect to see them again until the autumn. Nevertheless they did return the following week and worked hard laying rocks.

There was one saving grace about the weekend that followed that pernicious Friday. The roses started to flower. There is something about the season's first roses that outbids the others in enchantment. We are hungry for colour and starved of the sight of the curls and folds in rose petals, of rose forms and outlines. The vanguard that year was 'Charleston', 'Evelyn Fison' and 'Dickson's Flame'. If I never see perfection again the sight of that first 'Evelyn Fison' should soothe my wrinkled brow for years to come. It is a floribunda with a flower which opens like a perfect little hybrid tea of the brightest shade of red, and grows into a frilled rosette. No rose was ever more welcome or more rewarding in the sense that its very appearance almost compensated for the loss of those shoots of 'Faust' and 'Celebration'. Next came a bloom of 'Charleston', chrome yellow edged with pillar-box red, full-petalled and hybrid tea-shaped. That was a further opiate to my pained senses. 'Charleston' proved to be a mistake. Its blooms in summer are glorious, but the autumn flowers are a travesty of their summer selves —small and faded. It is a martyr to Black Spot, is reluctant to grow and sheds its leaves early.

Part of the excitement was that these were some of the new roses or roses we had not grown before. New roses have their own special charm. They keep interest alive in the garden and for that they need only be new to the gardener as 'Chinatown' was to us.

No one can become acquainted with every new rose immediately it makes its debut. Some you hold back in your memory to savour at a later date. I am glad I did not forget about 'Faust'. I must have passed by many others. There are so many! There is also a fascination about new roses, which has something to do with "Hope springing eternally"; hope that you may have found the perfect rose; optimism that you have found lasting beauty. We need to retain flexibility of mind united with intensity of spirit in a search for beauty without material gain. Perhaps we imagine novelty can lead to constancy or blind us to faults that may come to irritate or frustrate. The very novelty of the new rose and our own ignorance of its behaviour and characteristics gives it a halo and a promise probably completely undeserved. But until familiarity clouds the ideals with which we surround it, while its performance still remains an unknown quantity, imagination gilds it with a personality and an aura it will probably never attain. But if we have chosen the new rose from the nursery and the show bench to suit our fancies and expectations, what a potential for a few years of enjoyment, perhaps many summers of contentment and winters of looking forward, lies ahead.

The iconoclasts may have shattered a few ideals but the rose trees grew again, and by building the rock and water garden they furnished us with a fresh arena for flights of fancy and imagination involving the senses of vision and hearing.

Beauty on High

ROSEMARY JAMES

It is difficult to understand why so many people today appear content with the ill-designed houses the builders offer, and particularly with the pre-cast concrete horrors sold as garages. One would have thought that the high prices demanded would at least have made it possible for the architect or builder to have produced something a little less offensive. Gardeners who appreciate beauty surely cannot willingly buy these things; but, somehow, they are bullied or mesmerised into having them. Like greatness, they are thrust upon them.

However, on finding oneself encumbered with a garage resembling some sort of machine-gun emplacement, the only thing to do is to hide it as speedily as possible. By that I don't mean that a rose should be flung against the sides in the vain hope that it will soon cover this eyesore. A support must be made against which to plant the roses, and this should be about 12 or 18 in. away from the building to allow a space for air. The materials used for the support must depend on what one can afford, the cheapest being strong posts with wire between, but as the idea is to hide the garage, it would be preferable to use something stronger such as posts with fairly thick cross bars, or trellis in between. When using posts, I always insert an angle iron at the back, because no matter how good the wood, and whether put into drain pipes or not, the base always rots in time, and if the angle iron is placed in at the same time as the post, it saves having to do it in later years and probably damaging the roots.

Having prepared the planting sites, adding manure and compost, we can come to the question of varieties, bearing in mind that in such a position the main requirements are healthy, free flowering plants which will produce as much colour as possible over the season. This brings us to those which some nurserymen insist on calling "perpetual flowering", a term which the novice takes literally. He sees some new cultivar at a show where he is assured it will flower "all the season", and goes away with a picture in his mind of a pillar of colour from June until September, only later to be disappointed. A little common sense should tell us that no plant can have unending bloom, and that time must be

79

allowed for it to make new growth on which to produce further flowers.

Unfortunately, shows are places where common sense often flies to the winds, and we find ourselves believing silly statements because we want to think them true. I've done it myself! We can have repeat-flowering climbers which will either flower early and again late in the season, as in the manner of the hybrid teas, or which will bloom on and off during the summer, giving a certain amount of colour for a great deal of the time. Most of the new cultivars give more "on and off" bloom than the older ones, and with one or two exceptions neither old nor new give such a heavy crop in autumn if they have provided a really generous flush early. Those which produce less growth will give more bloom, because they can't do both at once. In other words, it's no good expecting the impossible!

It is not easy to advise others on a selection, and the oft-given advice of going to see them growing is still the best. We all have different ideas of beauty, and I am prepared to sacrifice repeat flowering (although, of course, I prefer it where possible) for an exquisitely shaped bloom or subtlety of colouring. On the other hand, I don't mind a "flippy-floppy" flower on a climber if it is really strongly scented and has a certain charm. The rose I cannot become enthusiastic about is one which is harsh in colour, or similar to many others and lacks character.

A couple of years ago I was writing about climbers for this *Annual*, and mentioned that I had replaced some of the older types with the hybrids of R. *Kordesii* and other newer cultivars. While the moderate habit of growth of these has proved a boon where space is restricted, and they are easy to manage, this hardly compensates for lack of fragrance, form and general character. With one or two exceptions, all my moderns have gone, for after a while I came to the conclusion that although they provided a certain amount of welcome colour on and off during the season, they were a rather undistinguished collection, and certainly could not compete with 'Clg. Mrs Sam McGredy'! Her lovely blooms of coppery-orange, shaded with scarlet and salmon-pink, set amid most handsome bronze-tinted foliage, are unique.

However, in a position such as we are considering, it would probably be more practical to choose a less vigorous rose, and one which will give as much bloom as possible again after the first crop. The orange-scarlet 'Danse du Feu' is most good-natured, bright without being

The recurrent-flowering climber 'GOLDEN SHOWERS' (*see page* 81)

Top: 'MME CAROLINE TESTOUT' (*see page* 91)
Below: Part of an excellent specimen of the climber 'MAIGOLD' on a wall in
Maj.-Gen. Naylor's garden (*see page* 81)

harsh, and particularly good in late autumn. The rose-pink 'Aloha' is a modern cultivar with character, bred from the inimitable 'New Dawn', with a strong "old rose" fragrance. It flowers quite freely again later in the year when the blooms are a deeper, more salmon colour. Incidentally, although it will in time reach 7 or 8 ft, it is like so many we have today, more of a shrub and may be thus grown. I find this shrub-cum-climber type rather "neither nor" in habit, although when one becomes well acquainted with them, they can be useful.

There is a shortage of good yellow climbers; the deep golden 'Royal Gold', while showy, is not in my opinion worth garden space, for the habit is not robust and it does not seem to care for our winters. The amber-tinted apricot yellow 'Maigold' is exquisite, but has very little repeat bloom, so that leaves us with the bright 'Golden Showers' and paler 'Casino'. Both are good, but the latter might prove the better for this purpose, with its handsome, shiny foliage and shapely, freely produced blooms.

Two of the best hybrids of R. Kordesii are 'Hamburger Phoenix' and 'Parkdirektor Riggers'. The large, rather loose crimson blooms of the former are borne freely, although I think the deep scarlet of the latter more attractive. The foliage is good and glossy, while both are very hardy and healthy. There does not appear to be anything particularly breathtaking among recent introductions, although the new pink 'Galway Bay' is pretty, while the creamy rose-edged 'Handel' is unusual for a climber, and will undoubtedly be popular.

The scarlet, sweetly scented 'Copenhagen' is most satisfactory and probably the best of the newer ones, not only in appearance, but for health, habit and freedom of flowering. It may well be widely grown when better known. For a dark scarlet, the older 'Guinée' takes a lot of beating, for the flowers are shapely, it has a delicious scent and blooms freely when established. I still grow one of its parents, the light red 'Souvenir de Claudius Denoyel' because it has a very sweet fragrance, is always free from disease, and produces quite a good number of blooms again in autumn. In addition, the rather loosely formed flowers, which make no claim to sophisticated elegance, have an indefinable charm.

Twenty-five Years On

F. C. H. WITCHELL

All life is irresistibly involved in a system of gradual change and development. As we live through it, we tend to accept what seem to be minor developments without appreciating the cumulative outcome. Yet, if one stops and looks back over a considerable span of time and attempts to make a rational "then and now" comparison, the sum of all the small changes appears to border on the revolutionary.

Having passed the quarter century mark as a member of the Society, I chanced recently to look back and make the aforesaid comparison and was intrigued as much by the nature as by the extent of the changes that have taken place. These have been concerned not only with the roses themselves, but encompass our very attitudes towards the queen of flowers and the techniques we apply in trying to grow our favourite roses to perfection.

A comprehensive review of every kind of change that has occurred in twenty-five or more years could quite obviously fill the entire *Rose Annual* but, as the Editor is, for some strange reason, unwilling to grant me that much space, I must restrict myself to comment on those aspects which appeal to me, as an amateur, as being particularly significant.

Of special interest to me has been the development of the Royal National Rose Society as a body. Societies of this nature are traditionally conservative and frequently find themselves targets for charges of obsolescence in attitude and general old fogyism. The amazing growth of our Society during the past twenty-five or so years (and especially in the period since the war) demonstrates its consistent up-to-dateness and freshness of outlook. Without these characteristics, it could not possibly have become acceptable to such a large multitude as its present membership of over 100,000. This figure looks almost astronomical when compared with the immediate pre-war total of a mere 10,000.

Equally astonishing has been the tremendous rise in popularity of the Society's shows. I well remember what ultimately proved to be an important milestone in my rose-growing life—my first visit to a "National" in 1939. On that occasion some 390 amateur exhibits were staged in 41 classes and an estimated 8,000 people turned up to look at them. But the whole affair was almost of village fête proportions when measured against the fabulous shows we have seen in the 1960s with around 750 amateur entries on view and nearly 60,000 people coming to view these and the breathtaking nurserymen's displays at Alexandra Palace.

And what of the exhibits that these teeming crowds so eagerly come to see—are they that much better as well as that much more numerous than in days gone by? I am quite sure that they are. Basically, most of today's roses have a greater potential than the old varieties, they are much better grown and more attractively staged, especially by the trade.

In considering the roses themselves, one sees great and significant differences in the types, their habits of growth and flowering and in the colour range. In pre-war days the popular kinds of bush roses we grew in our gardens were classified into four main groups: the polyantha pom-pons, the hybrid polyanthas, the hybrid teas and the pernetianas.

The polyantha pom-pons, which are rarely seen outside public parks today, made small bushes about 20 in. tall, carrying tight clusters of flowers of the form associated with ramblers of the 'Dorothy Perkins' type and were, even then, beginning to fall out of favour. The rose-growing public has always had a discerning eye for beauty of form in the roses it grows and the polyantha pom-pon could never satisfy a well-developed and fastidious taste.

Hybrid polyantha was a title that had then only recently been adopted to distinguish from the rest a new group of bush roses. This had been developed largely as a result of the efforts of that great Danish hybridiser, Svend Poulsen. He had sought to breed a race of really free-flowering roses, hardy enough to withstand the vicious Continental winters and had succeeded in developing a tough, vigorous race of mostly single or semi-double large-flowered varieties which produced their blooms in big sprays or trusses. These did not seem to fit into any existing category and so the Society originated the term hybrid polyantha to identify them.

As time went by, and as more new blood was introduced into the group, hybrid polyantha, in its turn, was discarded as a distinguishing mark. This occurred in more recent years, with the appearance of yet bigger, more free-flowering strains, a gradual trend towards hybrid tea shape in the flowers and the development of scent in the race. The title floribunda then seemed to be more appropriate than the old term hybrid polyantha. Now, such is the current rate of development in the group, it is being found necessary to qualify even this latest title.

Hybrid teas, in theory, were then much the same as they are today. That is to say, bushes producing large flowers of good form in three or so flushes during the season. In fact, today's varieties are generally distinguished from those of yesteryear by markedly improved health, strength and hardiness and considerable extension of the colour range. There was no 'Stella', 'Super Star' or 'Blue Moon' in the 1930s and, although there were occasional enormous growers (like 'President Hoover') the overall level of vigour was very much lower.

The fourth group, the pernetianas, which have since been merged with the hybrid teas, were yellow, apricot and orange-hued roses with glossy foliage and very thorny wood which in all other outward respects seemed to be indistinguishable from the hybrid teas.

Turning next to consider how much better we grow roses today than we did, I appreciate that there is the problem of assessing how much the high standards of quality now achieved are due to better varieties and how much to better methods of cultivation. That the part played by improved techniques is both significant and measurable cannot be doubted. I am sure that pre-war cultivation methods were not such as to get the best out of varieties then available and that, if the cream of the old favourites had received the benefit of modern treatment, they would be around and appreciated today. As a case in point within my own experience, that lovely old rose 'Mrs Sam McGredy', which I could never persuade to grow satisfactorily using the techniques of the pre-war era, made enormous trees in response to modern methods of cultivation. On the other hand, I have seen gardens where new varieties have been subjected to the kind of treatment that used to be meted out to their unfortunate ancestors. The resultant displays were quite pitiful.

Of course, in twenty-five years there have been many important developments in cultivation techniques, but those which seem to me to be particularly significant are related to pruning and feeding. In particular, it is now accepted that quality as well as quantity is easily obtainable with quite moderate pruning and that the man planting a fresh bed does not have to hack new trees down almost to ground level on pain of certain disaster if he shows the slightest trace of pity.

The viciousness of the old-time spring pruning, the lateness of the recommended dates—the end of March or early April—and the then common habit of "summer pruning" all conspired to delay the first flowering and then to ensure a flowerless gap before the second flush came along. In addition it tended to restrict unnecessarily the number of flowers a tree could possibly produce in a season.

If today's approach to pruning grants to the trees freedom to make a good display, the attitude to feeding complements it by providing the wherewithal to make the effort. Twenty-five years ago foliar feeding, as an additional technique available to the amateur, was unknown. Now, an increasing number of us regularly feed through the leaves as well as through the roots and attain measurably more growth as a result. It is particularly effective in getting young trees away to a good start in their first summer in the garden.

So far, then, this is a success story. A story in which the obvious and visible manifestations of that success are seen in the extraordinary popularity of the rose, the spectacular shows, the enormous Society membership and a flourishing rose nursery industry. But this kind of success does not just happen. There must be an influential connecting link. As I assess the situation, that link is the Society and its Trial Ground.

Before the war, trials of new roses were carried out on land made available through the generosity of the then Hon. Secretary of the Society, the late Courtney Page. Now, we are the proud owners of the delightful Bone Hill estate, with not only ample space for trials and display gardens, but excellent headquarters offices as well. Here, a raiser can obtain an assessment of how a new variety compares with existing varieties and with the novelties of other hybridisers from all parts of the world. Since all the trees are grown in conditions as nearly identical as possible, the comparisons are valid.

To me, it is of great import that raisers really do make use of this facility and that practically every new variety marketed in this country has been freely and voluntarily put through the Trial Ground and has been objectively assessed and reported on before being offered for sale. Can you think of another product that is independently tested for you and which you can go and see for yourself actually undergoing that test? If the test is valid and proper, it must clearly provoke rapid progress in the development of better varieties and, because the market can absorb only a certain number of novelties each year, must tend to eliminate all but the kinds the public really wants.

The superiority of the varieties of the 1960s over those of the 1930s is so marked that very few of the Trial Ground Certificate winners of that earlier decade could possibly reach the standards now set to obtain an award.

Obviously, the value of the trials depends upon who carries them out. Well, we know that the Society carries them out, but who is the Society? The Society is *you*, dear reader, and the trials are judged by those worthy people that you elect to the Council. Fortunately, you are wise enough to elect a nice balance of nurserymen and amateurs— both sides of the fence so to speak. Thus, we have the unusual situation of new products being rigorously tested by an amalgam of trade and customer working in a proper harmony and producing a remarkable result.

Unfortunately, such success has not been achieved in all fields. That exhibitors and flower arrangers manage to produce such gorgeous displays is in spite of rather than because of the progress made in pest and disease control. This has been most disappointing. It is true that we have systemic insecticides which can be a great help against aphids but they control nothing much else. For combating disease, I concede that the latest fungicides are less smelly and unpleasant to handle than Liver of Sulphur, Bordeaux mixture and the like, but they are very expensive and they are not all that much more effective. We still lack a real fungicide—that is, a substance that will actually eradicate an attack of Mildew or Black Spot. The relative healthiness of our modern rose gardens is, I suspect, as much due to the stronger constitution and disease-resisting characteristics of post-war varieties as to the introduction of new and supposedly better fungus preventives. I wonder if there could be any significance in the fact that the area where there has been least progress of value to the rosarian—the chemist's laboratory—is also the area where the Society has the least influence?

Photographing Your Roses in Colour

LEWIS FROST

It's odd that, even in these days, a mention of photography conjures up for some people a vision of alchemy and mystery; of the magic box under a black cloth. In order to allay any doubts or fears which may spring to the mind of the reader, let me begin by saying that it is not my intention to try to teach expert photographers. I want to help rosarians who are also occasional photographers to raise their standard of photography to a point where it can complement and do justice to the roses they grow and love.

I know that countless rose pictures are taken every year and many of these must give great pleasure to the people who take them. On the other hand, some of them just do not ring the bell, perhaps without the owners quite realising where the failure lies.

Most people own a camera, usually a comparatively simple one, with a limited range of adjustments. With such a camera it is quite easy to take colour pictures, either transparencies or colour prints according to personal taste, over a wide range of weather conditions. This can include shots in shade, indoors, or shots taken in poorish light but which depend on short exposure times in order to "stop" a moving subject.

Your photographic dealer will be able to advise you on the film best suited for your purpose if you explain what the limitations are. For instance, rosarians know only too well that a rose bloom is only at its peak of perfection for about an hour and, if this time happens to coincide with a period of adverse weather, one of the high-speed films such as High Speed "Ektachrome" will prove the means of saving the day.

Dealing first with composition, remember that the keynote here is *simplicity*. So often one sees pictures of large rose gardens which appear to be overflowing all round the edge of the frame. To the eye of the beholder, no doubt, the expanse of roses looked a beautiful sight, but a camera lens cannot cover as great an area as the human eye. Result, the picture loses impact. So, never try to cram too much into the picture. On the other hand, do make sure that what you really want to photograph fills the viewfinder. All too frequently the subject occupies a small part of the picture area with a large expanse of distracting background or foreground filling the remainder of the space. Compose the scene in the viewfinder and get close enough to make the most of the subject.

One way to get in close to a subject is by using a close-up attachment. This may be either a supplementary lens attachment, a bellows extension or an extension tube. Whatever the means employed, the ability to focus down to distances well below the normal range of the lens will mean that you can record detail which is not normally possible. Roses photographed at distances beyond 4 or 5 ft tend to lose their clear outline and become blobs of colour. This does not matter if you are taking a general shot. But if you want to get the detail of form and texture and the subtle changes of shade across the bloom, then you should get close and concentrate on the individual bloom.

When working at these close ranges the measurement of the distance must be very accurate. The depth of sharp focus is small, especially when larger apertures are being used. There are several ways of effecting the necessary accurate measurements. Some types of camera can be fitted with a close-up rangefinder, a device which not only takes care of the distance problem, but also shows accurately the size of field at the given distance. Other cameras can be equipped with a set of gauge rods. These are fitted to the base of the camera and extend in front of it to form a frame within which the subject is composed to get a sharp result.

If your particular camera does not have a set of these rods available as an accessory, it is quite simple to manufacture a set of focal frames suitable for the various close-up lenses available for your camera.[1]

Failing all other aids, simple measuring devices such as a length of dowel rod cut to the correct length, or a piece of string knotted at the appropriate point can be used. In use, these are held between the lens of the camera and the subject so that the ends of the measuring device just touch the front of the lens mount and the centre of the flower. When you are sure of the correct distance drop the measure out of the field of view and make the exposure.

Most of these devices, in addition to providing accurate distance

[1] A pamphlet describing how to make these frames and giving all measurements for the whole series of "Portra" lenses may be obtained by writing to the Sales Service Library, Kodak Limited, Kingsway, London, W.C.2, asking for Leaflet B 10.

measurement, also provide a means of overcoming "parallax". This is the effect caused by the camera lens not "seeing" exactly the same picture area as that which appears in the viewfinder. In most cameras the viewfinder is situated a little way from the camera lens and consequently the areas covered differ somewhat. The effect is not of great importance when working at distances above 5 ft or so, but at the close-up ranges it becomes very marked and allowance must be made for it.

I have already mentioned the necessity of keeping large areas of distracting background out of the picture, and failure to do so is probably the most frequent cause of disappointment with close-up shots. It can be avoided by providing a false background, a sheet of neutral material, grey or black for preference, which can be supported behind the subject. The sky is always available and by sighting the camera so that the rose is set against a blue sky a pleasant effect will be achieved. If it proves impossible to provide a suitable background, you can reduce the effect of a messy background by using a small depth of field so that the subject is registered as sharp against an out of focus surround. The greater the size of aperture used, the shallower the depth of field, so, open up the aperture as far as possible and adjust the exposure by decreasing the exposure time.

A photographic record of Rose Shows is not a difficult undertaking. Since the best of the blooms are all assembled in one place and are displayed to their best advantage, it is an excellent opportunity to get wonderful pictures of roses as they should be under ideal conditions. Most societies do not object to visitors photographing their shows so long as no inconvenience is caused to other people, and the exhibits are not interfered with.

The difficulty, in my experience, is one of too much to photograph rather than too little. Exhibits are frequently placed close together without too much attention to clashes of colour and form. Hence it is strongly recommended that special attention be paid to getting the picture composed carefully, so that only what you want appears. This may involve a bit of manoeuvring but the result will be well worth while.

A fruitful source of good rose pictures is a Flower Arrangement class or show. These competitions are rapidly gaining popularity in this country and are well worth recording.

Getting away from the photography of the beauty of roses, I want to touch on the use of the camera as a scientific instrument. You will have seen examples of this over the years in *The Rose Annual* and will probably have attended illustrated talks on technical aspects of rose growing, where the use of projected slides or movie films has been the means of demonstrating rather complicated and perhaps quite new techniques, so that all present have been able to see for themselves exactly what is being done. A well-planned picture can replace hundreds of words of explanation.

The majority of the remarks made so far can apply equally to movie film as to still pictures. It is true to say that a good picture is good for the same reasons whether it is still or movie. There are, however, a few differences in movie camera technique which should be used to improve the standard of your movies.

A point to remember when taking moving pictures is "Let the subject do the moving, not the camera". If you wish to "pan" the camera, i.e. to rotate it horizontally (or more infrequently vertically) while filming, in order to cover a large subject, move it only half as fast as you think you should and you will find the effect will be natural when the film is projected. Incidentally, do not wait for the rose to be absolutely still before you start filming. The slight movement will look very attractive and will not appear blurred as might be thought. Just remember to keep the camera centred on the spot the flower would occupy if it were still.

Finally, do not put your camera into hibernation for the winter. Some of the species produce fine ornamental heps and these, taken in contrast to the rather sombre monotones of winter, make startling colour pictures. There is a point to watch when taking pictures in winter, and to a lesser extent spring and autumn too. The light from the sun, although it may appear strong, is rather weak compared with the summer sun for which most exposure recommendations are made. Manufacturers usually include in their film instruction sheets a correction for exposures at these times of year and this should be followed, even though it may seem excessive at the time.

Rose Indestructible

W. P. BROOKS

Some time ago I read in a gardening magazine a paragraph about a 'Mme Caroline Testout' bush which was estimated to be well over fifty years old. I cannot claim such longevity for my "Caroline", but she is more than half that age and she has had a remarkable life so far. If I wanted to rename her, I would call her 'Resuscito', for she has overcome many trials and apparent death only to rise again in triumphant flowering.

I bought this variety as a bush in 1938. It grew well from the start and provided a wealth of bloom each season. During the dark days of the war, "Caroline" presented us with masses of flowers every summer. About 1944 or 1945, when everyone was looking to the future with hope and confidence that peace was at last coming to a war-weary world, "Caroline" decided on her contribution to change for the better. She decided to change from a bush to a climbing habit, lengthening her stems and trailing them across my front garden path. I pruned and tied back these leaders but without success for "Caroline" was set on her purpose, determined to follow a new fashion.

As nothing I did would stop her, in the autumn of 1946 I dug her up and conveyed her tenderly to a small fence dividing the garden from the public footpath. There I trained the ever-lengthening trailers along the fence and for years they bore masses of bloom. Although "Caroline" produced a wealth of bloom which was the admiration of the neighbourhood, she overdid it to such an extent that she became a public danger. Thorny branches threatened passers-by and her roots dislodged paving stones.

Once again, I decided, she must move home. In the autumn of 1963 I set to work on removal and this time I had a truly herculean task. I struggled for hours before finally great roots parted from the soil, and they were perforce considerably damaged. I suffered painful wounds and scratches, which later entailed a different type of digging—to extract great thorns from my flesh. I hauled, pulled and dragged "Caroline"—much too heavy and cumbersome now to carry—to the back garden.

There at last I bedded her down safely with ample nourishment and strong support. I watered the plant well and often and pruned the massive limbs of this bush-cum-climber, but I hardly dared to hope that it would recover from uprooting so late in life. It was autumn, so I was not at all surprised that the leaves shrivelled quickly, but in the next spring no new leaves appeared. I cut back still more, watered and tended the plant, but throughout 1964 there was no sign of life. The branches were now just bare dead sticks. I intended disinterring the "corpse", but because of other work I never found time to do so that year.

To my great surprise, "Caroline" stirred back into life in the spring of 1965. Two spindly stems came up from the base bearing sickly looking leaves. I thought, of course, that these must be suckers, but on closer inspection I was able to confirm that they were in fact rose stems. But there was no flower bud. Again I delayed and left "Caroline" alone. The spindly growths grew and soon reached a height of three or four feet. This year they sped on and, early in April, I found buds forming. Now as I write, in June 1966, "Caroline" has a score of fine blooms. After all these years she promises a full return to her former undoubted glory.

The Society's handbook *A Selected List of Roses* gives the date 1890 as the first introduction of 'Mme Caroline Testout'. My specimen confirms the comment: "vigorous. An old rose which still retains a remarkably good constitution".

To gather life's roses unscathed by the briar.
Walter Scott—*Ivanhoe*, Ch. 18 (1819)

Roses at Kew

G. J. E. YATES

Some five and a half thousand roses are grown adjacent to the Palm House, planted in a formal setting designed by W. A. Nesfield. The site is very open and due to the different levels is frequently subject to extremes of temperature and wind; the latter, of course, is at once noticeable whenever spraying is about to commence. Though the beds are made up with imported materials and much care has gone into their preparation, the growing conditions tend to be hot and dry due to the natural poor gravel soil of Kew, resulting in regular red spider mite attacks which can rapidly cause bronzing of the rose foliage and subsequent loss in vigour.

The current rose varieties can be seen in the larger beds but a closer look will reveal a number of old-timers whose survival and continued display should not go unnoticed. A few, if not more than twenty years old, have been replanted in new loam and except for the occasional loss have rapidly grown away as strongly as maidens.

Of hybrid perpetuals and early hybrid tea types the soft pink full blooms of 'Mrs Wakefield Christie-Miller' (1909 McGredy) open very early in the season. Always early, too, is 'Hugh Dickson', with sweetly scented crimson flowers; this variety is tied down in a large circular bed, a task best carried out in November, along with pruning, before it is too cold to carry out the work comfortably.

'Frau Karl Druschki' was growing at Kew in 1906 and was re-introduced—as it has been in so many gardens—in 1962. Forty-eight plants in a bed 9 yds long rapidly made 6-ft-long growths which in the second winter were tied down to a height of 2 ft; a dense framework was rapidly formed which now carries a fine display of the white flowers, Another tie-down bed close by is the charming cerise-pink Bourbon 'Mme Isaac Pereire' (1881) with quartered petals (see coloured illustration, *N.R.S. Annual* 1962, page 64).

Great landmarks in the evolution of the modern rose are given their place here with small beds of 'Crimson Glory' and 'Independence', though neither can be said to grow well even when on freshly budded stocks. The latter variety is used to show how the bright vermilion shades have been bred into the new varieties.

Several of our current varieties may have their ancestry traced back to 'Mme Caroline Testout'; two beds of this variety are still growing at Kew, one without planting record at least forty-six years old and a second growing close to Lion Gate which has grown successfully for sixty years on its own roots. A bed of 'Ophelia' planted in 1930 flourishes with large flowers, and it must be admitted that the subtle salmon cream colouring still has great appeal. Of 'Ophelia' and her relatives, 'Mme Butterfly' and 'Lady Sylvia', it is difficult to choose one in preference to the others, yet with the turbulent colours that we plant today there is still a place for these soft shades.

However, replacements with standard varieties are made each year, often favouring the floribundas and the strong-growing modern shrub roses which might, by their use, be termed Park Roses. Always a focus of interest is a large bed of 'Gustav Frahm' (Kordes) 5 ft high—a little less in height than the plants at Regent's Park. The trusses of pleasing red flowers are quite massive and, being continually produced in great numbers, are most frequently noted down by visitors. 'Kassel' and 'Prestige' are planted in prominent positions and the latter with its few but brilliant petals does take the worst weather that we can experience. 'Kassel', with more refined cherry-red semi-double flowers, is very worthy of a bed on its own. Surprisingly the floribunda 'Allgold' does not do well here and for yellow tones reliance is placed on strong growers such as 'Buccaneer' and 'Golden Giant', not forgetting such consistent old hybrid teas as 'McGredy's Yellow' and 'Mrs Pierre S. du Pont'. A large planting of 'Coronet' budded on R. multiflora ("Simplex") has been made after seeing how Mildew free it remains in all seasons. On this stock more flowers per stem are formed compared with a similar bed on R. canina. This very dusky crimson floribunda, raised by De-Ruiter, grows rather tall with clean stems and has wonderful foliage; to some the velvet petals are too dark, but planted next to the modern vermilion 'Super Star' the change of tone is very satisfactory.

With many other horticultural activities to attend to and the need for a high standard of maintenance—not easy when one has caught a voluntary student tearing out all the new basal growths from a newly planted bed of 'Super Star', in mistake for suckers!—spraying is best achieved by adhering to a strict calendar with a changing range of sprays as dictated by frequent observations. The sprays are based around a regular application of Karathane and to achieve a satisfactory control of Mildew a second application is always given from five to seven days after the first, followed by a space of sixteen days—thus giving a whole working week free of spraying. In practice 200 gallons of liquid is required and a Wednesday spraying is followed up on Monday or Tuesday and in this way unfavourable weather and weekends do not deter the important follow-up second spraying.

Foliar feeding with seaweed preparations gave encouraging results by the second year and is now used as a standard feed throughout the season to augment the March and July solid fertiliser applications. The latter are a mixture of fish meal with an equal weight of Chile nitrate of potash plus superphosphate and bone meal. The only time the beds are hoed is after pruning and again in July after fertilising. It is interesting to see just below the undisturbed mulches the very fine translucent feeding roots through the beds. I think we tend to imagine that roses achieve their root functions by a relatively sparse system of old thick black roots; here is an object lesson to every student working in the rose garden.

Early pruning is avoided because many beds are situated in undrained frost pockets. The method practised in the first week in March is to obtain a continual renewal of growth coming from as low as possible but without hard pruning; a full explanation of this approach would require more space than is available here.

In 1960 an extensive feature was constructed in the herbaceous ground extending northwards from Cumberland Gate; this is a pergola of brick, tile and oak timbers accommodating a collection of common climbing roses. To cover such an area one has to be patient and much trouble has gone into selecting varieties to fill the bill. Full of vigour with bright red flowers is 'Décor'. 'Lawrence Johnston', with early semi-double yellow blooms, is quite attractive and has a difference of form that is probably inherited from R. *foetida persiana*, one of the parents. Two roses that have amply covered the timbers are 'Sanders' White Rambler' and 'François Juranville', a R. *wichuraiana* hybrid with fragrant double pink flowers.

The enthusiast should not miss the species collection which is grown in twenty-one large beds continuing from the Holly Walk in the southern half of the garden towards The Old Deer Park and Richmond.

Though arranged botanically under the sub-genera of Rosa as found in Rheder's *Manual of Cultivated Trees and Shrubs*, a wealth of valuable landscape material can be chosen here, especially with regard to the way they thrive on the pure sandy subsoil. As shrubs these species and cultivated forms include plants that are invaluable, even in small gardens, towards the back of borders. *Rosa spinosissima* and *R. hugonis* are welcome for early flowers in May and *R. rubrifolia* with plum-coloured foliage is attractive throughout the season, even though its seedlings come up in the most unexpected places. We do not think of heps until the winter, but by early August a fine display has usually coloured up on *Rosa moyesii*, *R. sweginzowii* and its related species *R. macrophylla* whose heps really shine brightly. In the same context the Sweet Briar *R. eglanteria* (*rubiginosa*) should not be missed, with fragrant foliage and masses of heps.

Finally, come to Kew in earliest June when the lovely fully developed "Hybrid Musk" rose hedge of 'Penelope' begins its long season, with trusses of scented salmon and cream flowers, just west of the rock garden. Here surely is a lesson to all those who still drearily persist in planting far too much privet everywhere.

So sweet a kiss the golden sun gives not
To those fresh morning drops upon the rose,
As thy eye-beams, when their fresh rays have smote
The night of dew that on my cheeks down flows.
Shakespeare—*Love's Labour's Lost*

'GEISHA GIRL' (floribunda)
'Gold Cup' × *'McGredy's Yellow'*
Raised by S. McGredy IV, N. Ireland
TRIAL GROUND CERTIFICATE 1965

Clematis 'Jackmanii superba' sharing a pillar with rose 'Clg Michèle Meilland' in the Hon. Editor's garden in August. The rose provided the display in June and early July.

(Photo by courtesy of W. H. & L. Collingridge)

Clematis as Companions for Roses

CHRISTOPHER LLOYD

There are a great many gardeners who admire and would like to grow clematis, and who yet imagine that they have no room for even one in their gardens. Now, the climbing type of clematis are weak stemmed and must have some kind of support. They can be grown up a trellis or some other man-made framework, it is true, but by nature they are the companions and associates of other shrubs, through which they like to climb so that their roots remain in shady coolth while their flowers appear at the summit in the light. It is my experience that, of the count-less shrubs with which clematis may so well be grown, they and the rose suit each other best of all.

For they have much in common. Both are exquisite in flower, yet dowdy when not, and we can therefore train our eyes to look towards or away from them, according to their deserts. Both enjoy the same cultural conditions: a soil that is well drained yet moisture retaining and rich in humus and other well decayed organic matter. Then, turn-ing for a moment to a more gloomy feature of growing things, if you have to spray your roses with captan to control Black Spot, the same spray will also help to control possible trouble from wilt disease in clematis, while a Mildew-controlling spray will similarly benefit the one and the other, for some summer- and autumn-flowering clematis are subject to Mildew.

Now to consider the positive advantages and enjoyment to be derived from a rose/clematis association. You can double up on both the quantity and quality of colour in any piece of garden where both are growing. As regards quantity, you can either plan to have one tre-mendous outburst of clematis and rose flowering together, or you will associate with your roses a clematis that is likely to fill in the blank spaces of the former's flowering. Thus, you might grow a 'Clg. Shot Silk', or the terracotta 'Clg. Mme Edouard Herriot' or butter-yellow 'Lawrence Johnston' with the rich blue of a clematis 'Lasurstern' or a 'Lady Northcliffe', thereby gaining a prodigious spectacle in late May and June, with nothing much to follow. Or you might grow over these same climbing roses, say, a pink clematis, 'Comtesse de Bouchaud', that would make its bow from mid-June until August, immediately after the roses had completed their main contribution; or a purple-flowered 'Lady Betty Balfour', with a September season, giving you a break in July and August, when you perhaps take your holidays, anyway.

If you play Cox and Box with your clematis and roses, so that the one flower is blooming when the other is not, it obviously does not matter what their respective colours may be. However, if their seasons overlap, you can work for all sorts of colour contrasts or colour harmonies. Clematis include, in their varied palette, a host of purple and near-blue (but not pure blue) shades, that are outside the rose's repertory. So, the purple 'Jackmanii' or the light blue 'Perle d'Azur' could safely be associated with any rose colour you like to think of. The contrast will be striking. Other gardeners may prefer effects where shades of the same colour are in association. You might be surprised at the idea yet gratified by the result of growing the white-flowered climber 'Mme Alfred Carrière' together with the enormous milk-white blossoms of clematis 'Marie Boisselot', against a north wall. Both will tolerate this position; both will give light to its sunlessness and while both are, admittedly, white, there will be a complete contrast in form and texture that will harmonise most satisfactorily. 'Marie Boisselot', incidentally, has two very marked and reliable flowering seasons, in May–June and again in September–October; it is the finest of all white clematis.

Some of the large-flowered clematis have double flowers at their first appearance in May and June, and are themselves not unlike roses in form. 'Proteus', for example, is a double-flowered clematis of soft rosy-lilac colouring, similar to that of modern roses like 'Magenta' and 'Lilac Time'; it could subtly be associated with such as these. From July onwards, it carries on its young shoots single blossoms that are no less beautiful in their way.

It will be appreciated that the vigour of different clematis species and cultivars varies enormously, just as it does in roses, and that the ideal for which the gardener strives is to match them so that neither overwhelms the other. On the whole I have found it best always to give the rose a start. Get it planted, say, a couple of years before the clematis, and then the former will have made a good frame-work of young branches by the time the latter is there, ready to twine among them.

Gardeners quite often have the idea of planting a trellis or pergola with roses and clematis alternating at several feet intervals. It is always a mistake, however, to try and isolate a clematis, even to this extent. Plant it as near the rose as you can, so that it casts a shade on the clematis roots and also gives the clematis ready access to its branches for support. As roses tend to be pretty deep rooting, there will be no problem in planting a clematis close to one that is already well established. And this convivial arrangement has the additional advantage that you can manure the two plants simultaneously.

You can use clematis in quite a different way among lowish growing hybrid tea or floribunda roses. Obviously the latter would not have a bulky or tough enough framework to support any weight additional to their own. But if you train a clematis up an 8- or 10-ft pole set fairly centrally in a rose bed, this vertical feature rising out of a low froth of roses is altogether delightful. And it is easy to imagine the colourful contrast to be obtained, say, from a pillar of the crimson and purple clematis 'Star of India' on a pale pink carpet of 'Mme Butterfly'; or the rich blue of clematis 'Ascotiensis' against the pure brilliance of 'Super Star'.

Even more effective, in a way, are pillars of clematis among hybrid perpetual or Bourbon roses. This type of rose makes long, strong young canes, most of which I peg to the horizontal, to make them flower with extra freedom; but some I tie to a nearby post, which they share with a clematis. This, in its turn, is allowed to send a few of its shoots straying at a low level among the pegged roses. The mutual act of sharing is outstandingly successful. The roses have to be fairly drastically pruned, each winter, and, for simplicity's sake, I use among them such clematis as flower on their young shoots from mid-June onwards, and can themselves be pruned hard, ripping off all their old flowering shoots before a start is made on tackling the roses. Clematis that I can particularly recommend for this purpose are 'Huldine', white; 'Belle Nantaise', lavender; 'W. E. Gladstone', with mid-blue flowers up to 10 in. across; 'Perle d'Azur', light blue and of medium size but extra prolific; 'Ascotiensis', deep blue; 'Mme Jules Correvon', wine red; 'Margot Koster', deep pink; 'Comtesse de Bouchaud', vivid pink and 'Hagley Hybrid', a softer pink shade with dark stamens; 'Star of India', crimson and purple; 'Victoria', lilac and light purple; not forgetting the most popular of all clematis, the deep purple 'Jackmanii', to which 'Gypsy Queen' makes a welcome change in shape.

It is only a step from clematis straying from a post and wandering among hybrid perpetual roses, to the rose (if it is a strong shrub) entirely supporting the clematis by itself. A shrub like 'Frühlingsgold' or 'Nevada'; R. *moyesii* or any of the Rugosas, among many others, is well able to cope with this situation. And if the shrub rose is not so vigorous, you can choose a less vigorous clematis to go with it, such as the crimson 'Gravetye Beauty' or the pink 'Duchess of Albany' or 'Etoile Rose'. These can be cut to the ground in winter, without detriment to the next season's blossom. Should you find, after a few years, that the growth of your clematis is rather too heavy for the rose to sustain, you can easily relieve the situation by putting in a post (it need not be much taller than the rose itself) close to clematis and rose, and tying some of the climber's shoots to this while allowing others to continue to twine among the shrub's branches.

Gardeners tend to get worried about how to cope with the pruning of roses and clematis when both are of a climbing habit. If the rose has a more or less permanent framework, such as all the climbing sports, 'Paul's Lemon Pillar', 'Mermaid' and many more, then the clematis can very well be of the same habit. 'Nelly Moser', 'Lasurstern', 'Marie Boisselot' and, indeed, all the large-flowered hybrids that start blooming in May or early June, will themselves require no more pruning than the annual removal of old flowering and other dead shoots. If you want later flowering clematis to go on this type of rose, there is nothing against it, either. These clematis are the better for hard pruning. What you do is to cut all the shoots back to within a foot or two of ground level in February or early March, and then just tug at the severed strands, pulling downwards and outwards, so that they come right off the rose.

With rambler roses acting as host, a large proportion and sometimes all of the branches are cut away annually, and it is almost essential to use the later-flowering clematis with these, for they respond to a similar treatment.

Roses as Cut Flowers

ENA HARKNESS

When I have pluck'd the rose,
I cannot give it vital growth again
It needs must wither: I'll smell it on the tree.
SHAKESPEARE—*Othello*

For how long can the rose be smelled upon the tree? Only as long as she lives, and conditions are perfect. A cut rose on the other hand distils her fragrance through the warmth and stillness of a quiet room. From bud to full-blown flower her scent lies upon the air, sometimes faint and elusive; sometimes full and rich, almost as though the bloom is sensuously enjoying the comfort of being safely inside away from hot sun, or cold winds and rain! Even roses for which no scent is claimed seem to produce a subtle sweetness when cut. Perhaps if Othello could have grown the modern roses he would have been more ready to "pluck the rose".

Very few modern roses *cannot* be cut and used indoors to the satisfaction and pleasure of all who see them. Some, of course, are more suitable than others and easier to manage. It is generally assumed that those with thin thornless stems are the best roses for what the nurserymen's catalogues often describe as "indoor decoration". Undoubtedly it is the roses with thick short petals firmly and closely held at the base of the flower which are the longest lasting. Even when the petals are few and thin roses can be enjoyed when cut. Take them in the early morning in bud; give them a good deep drink in a cool and preferably dark place for several hours. They will emerge bright and crisp, ready to open their wings in a light and pleasant place, gradually expanding to full beauty, holding it perhaps for a shorter time than their more robust and fuller-petalled sisters, but still lovely.

'First Love' is such a one. Soft delicate pink, carried on a nearly thornless stem clothed with light green pointed leaves, the bloom has not many petals, but the graceful appearance makes it a favourite. Crossed with 'Pinocchio' this rose produced 'Pink Parfait'—the perfect floribunda for cutting. The beautifully shaped blooms are hybrid tea formed and well spaced in loose clusters, and there are sufficient pinky-apricot coloured petals to ensure that the flowers hold their shape even when fully out. Faint sweet fragrance enhances this charming creation. The modern floribunda is invaluable for cutting; the blooms take up water well and have the great advantage of lasting five to seven days or more. 'Allgold' has small hybrid tea-shaped buds and opens to round, full-petalled blooms carried on slender stems. There are many laterals on the plant which carry only one or two flowers; these are ideal for cutting. 'Woburn Abbey' has the same advantage, but the truss of bloom here is full and strong, and if used for arrangement must be trimmed out. The colour is so wonderful that it is worth searching low down on the growth for the laterals carrying only one or two perfectly formed flowers. Few floribundas have perfume, but one has much—this is 'Orange Sensation'. Glowing with warm, iridescent colour and revealing soft golden stamens in the fully opened semi-double flowers, this rose pours out the sweet light odours that characterise *Rosa canina* in the June hedges of English country lanes. One spray in a slender vase will fill a room with light and scent. 'Alison Wheatcroft' and 'Circus' are gay with colour changing from cream to pink to red in the small, firm camellia-shaped flowers; and 'Golden Slippers', a low-growing neat little plant, always seems to have blooms of glowing orange and gold to offer.

It is curious that red floribundas seem unhappy indoors—often they lose their light and sparkle. Our old friend 'Frensham' is one which does not do this. As a cut flower 'Frensham' is bright, long-lasting and glowing. It is a pity for this purpose that the stems are so thorny, but thorns can be removed. Mildew, too, bothers this plant, but the earliest flowers are usually clean, and as the variety is one of the first to bloom and produces prodigious numbers, it is still worth growing. 'Lilli Marlene' is another good red for cutting.

Everyone sniffs a red hybrid tea, believing a red rose must have scent! Those that have, like the floribundas, do not always look so good when cut. 'Chrysler Imperial', distilling glorious scent turns sadly blue and limp. 'Crimson Glory' hangs her head. So also does 'Ena Harkness' unless the earliest strong young blooms are cut, but she glows to the end and her perfume indoors is heady. Support her head with a thin stub wire if you like her at home. 'Papa Meilland' can be cut either in bud or fully out. He is glorious with velvety deep crimson colour and rich with perfume in all stages and lasts long, but the plant is sadly prone to Mildew. Early in the summer, before attacked, this rose is one which no lover of deep red blooms will care to be without. 'Josephine Bruce' is perhaps the best deep red. Perfect in form with deep crimson petals, she holds her head up well, but is often capricious with her scent, at times withholding it completely, and then spilling it in an almost intoxicating wave of sweetness. Bright with colour, 'Milord' has been known to last ten days in scentless beauty. 'Fragrant Cloud', so aptly named, is best cut when fully open. Then this rose is perfectly lovely in colour and scent and will last several days.

Who knows the parentage of the lovely 'Prima Ballerina'? Her cherry-pink sparkling flowers are carried on strong straight stems clothed to the ground with clean mid-green leaves. Her perfume is delightful and she lasts long in water. Unfortunately she does not produce abundance of bloom, but one flower in a vase is enough. 'Ballet', a splendid garden plant producing large perfectly formed deep pink flowers with many petals, will grace a room with colour but no scent. She will last five days without much change of shape because she carries so many petals, but needs plenty of water. Another full-petalled bloom, spicily fragrant, is 'Diamond Jubilee'. Undisbudded on the plant 'Diamond Jubilee' will produce long-stemmed sprays of bloom which can be cut fully out and still last three to five days in water. Tawny orange 'Bettina' too can be used in all stages, and carries her flowers on stiff strong stems.

An old favourite is 'President Herbert Hoover'—introduced in 1930, this rose is still hale and hearty and has very long straight stems. The blooms have creamy petals splashed with rose and orange and are strongly scented. This variety opens rather quickly and is somewhat niggardly with foliage, but a boon to the flower arranger who wishes to make a large, impressive group of roses. Add to this that good utility rose 'Queen Elizabeth' and a mass of handsome blooms up to 6 ft high can be assembled from a few dozen bushes without stripping all the colour from the garden.

'Spek's Yellow' is probably the best of the yellows; many in this colour have thin, loosely-held petals which open quickly, revealing the stamens. Early in the season 'Elegance' upholds its name to good effect, but this is a climber and has only one period of bloom. 'Peace' is a grand rose, but possibly only when fully open with the translucent pale yellow petals all expanded is it beautiful when off the plant. The buds are somewhat clumsy to arrange.

Who does not know the dainty 'Lady Sylvia'? Since 1927 she has been popular and is still the best pink florist rose. For small, delicate rose arrangements nothing except 'Pink Parfait' could be better.

A useful conversation piece is 'Super Star', another rose which can be cut in all stages of growth. The colour is so arresting that everyone will talk about it wherever it is displayed. Sometimes it hangs its head —especially the hot-house blooms. If this happens it is a good plan to remove a small piece from the base of the stems and place them about 1 in. deep in boiling water. Then fill up with cold water to the neck of the flower, and leave in a cool place until crisp and fresh again.

When white roses are needed 'Virgo' is perhaps the best hybrid tea. The blooms are slender and elegant in form, carried on firm straight stems without many laterals. 'Iceberg', the white floribunda, has a quality of dancing sparkling gaiety which can be brought into the house if the flowers are loosely arranged with their own light green foliage.

Except to mix with other colours and also other flowers, the so-called "blue" roses seem to be a doubtful asset. These roses are interesting rather than beautiful, in the opinion of many. 'Sterling Silver' has straight firm stems and a delicious scent, but is definitely better when grown under glass. 'Blue Moon' is deeper in colour and has more petals. The floribundas in this colour range are good when cut; 'Africa Star', with small hybrid tea-shaped buds opens to full, pretty pale mauve blooms which last quite five to seven days. Combined with pale yellow or pink roses they are enchanting. 'Magenta', an older variety, is lavish with deep mauve flowers reminiscent of the old roses.

Sentiment and the late Constance Spry did much to popularise the old garden roses, but they are droopy creatures, albeit lovely and appealing in a large garden. The species roses, Hybrid Musk, Rugosa and Scotch roses, all offer something. Unusual and beautiful foliage —heps round and wine coloured—scarlet and bottle shaped—small coral hued and clustering, and large tomato-red. In fact it would seem that the rose offers everything. But arm yourself with tough gloves and sharp secateurs for cutting, for nearly all roses are thorny and will scratch you if they can, even while smiling in your eyes with beauty, and titillating your senses with sweet perfume. Yet

Gather ye rosebuds while you may—
Old time is still a-flying—

On the right:
'STERLING SILVER'

Below:
A mixed bowl of
'GOLDEN MELODY',
'PRESIDENT HERBERT HOOVER'
and 'ENA HARKNESS'

Top: Twenty-one-year-old bushes of H.T. 'LAL' one year after replanting into fresh loam (*see page* 93)
Below: Palm House, Kew, 1966, with a general view of rose beds. In the foreground is a bed of 'DEAREST' (*see page* 93)

A general view in the Trial Ground at Bone Hill, St Albans

VEIN BANDING ROSE MOSAIC SYMPTOMS IN ROSE FOLIAGE

This is the commonest and probably the least damaging of the rose mosaic virus diseases which are known to be present in cultivated roses in the United Kingdom (*see page* 105)

Recent Research on Roses

E. F. ALLEN, M.A., Dip. Agric.(Cantab.), A.I.C.T.A.

Since most of my sources are mentioned in the journal *Horticultural Abstracts*[1] the relevant reference to this will be given where appropriate so that those members who wish to refer to the original paper may locate this with ease. Thus HA.36:3308 refers to volume 36 of *Horticultural Abstracts*, abstract No. 3308. This avoids burdening my paper with a long list of references.

Rose Virus Diseases

It is sad to record that a number of American-raised roses are being submitted to the Society's Trial Grounds already infected with mosaic viruses and, in my view, at least two potential Gold Medal winners have failed to receive this high honour recently for this very reason. Since virtually all mosaic virus infection in roses appears to be caused by budding on to infected stocks I regard the infection of promising new seedlings as evidence of carelessness during propagation. Furthermore the submission of such systemically diseased seedlings for trial constitutes gross discourtesy both to the Society and also to the eighteen experienced judges who devoted so much of their time during 1966 to inspection and marking of the 468 seedlings under trial.

Much has been learnt about rose viruses in recent years and Hunter,[2] in New Zealand, has described and illustrated the three types of mosaic which are present in that country. His Vein Banding Rose Mosaic, which is the commonest type in the United Kingdom, causes only a slight reduction in vigour of the infected bushes. (See photograph opposite.) This virus produces similar vein banding symptoms in *R. multiflora*, but in that species there is also a reduction in leaf size and the leaflet tips tend to be more rounded than usual.

Line Pattern Rose Mosaic produces characteristic narrow, wavy, yellow lines on leaflets and these lines often form oak-leaf patterns. On *R. multiflora* the patterns are less regular and may appear as pale green, creamy white or yellow spots, blotches, ring spots or broad oak-leaf

---

[1] Published by the Commonwealth Agricultural Bureau, Farnham Royal, Bucks.
[2] Hunter, J. A. (1966): "Rose mosaic virus", N.Z. *Rose Annual*, p. 79.

patterns. This virus Hunter reports as causing considerable reduction in both vigour and flowering. It is certainly present in several American-raised roses in the United Kingdom but is much less common than Vein Banding Mosaic.

The symptoms of both the mosaic viruses mentioned above are most conspicuous, in England, during April and May; they are less noticeable in the autumn and often not apparent at all in mid-summer.

Hunter's third mosaic he has named Chlorotic Mottle, which produces a leaf mosaic of creamy white small spots or large blotches. Affected leaves are usually distorted, showing puckering of the centre of the blades and crinkling of the margins. A coarse vein banding sometimes develops. One distinguishing feature of this virus is that leaf symptoms are apparent during the summer as well as in spring and autumn. This suggests that heat therapy is unlikely to be so successful as with the other two mosaics.

Posnette[1] has shown that apple seedlings bud-inoculated with virus from a rose with ring and line mosaic developed apple mosaic symptoms. Virus transmitted from one of these to herbaceous hosts reacted specifically with cherry necrotic ringspot antiserum. The same author (HA.33:6964) has noted elsewhere that apple mosaic is relatively easy to treat by heat therapy: virus-free plants can be propagated from the tips of young, actively growing shoots and the proportion of such healthy plants obtained in this way is increased by culture at 37° C. for two or three weeks. It would seem reasonable to conclude that heat-therapy would be equally successful in the rose, especially for those viruses of which the symptoms disappear in mid-summer.

Cammack (HA.36:5168), by sap transmission to indicator plants and subsequent serological tests, has confirmed the presence of arabis mosaic virus (AMV) and strawberry latent ringspot virus (SLRV) in roses in England. AMV has been isolated from the variety 'Masquerade' on two occasions and also from 'Jiminy Cricket'. The infected plants of 'Masquerade', in both cases, showed chlorotic ringspots and vein mottling on the foliage and a reduction in plant vigour. On 'Jiminy Cricket' symptoms were confined to a faint vein mottling on the young foliage which disappeared as the leaves matured. SLRV has been isolated from the varieties 'Ena Harkness', 'Sultane', 'Super Star' and 'Peace'. Symptoms varied considerably with the variety but infection

[1] Posnette, A. F. (1966): East Malling Annual Report, 1965, p. 46.

was associated with yellow vein mottle on the young foliage, strapping and reduction in size of the leaflets and loss of vigour.

At two localities SLRV was confirmed in plants which had been budded on to rootstocks imported from the same source, suggesting that infection may have been introduced in the rootstocks rather than acquired locally.

Schmelzer (HA.36:3308) has published an illustrated description of the various rose viruses, largely based on Brierley's work in America, and the following virus names are recorded: yellow mosaic, mosaic, streak, wilt and rosette. Unfortunately the illustrations are not sufficiently clear for me to correlate these names with Hunter's descriptions. Schmelzer also illustrates and describes certain non-infective abnormalities which might be confused with virus symptoms.

Rose Rust

In Rumanian trials with 12 fungicides (HA.36:1530) the best results were obtained from 0·2 per cent Polyram, followed by 1 per cent Bordeaux mixture, 0·4 per cent wettable sulphur and 0·2 per cent zineb plus 0·2 per cent wettable sulphur. In that country it is recommended that spraying should be repeated five times at fortnightly intervals, beginning in April.

In my own garden the new fungicide dithianon (at 1 fl. oz. Delancol to 10 gallons water) has proved to be a less effective protectant, in 1966, than was maneb in 1965.

Black Spot

In North Carolina (HA.36:1528) Phaltan and two other proprietary compounds are considered very effective against this disease but a rigorous seven-day schedule of spraying prior to infection is recommended. In the United Kingdom such a schedule would involve spraying one's roses about twenty-five times.

Saunders at Exeter[1] has shown that Black Spot spores (conidia) are dispersed mainly by water splash. Seasonal weather in August led to a characteristic, rapid development of the disease in September, 1963 and 1964, after an incubation period of two to four weeks. Hence protective spraying from August to October is all-important. The same author has shown that Black Spot is checked or eliminated in

[1] Saunders, P. J. W. (1966): *Ann. appl. Biol.* 58, 103 and 115.

areas where sulphur dioxide pollution of air exceeds 100 μg/m³ (micrograms per cubic metre).

My own trials suggest that dithianon (at 1 fl. oz. Delancol to 10 gallons water) is a very effective protectant against Black Spot. It is easy to mix and has excellent sticking qualities. At twice that concentration some leaf damage has been recorded at Fernhurst.

Powdery Mildew

Sprays listed for Mildew control in Russia (HA.**35**:8321) include various sulphur compounds, thiram and zineb, but the most frequently used fungicide is a copper-soap emulsion.

In Wisconsin (HA.**36**:1529) it has been shown that Mildew conidia from the varieties 'Christopher Stone' and 'Fusilier' would not infect *R. virginiana* in the laboratory although twelve other hybrid tea and floribunda varieties could be infected. Similarly conidia collected from *R. virginiana* would not infect these twelve cultivated roses although other plants of the same species could be infected. *R. rugosa* was susceptible to the disease from both sources, whereas *R. setigera, R. spinosissima, R. multiflora* and *R. hugonis* were resistant to both types.

Unpublished trials at Wolverhampton (W. T. Dale in litt.) suggest that both summer white oil (e.g. Volck at 1½ fl. oz./gallon) and the experimental material PP.781 are both effective fungicides against Powdery Mildew and cause little or no leaf damage. However, F.238, which seems to be entirely non-phytotoxic, gave disappointing control although it has been effective in my own garden. This last material can be used at very frequent intervals without damage. It may soon be on the garden market. Washing soda (2 per cent plus spreader) gave poorer control than last year and caused more damage.

Verticillium Wilt

Field inoculations of roses with *V. albo-atrum* in California (HA.**36**:5170) succeeded where conidia were applied with the bud or were brushed on to pruning wounds or when buds were taken from infected canes. Little or no infection resulted when rootstocks were planted in infested soil. 'Manetti' stocks were found to be very resistant; 'Burr' multiflora and 'Dr Huey' were resistant, while 'Ragged Robin' and 'Odorata' were susceptible.

Mites

At Aalsmeer, Holland (HA.36:3310), complete control of glasshouse adult mites, larvae and eggs was achieved by evaporating binapacryl (Morocide) at 2½ cc/100 cu.m. in 100-watt evaporators spaced at one per 80–100 sq. m. floor space (7½ cc acaricide per 100 cc water). The temperature should be 18–20° C. (64–68° F.) and the relative humidity at least 80.

In my own glasshouse, mites have become completely resistant to DDVP vapour although they were killed overnight by it only eighteen months ago. It remains very effective against insects. This strain of mites is now also resistant to other organo-phosphorus pesticides but can be controlled by a dilute spray of oxythioquinox (Morestan at 1 oz./25 gallons).

Nematodes

In Californian glasshouse tests (HA.36:1531) root-lesion nematode disease of roses, caused by *Pratylenchus vulnus*, was most severe when the soil was light and sandy and the soil temperature relatively high.

In a survey of 25 rose gardens in Manatee County, Florida, twelve genera of plant nematodes were found (HA.36:1532).

At Rothamsted Experimental Station (HA.36:1533-34) D-D at 800 lb./acre killed *Xiphinema diversicaudatum*, the Dagger Nematode, in a Lea Valley glasshouse soil. Roses grown in soil steamed after such fumigation produced taller stems of slightly better quality than those grown in soil fumigated but not steamed. Nemagon at 5·8 gallons per acre, emulsified and drenched into the soil, was also effective in controlling the Dagger Nematode. This is the eelworm which sometimes transmits certain rose viruses.

Neither D-D nor Nemagon is suitable for amateur use.

Rootstocks

Swedish work with 20 rootstocks (HA.35:8315) has been described, the hardiest being *R. alpina* (= *R. pendulina*), *R. poppius* and *R. rubrifolia*. *R. poppius* is not listed by Rowley in *Modern Roses 6*.

Ten different rootstocks have been studied and classified in Belgium (HA.35:8317), these including seven named varieties of *R. canina* with 'Laxa', *R. multiflora* and *R. rubiginosa*.

A well-illustrated booklet, *Rootstocks for Roses*, has been published in Holland (HA.**36**:1519). This guide was compiled from research results at Wageningen. A list of ten recommended varieties is included.

Seed Germination

At Beltsville (HA.**36**:1520) seeds of *R. multiflora* 'Cathayensis', *R. X reversa*, *R. setigera* 'Beltsville', *R. setigera* 'Serena' and *R. wichuraiana* varied in after-ripening requirement from 30 days at 4·4° C. for *R. multiflora* to 90 days for 'Serena'. The compensating temperature was also studied for these five roses, this being defined as the temperature at which mature moist seed does not germinate, after-ripening does not take place and dormancy does not change.

In Belgium (HA.**36**:1521) five stratifying media for seeds of *R. canina* were compared, these being sand, peat, perlite, a 1:1 mixture of peat and sand and a 3:1 mixture of peat and perlite. The longest period of stratifying, three months, resulted in the highest germination. This was highest in peat and least in sand, but sand and perlite were easier to handle mechanically than peat.

Propagation

In Norway (HA.**35**:8316) three types of budwood, for the climber 'New Dawn', have been tested, buds being taken from plants without flowers, from shoots bearing flowers and from shoots without flowers but taken from flowering plants. Budwood from the second source— flowering shoots—produced plants which flowered the most profusely although they grew less tall than the others.

Cultivation and Varieties

Cultural and variety trials have been described from Norway and Finland (HA.**35**:8315) and from north-east Georgia, USA (HA.**36**:3306). The latter were concerned with 136 varieties and recommended ones are listed and described.

In Michigan (HA.**36**:5166) glasshouse plants of 'Better Times' roses grew larger and produced more flowers when grown in a CO_2-enriched atmosphere (1,200–2,000 ppm CO_2) than where extra carbon dioxide was not added.

Manuring and Nutrition

In an Oregon manurial experiment (HA.**35**:8318) plots of 'Peace' and 'Condesa de Sástago' received seven different treatments comprising, per acre, 100 lb. P_2O_5 with and without 1 lb. B (boron), 100 lb. K_2O as either chloride or sulphate, 100 lb. K_2O + 100 lb. P_2O_5, 1 lb. B alone and no fertiliser. In the second year all plants were given 100 lb. N per acre as either urea or sulphate of ammonia. Growth of both varieties was improved by the PK combination but not by P alone. None of the other treatments had any effect on 'Condesa de Sástago' but all treatments except P and PB led to improved growth of 'Peace'. There was no difference in the responses of either variety to the two sources of nitrogen.

In a Belgian nursery experiment (HA.36:5165) manures were applied before planting rootstocks (April 1963), before budding (July 1963), before pinching back the scion shoots (April 1964) and during growth of scions (June 1964). Total amounts of nutrients applied during the two years were 0, 300 and 600 kg/ha (kilograms per hectare) N; 0, 300 and 600 kg/ha K_2O and 320 kg/ha P_2O_5. The rootstocks of R. canina were budded with seven varieties. An increased application of N led to a larger collar diameter at budding but K had little effect. When the plants were lifted, in October 1964, the number of top quality plants had been increased by the first level of N and K but there was no further benefit from the double application. Varieties did not differ between themselves in their responses to the fertilisers. The optimum dressing of 300 kg/ha is equivalent to 268 lb./acre for the two years. This would be provided by four applications, each made up of 319 lb./acre of sulphate of ammonia and 134 lb./acre of sulphate of potash.

In a nutritional study at the Everglades Experiment Station, Florida (HA.36:1524), pot-grown plants of 'Pink Frills', a pale pink sport of 'Garnette', were grown on R. X fortuniana stocks. Deficiency symptoms of nitrogen, phosphorus, potassium, calcium, magnesium, boron and possibly copper, and toxicity symptoms of zinc and boron were observed and described. A low potash leaf analysis was associated with a low iron value and the leaf symptoms associated with absence of potash were those normally considered to indicate an iron deficiency. Analyses of leaf tissue are tabulated.

Miscellaneous

Research workers will also be interested in the following abstracts: HA35:8319–8320, 8322–8324. HA.36:1522–1523, 1525–1526, 1535–1542, 3305, 3307, 3309, 3311–3313, 5167 and 5169.

Conifers in the Rose Garden

E. B. LE GRICE

My first reaction to this title was "never", for conifers and roses are both demanding and competitive in their requirements. On further thought the "never" was turned to "perhaps". The first lesson one would have to learn would be restraint.

A successful rose garden must have moving air in abundance and anything which would tend to prevent this must be precluded ruthlessly. Considering conifers with such a thought in mind, elimination should be made by bulk rather than height. A wide conifer must be excluded, as when full grown it will interfere with air circulation, increase shadow and rob the surrounding soil of food and moisture. This is why knowledge of the cultivar is so necessary. When we see these neat little shrubs 3 ft high with a diameter of 15 in., it is hard to envisage the mature specimen which in a period of fifteen years may become 25 ft high and 6 ft through. Here are a few examples of trees which were about 2 ft high fifteen years ago: *Chamaecyparis lawsoniana lutea*, now 12 ft high and 4½ ft wide; *C. l. wisselii*, 12 ft high and 3 ft wide; *Cupressocyparis leylandii*, approximately 30–40 ft high and 8 ft wide.

The answer lies in the choice of the right shrubs; firstly, they must be fastigiate (columnar in shape); secondly, they should be slow-growing and, thirdly, they must be hardy. The second consideration may be waived if we consider immediate results essential and are prepared after seven years to begin again. This is not as wild a suggestion as it may sound, for the immediate effect can be obtained at the cost of perhaps half-a-crown a year.

Having said so much which might sound denigration, why attempt to grow conifers at all? The answer is two-fold. A well-placed conifer enhances the beauty of the garden, and if the rose garden is seen from the house it gives variety in the dull days of winter and breaks the level of the site.

This leads to a suggestion as to where conifers can play a useful and decorative part in the rose garden. The north border which gets little sun and often funnels cold wind into the garden may make a pleasing and useful contribution to the whole area. Well planted with hardy

112

Princess Mary's Rose Borders, showing the
effect of conifers in the rose garden

'PERNILLE POULSEN' (floribunda)
'Ma Perkins' × 'Columbine'
Raised by Niels Poulsen, Denmark
TRIAL GROUND CERTIFICATE 1965

types of conifers at the back and more ornamental and colourful types at the front, it will come into its own in the dreary days of winter and also afford protection when the roses would otherwise be torn by summer gales. In such a position height may be encouraged, but a knowledge of varieties is essential. This will be dealt with later, but particular care should always be taken when choosing golden varieties. These are far less hardy than their green and glaucous forms, as many found to their sorrow in the spring of 1963, when many choice specimens died, leaving sad gaps in the planting scheme. This is why green, and especially the glaucous blue-green, varieties should be placed to take the maximum brunt of the weather. If the area is very cold, high or windswept my personal preference would be to forget the golden conifers except the upright and very slow-growing forms of yew. The golden variegated hollies could be used instead.

There is a further use for a different form of conifer which I would call the "approach" type. Where steps are used as a form of ingress to the garden, many of the slower growing flat type of Juniper make a pleasing welcome. For this purpose *Juniperus pfitzeriana aurea* is excellent for quick results, but one must be absolutely ruthless with it and prepared to root it out and replant every few years unless one has a very large area to cover.

There are less vigorous and very delightful forms, both in golden variegation, silver grey, brown, bluish green and bright green. I feel a plea should be made for allowing all these forms to retain their natural shape. Clipping should be studiously avoided. Obese "plum pudding" effects are painful in the extreme and the trees can seldom be clipped into perfect symmetry.

Having said so much one is left with a descriptive list as an appendage to a few brief suggestions of those which give the best results. To sum up, one may use conifers in three ways in the rose garden. As a wind protection and screen where they will not overshadow or rob the rose beds; as specimens to accentuate a focal point or prevent monotony, or as an evergreen approach to merge the rose garden with the remainder of the area. Perhaps under present conditions, when a few square yards are as costly as an acre of ground used to be, the term "rose garden" is a dream for most, but the same principle can be applied whatever the area, if one uses more and more restraint as the area becomes less and less.

Possibly one may be allowed to digress for a paragraph and briefly consider conifers as hedges. They can make admirable foils for the roses in the garden, but their rooting capacity must be allowed for. If a yew hedge is planted two methods of root control should be used. The ground should be well trenched and heavily fed and manured. This will encourage growth but will also keep the roots at home where they will have a cool rich root run. In addition, the further precaution of dropping an asbestos corrugated sheet width on edge between the yew and the roses is extra labour well repaid. Either the darker green *Taxus baccata* or the faster growing *Taxus 'Hicksii'* with its brighter green is suitable. *Chamaecyparis lawsoniana alumii* with its deep blue-green conical growth tapering from base to point is absolutely hardy, fairly fast in growth and needs no clipping. Where a more rapid hedge cut square or wedge-shaped is preferred, the Lawson Cypress itself may be used. On some sites near water the Thuyas are more amenable and the form *T. lobbii* (*plicata*) is as good as any. Where space is limited but an evergreen is essential *Chamaecyparis l. columnaris glauca* closely planted will give height without undue width or root trespass.

Chamaecyparis (Cupressus) probably embraces all the more vigorous cultivars which may be suggested where height is possible and where area per plant is generous. No forest tree type should be allowed under any circumstances, and over-vigorous varieties such as *C. leylandii* should be avoided like the plague. Of all the Chamaecyparis I would give pride of place to *C. l. columnaris glauca*. Absolutely hardy, of erect compact growth, a good specimen of 5 ft need not be more than 18 in. through. Like all very compact conifers its root run is restricted and as a separate specimen or paired to end a vista it is ideal. Growth is at the rate of 9–12 in. a year. Where a hedge is required in a very restricted border this is ideal.

C. lawsoniana alumii, a little more green than the previous cultivar but with a wider base and tapering to a pointed top, is very compact and hardy and it should be used with very great restraint as a specimen. It can make an excellent hedge where ultimate height and width are permissible. No clipping of these two specimens is required, but their height may be restricted by taking out the point. A 10-ft high specimen would be 3–3½ ft through. Growth is at the annual rate of about 15–18 in.

Other varieties such as 'Pottenii' (less hardy), *erecta viridis* and to a lesser degree 'Fraseri' are as vigorous as *alumii* but less inclined to retain their basal foliage.

Of the golden varieties of Chamaecyparis, *C. l. lutea*, clear light golden yellow, is probably the most striking although the greenish yellow 'Stewartii' makes an equally compact plant. Golden varieties like *C. l. obtusa* 'Crippsii' are less easy to maintain in shape and health. Providing the site is protected these may lighten the whole border, but I would prefer to keep the coloured types out of the actual rose area to avoid detracting from the colour effects of the roses.

A shorter but useful type in reasonable shelter is 'Fletcherii'. This has feathery grey-brown foliage and is compact and short in growth, carrying a number of erect growths which are improved by judicious pruning. Where a 5-ft specimen of equal width from top to bottom is needed this is the variety.

A dwarf form with similar foliage is 'Ellwoodii'. This makes a beautiful compact columnar mound and being slow-growing it can be useful, but it is not normally vigorous enough for an isolated specimen. Another of the same height, but a delightful contrast in blue-green and silver with compact pyramidal growth and feathery foliage, is *C. pisifera* 'Boulevard'.

A less widely grown fairly vigorous columnar type with more open growth is 'Wisselii'. This carries curiously contorted bunches of leaves, making a pleasing and distinct feature. Again rather vigorous, it would be better confined to the border, or it could be used at the entrance approach to act as a screen for surprise effect when the corner is turned.

Two suitable erect Junipers may be mentioned. These are *Juniperus communis hibernica*, a grey-green narrow columnar form which may be restricted to a maximum of 8 ft high and 18 in. wide, and Juniper 'Skyrocket'. The latter is very rapid in growth and of a neat and narrow upright habit.

One spreading Juniper for approach has been mentioned already, but there are numerous delightful forms to drape near steps leading to the garden. Of these *Juniperus communis* 'Hornibrookii', with fine bright grey-green prostrate foliage, and *J. sabina tamariscifolia*, with bright blue-green layers of low branches, are among the best.

Dwarf Chamaecyparis, such as *C. l. obtusa nana gracilis* and *pisifera filifera*, with its delightful mounds of thread-like foliage, add variety but are probably more for the rock garden specialist, although planted in conjunction with *Juniperus communis hibernica* these make an interesting approach.

Yews should be used with very great restraint, for their roots can spread far. Three types may be mentioned, the upright green 'Irish' yew, *Taxus baccata fastigiata*, the upright golden form *T. b. fastigiata aureomarginata* and the more rounded but upright golden variety *T. b. fastigiata* 'Standishii'.

To close my subject I would mention the excellent but deciduous conifer *Ginkgo biloba fastigiata*. In the first twenty years of its life at least it may make un unusual but excellent focal point to give height and interest to an otherwise flat lay-out.

Each morn a thousand roses brings, you say;
Yes, but where blows the Rose of yesterday?
Edward Fitzgerald, tr. *The Rubáiyát* (1859)

"Kinja", a Rose Nursery in Kenya

INGER MAGIUS

In Kenya, the "Land of Sunshine", roses have been cultivated for many years, at altitudes ranging from sea level with tropical climate to 10,000 ft, where night frost occurs frequently; and from semi-desert, where watering is a necessity, to luxuriant tea-growing country with its heavy rainfall. Nowadays most new varieties are imported from leading nurseries all over the world, as budding eyes, and are immediately budded on Multiflora stock, which has proved the most satisfactory for Kenya conditions.

My husband and I came to Kenya just after the last war. Soon after, we bought a small farm and established a good stock of what were the most popular varieties in those days: 'Picture', 'Comtesse Vandal', 'Etoile de Hollande', 'Madame Butterfly', 'Autumn', 'Clara Curtis' and the like. All were doing extremely well, and almost before we knew it 'Joyous Cavalier' was 10 ft high! Kinja Nurseries was a reality and we could start business.

When we started, my husband budded all roses himself, and I did the tying in, but very soon we started looking round for suitable men among our Kikuyu labour force. They took to it very easily, but as none of them could read or write, and their vocabulary for the various colours was limited to red, white and black, we had to be much on our guard to prevent a mix-up of varieties.

I should like to mention some varieties, most of which have disappeared from English catalogues, but, with us they are still going strong, doing well at all altitudes, even in the rather dry districts: 'Tahiti', 'Anthéor' and 'Suzon Lotthé', the last-named being the best for the coast area. There are also 'Mission Bells' and 'Michèle Meilland', which have given us two lovely sports: 'Tocsin', with flowers apricot to light buff inside and salmon outside, distinctly different from the parent, 'Mission Bells', but the leaves, healthy growth and habit are the same. 'Kinja Michèle' shows all the shades of 'Michèle Meilland', but intensified.

The nursery expanded, and in spite of little advertising we could hardly keep up with the demand, and the future looked rosy; but sud-

117

denly some very dark clouds appeared on the horizon. The "Mau-Mau" had started. Our good and faithful headman and another African were abducted from their huts one night and murdered. All our labourers were arrested by police, and as everyone appeared to be involved in it, they were sent to prison camps. We were left with only one toothless old man to herd our cattle. Owing to our position, with our backs almost against the forest on the Aberdare Range, it was almost impossible to get other tribes in to work. The few we were able to tempt with much higher wages than normal were not suited for the special work with the roses.

I started budding again with my cook's wife to tie in and my good Alsatian dog on guard against unwanted intruders.

At long last, a friend sent us an ex-soldier of the Wakamba tribe. This man proved a great help, being able to recruit labour from his own tribesmen, who have very nimble fingers. They produce most of the wooden carvings of humans and animals, almost world famous now. Very soon we had three teams working again.

The only advertising we did was showing at the various agricultural and horticultural shows. In spite of the emergency, we decided that it was a good idea to show at Eldoret, the year Her Majesty Queen Elizabeth, the Queen Mother, visited Kenya. Eldoret is a town not far from the Uganda border, about 150 miles from us, and in those days almost the whole way was earth road.

In no time my husband had erected a stand. Staging was covered by natural moss, and on the walls there were little shelves each with its own bowl of roses. Somebody from the local show committee came along and told us that if the stand was looking as lovely the next day, the Queen Mother was sure to pay us a visit. My husband started immediately after lunch, all the way home to Kinangop, to fetch a fresh lot of roses. By two o'clock in the morning he was back at Eldoret again; a short sleep, and by daylight we started renewing as much as necessary.

After lunch the Queen Mother was taken on her tour of the trade stands. We watched anxiously as the guest of honour and her party went into a large stand opposite us. At that moment rain broke, and the Queen Mother was hastily brought to the Grandstand at the main arena, so did not visit us after all. However, as the Royal visit had brought lots of visitors to the show, we received many orders, so it was well worth the trouble. Time went on, and trade increased rapidly.

Then again black clouds appeared on the horizon. The Lancaster House Conference opened, and the uncertainty of the future made even the keenest rose growers hesitate to invest more money in roses. Sales dropped considerably and when the Government some time later wanted to acquire all the land on the Kinangop for its re-settlement schemes, we were landed with a very large stock of roses. As the Government was unable to make use of our roses, it was not prepared to take over these at valuation price as it did with other standing crops. So we offered them for sale at £5 per 100, and even then thousands were left behind when we moved to our new premises.

The new owners had moved in before we paid our last visit to the place, and potatoes were sprouting everywhere in the beautifully laid out rock garden along the river, but we had found a lovely piece of land on the shores of Lake Naivasha, where the budding of roses was already progressing well.

On the Kinangop, at an altitude of 8,300 ft, roses thrived, almost without care, in the cool, moist climate, on very clayey, slightly acid soil; but the cold nights and wet weather, with occasional hailstorms, often made it difficult to produce good exhibition blooms. At our new place, altitude 6,200 ft, the soil is volcanic ash, very light and alkaline (pH 8·5) and rainfall very low. However, when given sufficient water and fertiliser, the growth is satisfactory, and the blooms respond well to the milder climate, also much appreciated by ourselves.

Hybrid tea roses are by far in the greatest demand. Floribundas, except for such outstanding varieties as 'Queen Elizabeth', 'Elizabeth of Glamis' and 'Iceberg', are not very popular. Dwarf polyanthas are hardly ever sold, except for 'The Fairy', while there is a certain demand for miniature and China roses. We have tried many shrub roses and species, but R. laevigata is the only one that has proved a success, as it does very well in low, dry districts. This also applies to 'Mermaid', which does well too at high altitudes, whereas many ramblers are shy bloomers below 7,000 ft.

There is a demand for standards and weeping standards, but it took some experimenting before we found a suitable method of producing a good stock. Although Multiflora produces long and suitable shoots, it is not so easy to make a 4-ft cutting for the ordinary standards (or 6 ft for the weeping standards) strike in a climate with an atmosphere lacking humidity, and with strong, dry winds. We solved the problem by enclosing each cutting in a bamboo stick, which had been split open and lined with moss, and then again tied with pieces of wire. Four in. of the cutting are left protruding at the top for the budding, and 8 in. at the bottom for the root formation. They are planted in the field at the beginning of the rainy season, but even so it is necessary to pour water down inside the bamboo, from time to time, to keep them moist. Within six weeks roots have started developing and after six months we are able to bud them. This method also ensures straight stems.

During spring of this year we had an interesting visit from J. W. Mattock, of Oxford, and we went round the nurseries together. He was struck by the great difference in colouring of certain varieties compared with what he knew of them in England.

Mr Mattock also remarked that we had got Black Spot; and I am afraid that all the usual diseases and pests are found everywhere in Kenya rose gardens, but plants respond well to treatment. Besides the common, well-known insects, termites are a special pest in the tropics, ready to kill a weakling within days; but with the modern remedies they can now be kept at bay. Perhaps the most difficult rose enemies to tackle are the buck, which all feed at night, and even in the outskirts of Nairobi are a pest. The little Dikdik, not larger than a hare, and also the Duiker are able to squeeze through the thickest hedge; and the larger ones, like Bush- or Reedbuck, will jump any fence under 5 ft. They all love the young shoots and especially those from the red scented varieties.

Here we are occasionally visited at night by a hippopotamus which, not heeding barbed wire, enjoys a walk amongst the roses, and always leaves some broken bushes in his wake.

As roses grow, and to a certain extent flower, all the year round, they must be fed and treated accordingly. We advise a yearly hard pruning in April with the onset of the long rains, and two months later they will produce a glorious flush. In the short rains in October a light pruning will bring on another flush, just before Christmas; with careful watering during the drier months, it is possible to have blooms all the year round. The sun is very strong and will kill much of the bacterial life, so heavy manuring and mulching are necessary.

Roses in the Arctic

VERA F. P. DAY

Incredible though this seems, roses flourish 100 miles inside the Arctic Circle, at Narvik in North Norway, which is roughly in the same latitude as Scoresby Sound, Greenland.

The Gulf Stream, flowing up the west coast of the British Isles, passes the Shetlands and continues up the Norwegian coast, rounding North Cape and reaching as far as the Kola Peninsula. This means that the whole of the sea coast of Norway, including the part within the Arctic Circle, is ice free throughout the winter. In fact the influence of the Gulf Stream is scarcely perceptible along our eastern seaboard, and it has been said that a fisherman is more likely to freeze to death in the Thames Estuary than in the Norwegian Fiords.

Narvik was built in 1900, to deal with the iron ore brought by rail from across the Swedish frontier. The docks were not constructed for really large ships, and cruise passengers are landed by launch. Almost entirely destroyed during the last war, Narvik has been rebuilt as a handsome modern town, with the usual blocks of flats, public buildings and good shops. The streets are wide and a number of open spaces are planted with grass and shrubs, and groups of deciduous trees. Evergreen shrubs would not survive under Arctic conditions. There are many attractive small private houses, mostly built of wood, with their own small gardens, usually protected by low stone walls—these are very necessary, for an icy wind blows all the summer from a snowfield overlooking the town.

The Norwegians love flowers, and every window and balcony is full of plants. All kinds of bedding plants are used, begonias being very popular, and permanent plantings are chiefly alpines and roses. As might be expected, floribundas predominate, especially the Poulsen hybrids. The Norwegians are fond of bright colours, especially red, so red roses of all shades are the favourites; pink varieties are also grown, and some white, but I saw no yellows as far north as this, though farther south all kinds are grown, and these include climbers, ramblers and a large selection of bush roses, but not the new mauves.

I saw no climbers in Narvik, but there were large hedges of Rugosa,

121

magenta and white, and a grass bank by the station was planted with a crimson-flowered Rugosa hybrid, fully double and scented, perhaps 'Roseraie de l'Haÿ', but more likely to be one of Kordes' hybrids. Planting in grass, besides helping to consolidate the bank, would no doubt protect the roots from frost. Other shrub roses are used in street plantings.

In these latitudes spring does not come until May, when I am told that trees with buds just breaking at noon will be in full leaf by mid-afternoon. Roses thus have a long season of rest, and no time for more than one flowering, being in full bloom in August—hence the useful-ness of the floribundas. It is evident from the size of the Rugosas that roses here are not killed back in winter. In the short time ashore from a cruise, and speaking no language but my own, it was impossible to find out anything about their culture, or methods of pruning. At a guess I should think an important point would be the prompt removal of sickly and weak growth, which is very liable to frost damage; and of course, the first essential would be to choose only varieties that can stand northern weather. I saw no sign of Black Spot.

Where capable of cultivation, the soil over the greater part of Norway is very suitable for roses, being neutral or acid, but not unduly acid, as on the whole rainfall is not heavy, especially in the far north; soil moisture is supplied largely by melting snow and mist.

A short train journey northwards, along a railway chiefly used for transporting iron ore from the Swedish border to Narvik, took us to Lapplandia, a resort for tourists in summer and ski-ing in winter, and where the Lapps come in spring for a great fair and an exchange of goods. There were roses at some of the small stations, but not as far up as Lapplandia, which is above the conifer line, and pleasantly situated among hills—where reindeer roam—small lakes and attractive deciduous woods. These woods consist of small silver birch, willows, aspen, alder and a few stunted ash trees, and there were many dwarf junipers. A surprising variety of flowering plants grew in these woods, with many beautiful ferns, and toadstools of all colours. There was some heather here, but it was beginning to be scarce, being too far north. At the places we visited along the coast I saw no wild roses except a bush of R. *villosa* close by the Briksdal Glacier, at Olden, midway between Bergen and Ålesund, and much farther south than Narvik.

Gibberellins—New Tools for Rose Breeders

E. F. ALLEN, M.A., Dip.Agric.(Cantab.), A.I.C.T.A.

In July 1965 Mr A. M. Cocker, of Aberdeen, asked my advice on a breeding problem concerning the premature abscission (dropping off) of fertilised rose flowers in the glasshouse. This was associated with secondary Botrytis attack and Mr Cocker had been advised to tackle the problem by treating the young green heps with various new fungicides known to be very active against Botrytis. Certain female parents, notably 'Piccadilly', were more susceptible to this trouble than others.

At the time I expressed the opinion that the Botrytis was entirely secondary and that fungicidal treatments would have little or no effect on early abscission of green heps. Later, in *The Rose Annual*,[1] I suggested that recent work by Jackson and Blundell at Bangor might hold the key to this problem.[2]

During 1966 I have had the opportunity to test this theory and the early results have been so promising that I am making them available at once, even though I do not yet know what the seed germination will be.[3]

Experimental

A pot plant of 'Goldilocks' produced two large and two small flower trusses in my glasshouse in mid-May of 1966. All flowers were pollinated with 7/62, a diploid seedling from the cross *R. ecae* × 'Canary Bird', this last being a sister seedling of my 'Golden Chersonese'. Most of these flowers were pollinated during the period 16 to 20 May. On 28 May all flowers on one large and one small truss were treated with three drops of a solution of gibberellin A.3, standard gibberellic acid, at a concentration of 250 ppm (parts per million) in 25 per cent iso-propyl alcohol and water. A total of about 30 flowers were produced and pollinated and about half of these were treated with gibberellin. Since

[1] Allen, E. F. (1966): *The Rose Annual*, p. 136.
[2] Jackson, G. A. D. and Blundell, J. B. (1964): *Nature*, **202**, 1027.
[3] See Addendum to this Paper.

'Goldilocks' is a tetraploid and quite unrelated botanically to the diploid male parent from the Pimpinellifoliae one would not expect a high take from this cross. By 18 June there were seven green fruit on the gibberellin-treated trusses and two smaller ones on the untreated stems.

During ripening it soon became obvious that the treated flowers had given rise to larger and earlier ripening heps than the untreated ones. The former were all red by the end of September while the latter were then still half green. All heps were harvested on 31 October, the sepals were rubbed off, the stems cut off flush with the hep bases, the heps weighed and the achenes ("seed") extracted at once.

The weight of treated heps ranged from 1·8 to 3·7 g. (grams) with an average of 2·9 g. The two untreated heps weighed 1·3 and 2·1 g., averaging 1·7 g. The former yielded 31 fat "seed" and a water test showed that 27 were "sinkers" and 4 "floaters". The untreated heps yielded only 2 "sinkers" and 4 "floaters".

One peculiarity of treated heps was the presence of large numbers of fresh white ovules, some with the styles still adhering. These were easy to distinguish from the fat achenes by their narrow, spindle shape and all those examined were found to be hollow. In the untreated heps most of the unfertilised ovules were darker and their styles had shrivelled.

This first test showed that not only had the gibberellin treatment led to a greater set of heps but also the yield of apparently good "seed" had been greatly increased. I therefore decided to conduct a second and more careful trial.

On 19 June a flowering pot plant of 'Elsinore' carried one very large truss of flowers and opening buds. All the fully open flowers and also the young buds were removed, leaving seven pairs of opening flowers at the right stage for pollination. All the flower pairs were numbered and one flower from each was marked at random for subsequent treatment. After careful emasculation all 14 flowers were fertilised with fresh pollen from 'Rosa Mundi', *R. gallica versicolor*. Pollination was repeated the following day.

On 3 July all seven marked flowers were treated with three drops each of gibberellin A.3 solution. These flowers all set heps which developed steadily and ripened early. They were finally harvested on 31 October.

The seven untreated flowers yielded only two heps. Two others had abscissed early, before 22 July, while the other three dropped off between 6 September and 31 October. Two of these last three heps were recovered but one was black and mouldy: the third hep was lost.

In this test gibberellin treatment resulted in 100 per cent fruit set and the hep weight averaged 3·67 g. Untreated flowers yielded four heps, with an average weight of 1·75 g. "Seed" yield from the seven treated heps amounted to 37 "sinkers" and 6 "floaters"; untreated heps yielded 14 "sinkers" and 9 "floaters", 5 of the latter being black and mouldy.

Jackson and Blundell used 1 μl. (microlitre) of solution on each flower bud but such a dosage is not easy to reproduce outside the laboratory. I used three drops applied with a glass rod 3 mm. in diameter to the base of the exposed part of the stigmas, just where they emerge from the cavity of the receptacle. A standard acid bottle, as used by field geologists, has a suitable-sized glass rod attached to the stopper and this provides a convenient method of precise application. The gibberellin should be very fresh and I am indebted to Dr J. Stubbs, of Plant Protection Ltd, for the gift of gibberellic acid. This was actually sent in error for A.4, which Jackson and Blundell have already shown to be more active on roses than A.3.

Discussion

It has been postulated that one reason why certain "wide" crosses do not succeed in ROSA is because the pollen tubes in such crosses are slower growing than in closer crosses and they thus fail to reach the ovules and achieve fertilisation before normal abscission occurs. This hypothesis fits in well with my experimental results, where the action of the gibberellin is to hold on the treated flowers for a long enough period for these slow-growing pollen tubes to penetrate down the styles and reach the ovules.

Dr Jackson has warned me of one danger: if gibberellin is applied too soon after pollination parthenocarpic heps are produced containing pseudo-achenes which look like normal "seed" but contain no embryos. Anything less than seven days is probably too soon and a ten-day interval is perhaps about right. On the other hand, too long a delay should be avoided because, once the irreversible changes in the structure of the pedicel (flower stem) have commenced and a corky abscission layer has begun to form, no amount of treatment with gibberellins or with fungicides will hold on the flower. This stage appears to be reached just before the top of the flower stem is clearly seen to be yellower than the green stem lower down, the colour change being an abrupt one. At this stage black spots may appear on the immature hep, which is later often attacked by secondary Botrytis.

Gibberellins are unstable in solution. Ideally rose breeders should make up a fresh solution once a week during the pollination season. However, my experience suggests that once a fortnight might be adequate, provided that an extra drop or two is applied during the second week.

In theory the use of the less easily available and presumably much more expensive A.4 is to be preferred to standard gibberellic acid, A.3. In practice, however, with a direct cross between two tetraploids A.3 is probably quite adequate since it gave me 100 per cent fruit set in the second trial. Whether or not a wider cross would justify the use of A.4 can be determined only by further experiment. It must be remembered that too heavy a fruit set would result in smaller heps and the total achene yield might not increase beyond a certain level. In the case of my pot plant of 'Goldilocks' some 30 flowers were pollinated, about half of which received gibberellin treatment. This was quite a small plant and the final total yield of 9 ripe heps may well have been close to its optimum level.

I have since been successful with other wide crosses so I am placing these early results on record so that other rose breeders may have a chance to test the method during 1967.

Summary

1.   Treatment of tetraploid rose flowers, ten days after pollination, with three drops of a 250 ppm. solution of gibberellin A.3 in 25 per cent iso-propyl alcohol resulted in both an improved fruit set and also an increased "seed" yield.
2.   Where diploid pollen was used, from a tetraploid male parent, the resulting fruit set was 100 per cent.
3.   Treated flowers produced larger and earlier ripening heps than untreated ones.
4.   It is suggested that the mechanism of the beneficial effect is to

hold on the flower long enough for the slower growing pollen tubes to reach the ovules before abscission.

Addendum

Immediately after harvesting the heps, sample achenes were submitted to Drs G. A. D. Jackson and J. B. Blundell for an assessment of their germination capacity. All samples were selected at random from the "sinkers", except in the case of the untreated control heps from the 'Goldilocks' hybrid, where the entire yield of 2 "sinkers" and 4 "floaters" had to be sent.

Dr Jackson has since reported that all embryos were excised on 2 November and soaked for 17 hours in either distilled water or 6-benzylaminopurine (10 μg per ml). They were then placed in a germinator at 70° F. on 3 November and germination was completed by 8 November. The results are summarised in Table One.

TABLE ONE

	'Goldilocks' Hybrid		'Elsinore' Hybrid	
	Treated A.3	Untreated control	Treated A.3	Untreated control
No. of achenes	6	6	10	10
No. of full-sized embryos	6	3*	9†	7
No. germinated by 8 November	6	3	9	7

* One of the "floaters" contained an embryo.
† The tenth achene contained a half-size embryo.

Treatment with 6-benzylaminopurine led to slightly earlier germination and active development work on this is now in progress at Bangor.

It will be seen that gibberellin treatment has given a further bonus of a higher proportion of fertile achenes and this makes the technique of even greater value to rose breeders.

I am most grateful for this very prompt action by Drs Jackson and Blundell. There can be few comparable cases where academic research has led to such rapid practical application.

The Red Spider Mite Problem on Outdoor Roses

N. W. HUSSEY, Ph.D., F.R.E.S., M.I.Biol.

Despite the development, over the past twenty years, of a large number of potent acaricides some rose growers are becoming aware that their efforts to control spider mites meet with steadily decreasing reward. The typical damage which is caused by all the developmental stages of *Tetranychus urticae* (syn. *T. telarius*) occurs frequently in hot, dry summers when the mites breed and develop most rapidly. Both young and adult mites live beneath a fine weft of silken threads which they spin between the veins on the underside of the leaves. Each mite feeds by inserting its needle-like mouthparts through the epidermal cells and sucking out the contents of individual chloroplasts. This activity causes minute chlorotic patches which, in light infestations, give the leaves a mottled appearance but, as the numbers of mites increase, these patches coalesce, ultimately producing a completely blanched leaf which withers and falls prematurely. Extended damage of this severity naturally reduces the vigour of rose bushes with consequent reduction in the number of blooms produced the following year. Another form of damage, encouraged by high populations of mites during the summer, is an induced susceptibility to winter injury which usually results in an increase in the number of stem cankers.

Most of the available knowledge on the control of pests and diseases of outdoor roses has come from studies in America, particularly by workers in the U.S. Department of Agriculture at Beltsville, Maryland. Reliance on control procedures, developed in very different environmental conditions from those in Britain, may have led growers to misunderstand some aspects of the behaviour of spider mites on outdoor roses.

A number of factors which may be contributing to the current difficulties in controlling mites are now discussed.

Hibernation

Henneberry and Taylor (1961) showed that, in America, *T. urticae* overwinters on various perennial weeds commonly growing amongst

'PRINCESS MICHIKO' (floribunda)
'Spartan' × *'Circus'*
Raised by Alex. Dickson & Sons Ltd, N. Ireland
TRIAL GROUND CERTIFICATE 1965

'CHARLIE'S AUNT' (H.T.)
'Golden Masterpiece' × *'Karl Herbst'*
Raised by S. McGredy IV, N. Ireland
TRIAL GROUND CERTIFICATE 1962

roses. This behaviour, involving as it does continued slow breeding during the winter months, is quite distinct from that occurring in Northern Europe. Parr and Hussey (1966) have confirmed the conclusions of other workers that, in more northern latitudes, the developmental stages of the mites are sensitive to changes in daylength. In Britain, so long as the daylength is in excess of 13–14 hours, the maturing females are green summer forms which feed continuously and produce about 100 eggs each. Towards autumn, however, as the daylength falls below this critical period, the maturing female mites are bright red, hibernating forms. These females do not feed and, as their movements are governed by positive reaction to gravity and negative reaction to light, they descend from the leaves and seek out protected situations in which to pass the winter. Typical hibernation sites are cracks and crevices in the bark of bushes or supporting stakes or, most commonly, in pockets just below the soil surface. These red, hibernating forms are specially adapted to survive the cold, indeed many hours at temperatures far below freezing are not lethal to them. Before such females can resume normal activity they must experience a minimum period at temperatures below their threshold of development (42° F.). This ensures that they do not become active before new leaf growth is available. With the onset of warmer conditions in spring the female mites resume feeding: they lay about ten eggs which initiate the normal summer generations.

The critical daylength governing this behaviour is dependent on latitude. In Northern Russia summer feeding forms develop only when the daylength is in excess of sixteen hours while, as one approaches the Mediterranean area, the critical daylength decreases until, in Southern France and Northern Italy, *T. urticae* breeds throughout the year.

This behaviour of the overwintering mites shows that hygiene methods directed to the removal of perennial weeds during the winter will have no effect on the incidence of mite infestations in early summer. Control measures must be directed either to the prevention of autumn hibernation or the destruction of mites as they emerge from overwintering sites.

While failure to appreciate the behaviour of hibernating mites may have led some British growers to rely on ineffective hygiene treatments there are other factors encouraging the increase in mite populations which are the direct result of pesticide applications.

Resistance

One of the most frequent causes of loss of efficiency in pesticide application is the selection of individuals which are resistant to the chemical concerned. Spider mites have a sexual mechanism which encourages the rapid development of these resistant strains. The females, which develop only from fertilised eggs, have diploid chromosomes whereas the males, since they develop from unfertilised eggs, are haploid. Because males are consistently haploid it follows that all characters are sex-linked.

The earliest records of resistance in *T. urticae* were those of Compton and Kearns (1937) who noticed reductions in the acaricidal efficiency of applications of selenium compounds to roses. Since 1947 the number of cases of resistance to synthetic acaricides has increased dramatically and, in recent years, a constantly fluctuating race has developed between the genetic plasticity of the mites and the skill of the chemical industry. One of the most difficult aspects of the development of resistance is the extremely slow process by which, at first, the proportion of resistant individuals increases. The grower is usually unaware of these changes and is then surprised by the dramatic suddenness with which a previously effective material ceases to kill the pest.

It is a common experience that, if the chemical to which the mites have developed resistance is dropped from the spray programme for some time, then it will recover some of its former effectiveness. This loss of resistance is caused by the frequent genetic linkage between the genes for pesticide tolerance and unfavourable characters such as reduced fecundity and vigour which afford them less chance of survival in competition with other susceptible brethren.

Study of the resistance problem in *T. urticae* reveals that tolerance to a wide range of organophosphorus acaricides and other compounds has developed. However, few of the records show close similarity in that there are large differences in the degree and range of tolerance recorded. This diversity of response is caused by the behaviour of the newly fertilised females. Young, newly matured females migrate upwards from the site of their maturation and settle on suitable leaves for oviposition. Each female deposits all its eggs within a limited area and the resultant progeny remain in close proximity until they, too, are ready for copulation. As each female mates effectively only once, within a few hours of maturation, she subsequently produces a mixture of fertilised and unfertilised eggs. From this localised distribution it follows that a high proportion of the mating occurs between brothers and sisters. Sibmating (inbreeding) of this kind encourages the production of individuals with identical genes with a consequent fixation of genetic characters. Such stability favours the persistence of rare recessive mutants. *Within* populations these genetic mechanisms restrict variability but the establishment of mutations ensures that great differences exist *between* populations. The restricted dispersal mechanisms of these plant-feeding mites encourages these differences, even between local populations.

It is widely believed that control programmes in which different chemicals are alternated can be expected to delay, or even prevent, the selection of tolerant individuals. There is some truth in this belief for, as outlined earlier, the reduced vigour of such mites reduces their chances of survival in competition with susceptible individuals. Unfortunately the tendency to homozygosity ensures that the resistant genes remain in the population for long periods so that further applications of the chemical are only temporarily successful. The greatest difficulty in developing practical control programmes based on "ringing the changes" lies in the fact that although there appear to be large numbers of different pesticides available to the grower many commercial products are merely different formulations of the same active ingredient manufactured by different companies. In addition, as the mites become resistant to pesticides by possession of specific detoxifying enzymes or cuticular structures, they become resistant to all chemicals which have the same mode of action. These modes of action are common to related groups of chemicals of which there are only a few, including organophosphorus, organochlorine and carbamate compounds together with a number of distinct materials such as pyrethrins and rotenone which occur naturally in plants.

Another complicating issue, when attempting to rotate materials with different modes of action, is the phenomenon of cross-resistance which is particularly common in spider mites. Selection for tolerance to one group of chemicals may confer tolerance to other, unrelated materials. For instance, a strain of *T. urticae* which had become resistant to parathion was found to be also resistant to a number of other unrelated compounds including sulfotepp, biphenyl, ethoxyquin and dicofol to which the mites had never been exposed.

As if these complications are not enough it has been shown that the rose appears to confer additional resistance to many pesticides merely by the nutrient status it affords the mites. There are numerous records of rose mites, selected for tolerance to organophosphorus materials, losing this tolerance merely by transference to another host such as beans. Saba (1962) has confirmed that, under identical selection pressure, mites of the same genetic stock develop resistance at different rates on different hosts. When the pressure is removed susceptibility too returns at different rates on different hosts.

Effects of Persistent Organochlorine Compounds

The practice of including DDT in pest control programmes on roses may have unexpected effects. Rodriguez *et al.* (1960) established that plants treated with DDT develop a modified nitrogen and sugar content within the foliage. Other workers, including Saini and Cutkomp (1966), have shown that variations in these nutrient constituents affect both the fecundity of the female mites and the survival of their progeny so that increased mite populations tend to follow applications of DDT.

An even more subtle effect of DDT upon mites is a tendency to make the adults more restless than normal on treated surfaces. This restlessness encourages the females to produce many small, isolated colonies of young which, in the absence of normal competition, are able to increase and develop at the maximum possible rate.

Complications of this kind have not hitherto been suspected but they are undoubtedly becoming more common as the practice of using mixtures of pesticides for simultaneous control of several pests becomes widespread. DDT is, of course, used against caterpillars and thrips rather than mites, but stimulation of population increase by Tetranychid mites has allowed the latter to become the dominant pest problem in fruit orchards throughout the world.

Although the use of "cocktails" to control pest complexes seems economically desirable, it frequently leads to the application of chemicals for purely "insurance" purposes. Many pests, although present on a crop, may not cause economic damage because of population limitation by some natural agency. Such overcontrol is one of the real problems of the present era of pest control. It is of course encouraged by the public demand for unblemished produce in various forms of prepackaging. As both commercial and amateur growers strive to attain completely clean foliage they are creating difficult pest control problems which may, in the long term, make the goal impossible without grave toxicity hazards. All growers must learn to live with incipient damage if we are not to present the chemical industry with impossible problems in developing a sufficiently rapid flow of safe, yet effective, compounds.

Interference with Biological Control

So far, only the direct effects of pesticides on the spider mites have been examined, but perhaps the most important effects of these materials occur indirectly through interference with biological control agents. As a general rule parasites and predators are particularly sensitive to chemicals long after they have achieved their target effect. For instance, applications of demeton methyl are normally effective against *T. urticae* for about three weeks. The predatory mite *Phytoseiulus*, an important enemy of Tetranychid mites under glass, may however be affected for as long as ten weeks. Apparently the spider mites, which reappear after treatment, are imbibing sub-lethal amounts of the chemical so that the predator, which eats about six adult hosts each day, takes in a lethal dose through a food-chain effect. Similar effects on the fecundity of this predator have been demonstrated following tetradifon sprays of the host plant three weeks earlier.

Since a wide range of natural enemies affects *T. urticae*—as many as nine insect and fourteen mite species having been recorded on one host plant—suppression of any one of them may encourage spider mite populations to increase.

It is of course impossible to use any chemical without upsetting this natural balance, at least to some extent, but it is obviously in our best interests to reduce such disturbance to a minimum. In this connection it should be stressed that persistent chemicals have the most deleterious effects and could well be dispensed with in programmes on outdoor roses where mites are becoming more troublesome.

Rational Pest Control Programme for Roses

During late April or early May a diazinon drench to the soil, within a foot or so of each bush, at a rate of 16 fl. oz. per 100 galls. of water, should help to prevent invasion of the new growth by mites emerging from their overwintering quarters. To prevent large numbers of mites entering hibernation in the autumn particularly careful treatment with acaricides should be made in the first week of September.

Routine control by commercial growers should be based on dimethoate (e.g. Rogor), dicofol (Kelthane), oxythioquinox (Morestan) and tetradifon (Tedion) high volume sprays, remembering that the last-named, acting as it does largely by reducing fecundity, achieves control only slowly. Each of the chemicals mentioned has a different mode of action and so forms the basis of a rotational programme designed to avoid excessive reliance on any one of them.

Amateur rosarians should rely on sprays of formothion (Toprose Systemic), petroleum white oil (Volck) and derris applied in rotation.

If other pests become troublesome where spider mites are difficult to kill, DDT and other persistent organochlorine compounds should be avoided and materials such as derris and pyrethrin substituted. The effect of some newer materials, like trichlorphon (Dipterex) on natural enemies is unknown and their use is therefore best limited to situations when control of caterpillars, etc., has become essential.

References:
Compton, C. C. and Kearns, C. W. (1937). *J. econ. Ent.*, 30, 512–22.
Henneberry, T. J. and Taylor, E. A. (1961). *J. econ. Ent.*, 54, 1256.
Parr, W. J. and Hussey, N. W. (1966). *Hort. Res.*, 6, 1–21.
Rodriguez, J. G., Maynard, D. E. and Smith, W. T. (1960). *J. econ. Ent.*, 53, 491–4.
Saba, F. (1962). *Anz. f. Schadlingskunde*, 35, 141–2.
Saini, R. S. and Cutkomp, L. K. (1966). *J. econ. Ent.*, 59, 249–253.

Taking the Plunge

W. D. ROBERTS

Sometimes a visitor to the R.N.R.S. Show will remark that his own roses could beat those on the benches "any day". An experienced exhibitor overhearing such a comment—and it is usually loud enough to be heard without undue strain—would probably query only the last two words, for in the expression "any day" is to be found the key to the fallacy in our visitor's claim. He is probably calling to mind all the best blooms his garden produces over a period of time, and arranging them in a Grand Reunion on his own imaginary show bench. Nevertheless, my purpose is to try and persuade him that his visions of success could very well be more prophetic than hallucinatory, and that they deserve to be translated into reality.

A successful exhibitor would concede that he is not necessarily a better rose *grower* than his non-competitive neighbours, but he would claim a more complete knowledge of how to produce a large number of high quality blooms for a certain date which he did not himself choose. This is the essence of the craft (a good word to use here) of exhibiting, and a newcomer to the game will quickly appreciate that there is a surprising amount to learn. He will also find that although the element of chance can never be eliminated, the exercise of judgement, backed by experience, will reduce the luck factor to manageable proportions, and enable him, on most occasions, to stage a worthy exhibit on the appointed day.

There will still be times when system goes awry, and the exhibitor finds himself in the position of having to make the best of some pretty substandard-looking material, and this is the situation in which the really good exhibitor shows his calibre; not only will he fulfil the classes for which he has entered, but he will, by clever staging, transform disappointing blooms into a very creditable show-piece.

The tyro can become proficient only by entering for shows, and chancing his arm in real competition; reading books and articles by experts is an invaluable road to further and quicker improvement, but can never be a substitute for the real thing. So, the sooner a start is made, the better, and let us recognise at the outset that the oft-repeated advice to begin with the local show can be good or bad, depending upon the standard of judging in the rose classes. Some local shows are judged by R.N.R.S. standards, and are obviously excellent, but at some others I have seen decisions which are so quaint that they could only confuse anyone who takes them seriously. Perhaps the best policy would be to support them all, learn from some and put the rest down to experience; whatever the result, you can never be a complete loser.

My own advice would be to lose no time in showing an entry or two in one of the Society's "National" Shows, even if this is your first-ever attempt. It is a step which is never regretted, and once the show bug bites, there is no known spray which will eradicate it. The new exhibitor will feel strange and a little lost for a while, and he (or she) would be well advised to arrive early, in order to allow time to get the feel of the place—and it has a very decided atmosphere all of its own—before settling down to work. Incidentally, after several years of exhibiting, I have now decided that nobody is ever the first to arrive; no matter at what impossible hour of the morning you get there, the hall is already buzzing with activity, and the strength of the rose perfume is evidence enough that things have been like this for some time. This is just one of those curious facts which you simply accept at first, and then, with the passage of years, the idea that some extra keen type must arrive at an empty hall still does not seem quite to "fit in".

Having arrived with all your impedimenta, it is time to go about your lawful occasions as methodically as you can, starting with the "official" desk. From that time until you are put out of the hall for judging to begin, your performance will be rather fumbling at your first attempt, but there will be plenty of people willing to help and to answer questions. You will be much slicker the next time, and the improvement will be maintained with each show your enter. The "new boy" will have no difficulty mixing in with the more established addicts, and should lose no time in doing so, for this is surely one of the most rewarding sides of the show scene, both technically and socially. Lasting friendships develop between rivals, and even although many are renewed only once a year, they seem to suffer very little from that. More is gained by exchange of experience than by any other means, and the exhibition is also a forum wherein the accumulated ideas of a year's growing and reading are ventilated, to the benefit of all concerned.

Roses which do not win prizes

1. Split bloom
Sometimes the petals of the outside row, or even two rows, reflex and reveal the split centre. The inner petals are "tucked in" rather than arranged symmetrically round the centre. This rose might have seemed perfect when first arranged but development took place before the judging, revealing a fault

2. Double centre
Occasionally a bloom, as it opens, reveals two centres—a development of a split bloom. This is another tragedy if it happens just before judging takes place

3. Quartered bloom
Except in classes for
"Old Fashioned Roses"
this type of centre
must be avoided in
hybrid tea classes. It has
obviously opened too
far and has developed
from a split centre

4. Too young
This rose has two
faults. It has three
damaged petals and is
too small, probably
due to being too
young

5. Too old
This shows the other extreme. While these fully blown roses are quite beautiful in the garden or for indoor decoration they are useless on the show bench, unless there is a class for fully-blown roses

6. Weather damage
Here is a rose of good form and substance which has suffered weather damage on several petals and which would thereby lose points when being judged

7. *Overdressing*

Fortunately this is less common at shows than it used to be, but one does find blooms which have been spoiled by having the outer petals pulled down much too far, leaving the centre cone tightly packed. Too young a bloom cannot be dressed effectively

But this one does

8. *The perfect bloom*

Here is a large, well-formed hybrid tea rose which has opened naturally and gracefully. It is as near as possible to the perfect rose

Before the judging, the time is pretty fully taken up with the job of staging, and on the whole this is not the time to engage another exhibitor in a protracted conversation; at this stage, the exchanges tend to be brief greetings or gentle leg-pulling. The first opportunity for more detailed chin-wagging on rose topics comes when the judges are busy sorting us out; we will have had a look, albeit a quick one, at the other exhibits, and tried to assess which will receive the awards. Making such lightning judgements of your own is a first class method of improving your eye for a good bloom, and it enables you to realise that faults are easier to see in other people's work than they are in your own. The judges are not encumbered with personal preferences, and will give clear-eyed verdicts on all the exhibits; comparing your own judgement with theirs is a very valuable exercise, and sometimes a revealing one. As the time approaches for the results to be seen, there is a mounting, but suppressed, excitement among the waiting exhibitors —a feeling which is sufficiently well controlled to enable them to walk, rather than run, into the hall to see how they have fared.

A quick tour of your own classes to see if you have won any prizes is the first and logical step, and as each class result is capable of evoking a fine selection of different reactions, your emotional make-up after five or six of them is likely to be temporarily traumatised. However, the more detailed inquest in the company of the other competitors will restore you to normality, and even as early as this, your mind will already be turning to the next show. Improvements in your growing and staging will readily suggest themselves by looking at the other exhibits and by talking to those who staged and judged them. Opinions on which varieties to grow, how best to feed, prune and spray them will be freely expressed, the merits of various commercial products will be discussed *ad lib*. The fact that you are an exhibitor naturally and inevitably puts you in the way of hearing more about what is going on in the rose world than would otherwise be the case; a good deal of what you hear will be repetitious, some will seem inapplicable to your own conditions and locality, but all will be of value ultimately.

It might be expected that a person's future as an exhibitor might depend rather heavily upon whether he succeeds or fails at the first attempt, but this does not seem to be the case. Win or lose, he comes back for more at the next show to try his skill again, and renew acquaintances; by this time, he knows that he is completely "hooked", and that the rest of his life is going to be, at least partially, governed by the necessity of growing good roses for certain dates. He knows that his garden will not necessarily look any better, that he must be prepared to laugh (with his family) at his own antics and moods, especially in the two or three weeks prior to the show. He will find himself talking to his plants, cursing the weather, getting up at outrageous hours of the morning, and generally following patterns of behaviour which would certainly give rise to concern if the cause were not so obviously benign. By way of compensation, he will have the advantage of an interest which will ensure that he is always looking ahead, for although the last show was a valuable and pleasant experience, it is the next one which really matters.

It is in the hope that these few observations will do something to entice the ditherers to take the plunge, that I offer this toast to "Absent Friends". It is all very well (and very natural) to criticise someone else's blooms, but your comments will have an enhanced value when your own efforts are also on the bench for 20,000 people to see.

"Come in"—as they say—"the water's lovely!"

But earthlier happy is the rose distill'd,
Than that which withering on the virgin thorn
Grows, lives and dies in single blessedness.
Shakespeare—*A Midsummer Night's Dream*

Field Notes on the Control of the Rose Leaf-Rolling Sawfly

E. F. ALLEN and MRS W. T. TOOGOOD

The Leaf-Rolling Rose Sawfly, *Blennocampa pusilla* Klug, is a widespread rose pest which is normally of sporadic occurrence but which sometimes assumes epidemic proportions locally, when it becomes very destructive.

This sawfly lays its eggs in the margins of unfolding leaflets from about mid-May until mid-June in southern England. Soon afterwards, but before the eggs hatch, the leaflet blades roll downwards and inwards to form a tight brittle cylinder of tissue which effectively reduces the leaf area by perhaps 80 per cent. It is this major reduction of photosynthetic surface which can be so damaging to growth and vigour, especially if the attack is repeated year after year.

The pale green larvae, which are often more yellow distally, have brown heads and a pair of simple eyes. This last character serves to distinguish them from the caterpillars of the Lepidoptera, butterflies and moths, which have paired groups of small eyes. These larvae feed within the leaf cylinders, eating away at the leaf margins, so that eventually they consume their own cover, leaving a narrow strip of curled tissue on either side of the midrib. By this time they may be 9 mm. long and very active and they may then migrate to a fresh leaflet. If this migration occurs by day they would then be vulnerable to attack by such birds as tits and warblers.

The fully fed larvae are said to descend to the ground in July or August (Wilson, G. F., 1954) where they remain below the soil surface within cocoons, until pupation takes place in early spring.

Both wild and cultivated roses are attacked and preference is shown for certain varieties. When the attack is only sporadic it is usually confined to bushes growing either close to a hedge or beneath the shade of a large tree. Such attacks are best ignored as they seem to be kept in check by natural predators.

The Purley Outbreak

About nine years ago leaf-rolling was first noticed in a garden in Purley,

Surrey, in some shrub roses growing close to a hedge and near a conifer tree. The pest increased gradually, year by year, until 1963, since when the outbreak has been of increasing severity in at least three adjacent gardens; so it was decided to attempt insecticidal control during the spring of 1966. Knowing that egg laying occurred from mid-May onwards, the following treatments were planned:

Group	Insecticide	Spraying Date	Number of Bushes
A	trichlorphon (Dipterex 80)	15 and 29 May, 12 June	180
B	DDT	15 and 29 May, 12 June	150
C	derris	15, 22 and 29 May, 5 and 12 June	150

In all treatments fresh packs of Ministry-approved formulations were purchased and the sprays applied at the recommended concentrations.

Field Observations

Spraying was carried out according to plan but for practical reasons subsequent observations were more detailed in Group A than elsewhere. Here it was noted that leaf-rolling first occurred on 12 May and by the following day all the young leaves on 14 bushes of 'Peace' were totally infested. A few bushes of 'Sutter's Gold' were also affected. No further outbreak was seen until 10 June, when more leaf-rolling was noticed on bushes of 'Sutter's Gold', 'Penelope', 'Elegance' and 'Iceberg'. After the third and last spraying there was no further attack, apart from a few rolled leaves on bushes of 'My Choice'. All rose bushes in this garden were pruned in early March and had made good growth subsequently.

In Group B about 75 bushes were attacked before the first spray application and many more by the end of May. Varieties affected included 'Albertine', 'Silver Moon', 'Clg. Ophelia', 'Rose Gaujard' and 'Woburn Abbey'. By the first week of June another large bed of mixed varieties, about 70 bushes in all, was attacked generally and it was noted that 'Peace' and 'Sutter's Gold' were both severely affected. This garden was also pruned in March.

The bushes in Group C were pruned very late, about mid-April, so growth was less advanced and no attack occurred before the first spray application. However, by the end of May all bushes were affected to some extent, 'Peace' again being severely attacked.

Leaf Examination

On 11 July a random sample of affected leaves was collected from all three gardens and these were placed in separate polythene bags for subsequent examination. This took place on 15 July, care being taken to examine and record every rolled leaflet. Some dexterity was required for this operation as the larvae were usually close to the leaflet margins, where the rolling was tightest and the leaf tissue most brittle. Examination with a ×10 lens was necessary wherever frass or other signs of larval activity were detected since the remains of dead larvae were sometimes difficult to spot with the naked eye.

The results of these leaf examinations are summarised in Table One.

TABLE ONE

Group	A	B	C
Insecticide	trichlorphon	DDT	derris
Number of leaves examined	72	43	29
Number of rolled leaflets	239	142	99
Frass present; no larvae	22	54	67
Larvae present; living	0	13	4
Larvae present; died recently	0	2	1
Larvae present; long dead	1	11	4
Hatching estimate, per cent	9	56	77

In Table One the hatching estimate was based on the number of leaves either occcupied at the time of inspection or which had been occupied, this figure being expressed as a percentage of the total number of rolled leaflets. The accuracy of this estimate depends on two assumptions: first that only one egg was laid in each rolled leaflet and, secondly, that in no case had there been time for any larva to occupy more than one leaflet. This second assumption may have led to an overestimate of hatching in Group C.

Discussion

In Group A not only was there a very low hatch but the small quantities of frass present in occupied leaf-rolls also indicate that those insects which did hatch had a short life. Although this treatment did not prevent attack this was largely due to bad luck in timing the first spray application, since leaf-rolling was noted two days beforehand.

Similarly, in Group B, three applications of DDT did not prevent attack nor did they have much effect on hatching. However, this treatment seems to have killed a proportion of the larvae, perhaps when they fed on exposed portions of the leaflets. Nevertheless, the high population of living, active larvae suggests that many earlier-hatched individuals may have reached the protection of the topsoil, from where they will emerge to repeat the damage next season.

The most notable feature of the leaflets in Group C was the very large quantities of frass which dropped from attacked leaflets in spite of the weekly spray applications of derris. Furthermore, a large proportion of rolled leaflets were so severely eaten that the rolled tissue had almost disappeared, leaving only a narrow blade on either side of the midrib. In view of the high hatching estimate it can be assumed that this treatment gave negligible control.

It is abundantly clear that only trichlorphon (Dipterex 80) has given a reasonable control of this very difficult pest. The high degree of control is somewhat surprising because this material is not recorded as having systemic action and its low volatility would seem to preclude a high fumigant activity. Perhaps a clue to its efficiency is given by its moderate water solubility, 15·4 per cent (Martin, H., 1963), but one would not expect a solution to penetrate far into such tight leaf-rolls.

It is most fortunate that trichlorphon has been found to control this sawfly because it is only slightly toxic to mammals and is thus readily available to amateur gardeners. The only other material likely to effect control would be the volatile and highly toxic mevinphos (Phosdrin) but it is very unlikely that this could ever be formulated for garden use because the dilute spray liquid has a short life (Peecock, P. R.).

For the particular area of Purley it would seem reasonable to recommend four spray applications of trichlorphon on 9, 19 and 29 May and 7 June. The ten-day interval derives from the fact that the spray applied on 29 May did not prevent a new attack on 10 June. This programme should also take care of tortrix and other caterpillars. Clearly all infested gardens should be treated in any one locality in order to achieve control in one season. Timing for other localities should depend on observation of the first date of the appearance of rolled leaflets. Although we do not know the interval which elapses between oviposition and leaf-rolling it is unlikely to exceed three days and may be as little as one.

Many authorities recommend applying a nicotine dust to affected bushes, the action of this insecticide being fumigant and dependent on an air temperature exceeding 65 to 70° F. However, this relatively high temperature requirement precludes such treatment being very effective in most English springs.

It is perhaps pointless to speculate as to why such a build-up of this pest has occurred in Purley since 1963. However, it is tempting to refer to the excessive use by gardeners of DDT and of other organochlorine insecticides which is known to aggravate mite attack on outdoor roses and which may well have other undesirable biological effects in the rose garden.

Summary

A build-up of *Blennocampa pusilla* is described in Purley, Surrey. Certain cultivars such as 'Peace' and 'Sutter's Gold' are more liable to attack than others.

Three spray applications of trichlorphon (Dipterex 80) between 15 May and 12 June did not prevent attack but gave a surprisingly good control of this pest.

Neither three applications of DDT nor five of derris in the same period were effective against this sawfly.

References
Martin, H. (1963). *Insecticide and Fungicide Handbook*, Blackwell, Oxford.
Peecock, P. R. (1966). Personal communication.
Wilson, G. F. and Ramsbottom, J. (1954). *The Enemies of the Rose*, R.N.R.S., p. 60.

THE CULTIVATION OF THE ROSE, 1966 EDITION:

Recent developments require a correction to be made to E. F. Allen's "A Short Guide to Pest Control on Roses":

> In Table I trichlorphon now rates ★★
> (very active) against sawflies.

British Standard Specification for Roses

C. F. ROBERTS

For many years past there has been some feeling that guidance should be given to the public as to the desirable minimum size and condition of various types of rose plants. Hitherto, amateur rose growers have had to learn by experience which nurserymen they can rely on to supply top quality plants budded on suitable rootstocks, which will transplant satisfactorily, not sucker unduly and will prove sufficiently hardy and long-lived.

The British Standards Institution formed a committee consisting of representatives from the relevant government departments and from the leading associations of those interested in the production of roses, with the object of considering and codifying the agreed minimum dimensions of and general requirements for rose plants for sale to the public. These have been published under the authority of the General Council of the British Standards Institution as *Specification for Nursery Stock, Part 2, Roses* (British Standard 3936: Part 2: 1966). It is stated to be "intended to provide a specification which will both encourage the production of satisfactory rose plants and reduce misunderstanding which may occur when plants are bought and sold. It is deliberately based upon schedules of minimum dimensions for rootstock, root system and shoots".

At present this standard applies only to roses grown on *R. canina* rootstock, except for standard roses, where the dimensions have been based on *R. canina* 'Pfander' and *R. rugosa* cultivated stems. It may become necessary at some future date to prepare a standard appropriate to other rootstocks, such as *R. multiflora* and the so-called "Laxa", which make very much larger plants in the first season than *R. canina* rootstocks.

The general requirements provide for the minimum dimensions applying to maiden rose plants (i.e. of one season's growth from the time of budding) which have been grown in the open ground, are budded on to rootstocks and are suitable to be transplanted and grown for amenity. Miniature roses are outside the scope of the specified standard. Other general requirements are that plants shall be true to

First Prize Arrangements, 1966—
Old Garden Roses—
Mrs W. Thomas
Class 83 (Summer Show)

"Red Roses for a Blue Lady"—
Mrs E. M. Woodcock
Class 69 (Autumn Show)

'SOLUS' (shrub)
'Kathleen Ferrier' × *'Dickson's Flame'*
Raised by Watkins Roses Ltd
TRIAL GROUND CERTIFICATE 1965

name, substantially free from any pest and disease and shall be materially undamaged. No roots shall have been subjected to adverse conditions (e.g. prolonged exposure to drying winds, frost or waterlogging) between lifting and delivery. General Requirement No. 7 covers trimming. It provides for the removal of damaged or broken roots, immature, dead and diseased growth and visible suckers. Snags must be removed immediately above the union. Packaging is required to be adequate for the protection of the plants and such as to avoid heating and drying out.

The dimensions as laid down in Section Two are intended as minima—probably most reputable nurserymen despatch plants larger than these defined minima. The Committee decided at the outset that the measurements should be stated in inches and/or millimetres, not in such vague terms as "a bushy well-grown plant". They also proceeded on the basis that the most important parts of the plant for which minimum dimensions are necessary are the root system, the scion at the point of union and the thickness of the stems, their length being immaterial.

In the case of bush roses, that is hybrid teas, floribundas (hybrid polyanthas) and polyantha pompons (dwarf polyanthas), etc., the following specific requirements apply. The root system shall include at least three main roots 10 in. or more in length. The distance between the union and the first root shall be not more than $2\frac{1}{2}$ in. The diameter of the rootstock, when measured immediately below the union, shall be not less than $\frac{5}{8}$ in. There shall be at least two shoots breaking from the union or one stem which branches out not more than $2\frac{1}{2}$ in. above the union. The combined diameters of the shoot or shoots arising directly from the union, measured just above the union or the point of branching, shall exceed the diameter of the rootstock. These shoots shall be hard and ripe and shall not yield to normal pressure with the forefinger and thumb at a point 3 in. above the union. As already mentioned, no minimum length of stem was recommended, it being the usual practice of the trade to reduce the stems to about 15 in. before despatching the plants.

For climbing, rambler or pillar roses the same measurements shall apply, with the additional stipulation that at least two of the shoots shall be not less than 2 ft 6 in. in length.

In the case of standard roses, these shall be at least double-budded, i.e. they shall have at least two unions which shall not be more than 4 in. apart, the length of the standard stem being left to the discretion of the individual nurseryman, but with a minimum height of 2 ft above the ground. A note, however, is included to the effect that the current trade practice is to bud standards at an average of 3 ft 6 in., half standards at an average of 2 ft 6 in. and weeping standards at not less than 4 ft 9 in. The stem when measured 1 in. below the lowest union shall not be less than $\frac{7}{16}$ in. in diameter. At each of two unions the combined diameters of the shoots arising directly from the union shall be at least four-fifths of the diameter of the stem measured 1 in. below the lowest union. The root system shall be the same as for bush roses.

From the foregoing summary it may perhaps be deduced that the most reputable rose nurserymen already make a practice of supplying plants of a rather higher quality than these minimum requirements. It is the supplier of sub-standard plants against whom amateur rose growers—and especially beginners—need some protection. But it is feared that there will always be people who will be unable to resist the bait of a relatively low price, irrespective of quality.

Roses have thorns, and silver fountains mud;
Clouds and eclipses stain both moon and sun,
And loathsome canker lives in sweetest bud.
Shakespeare—*Sonnets*

Obituary

EUGENE S. BOERNER

It is with a feeling of great loss that I pay tribute to Eugene S. Boerner, Director of Plant Research for the Jackson & Perkins Company of Newark, New York. I first met Gene some thirty years ago and since then he had been a frequent visitor at Newtownards and often attended the R.N.R.S. Summer Show.

I was greatly impressed by his vast knowledge of and his enthusiasm for plant breeding; he had a great love of roses and his special interest was rose hybridising. Evidence of his outstanding success in this field is illustrated by the All America Rose Selection winners. Twelve of his seedlings have been selected for this, America's highest award. It has been our privilege to introduce his roses in this country and perhaps his varieties best known here are the floribundas 'Fashion' and 'Masquerade', which created quite a sensation by reason of their novelty when first exhibited at the R.N.R.S. Summer Show. Gene was always trying to create something distinctive and in his latest floribunda, 'Apricot Nectar', he gave us yet another new colour.

He was the recipient of the highest honours from the leading American Horticultural Organisations.

Many years ago he told me of his conviction that a race of long-lasting, profuse-blooming floribundas would be the florists' rose of the future—and how right he was, for after years of patient research he succeeded in developing just such a type. His varieties, particularly 'Sonora' and 'Zorina', have become universally popular in the cut flower markets of the world and in Holland, in particular, they are being grown under glass in vast numbers.

Knowing he had not long to live, he quoted on his personal Christmas card last year the following lines from "Song of Life" by Sean O'Casey:

> "I have found life an enjoyable, enchanting, active and sometimes terrifying experience and I've enjoyed it completely. A lament in one ear, maybe, but always a song in the other."

This is so typical of the man, who enjoyed life and achieved much success with his roses.   ALEX. DICKSON

Reports on the 1963 Certificated Varieties

(1) AT HARLOW CAR, NEAR HARROGATE

F. FAIRBROTHER and F. A. GIBSON

As is customary the 1963 Certificated Varieties planted at Harlow Car have been inspected and pointed several times each year since they were planted. The results are appended, divided into: (A) those which have done exceptionally well; (B) those which have done well; and (C) those which have done fairly well.

It is interesting to note that by far the largest number come into group (A) and only a small proportion into groups (B) and (C), and as neither of the authors is a lax or over-generous pointer, northern growers can be assured that any variety which comes into category (A) can be relied upon to do well in their locality.

There have been only three casualties over the period, which is most satisfactory considering the bleak situation in which they are grown. What has impressed us quite definitely is that at Harlow Car rose trees take longer to become established than they do at St Albans, but once they are established they make sturdier plants. The original trees planted in 1961 are still in fine form.

During this year there has been very little disease, only slight Mildew and even less Black Spot.

Once again we wish to thank the Northern Horticultural Society for their care and attention.

CERTIFICATED VARIETIES

Group A	Group B	Group C
'Pink Supreme' (H.T.)	'Gavotte' (H.T.)	'Heure Mauve' (H.T.)
'Joyfulness' (flori. H.T. type)	'Elizabeth of Glamis'	'Scarlet Queen
'Vienna Charm' (H.T.)	(flori.)	Elizabeth' (flori.)
'Europeana' (flori.)	'Numéro Un' (H.T.)	'Wisbech Gold' (H.T.)
'Uncle Walter' (H.T. shrub)	'Fragrant Cloud' (H.T.)	'Pascali' (H.T.)
'Alamein' (flori.)		'Blue Diamond' (flori.
'Violet Carson' (flori. H.T. type)		H.T. type)
'Manx Queen' (flori.)		
'Marielle' (flori.)		
'Rose of Tralee' (flori.)		
'Bel Ange' (H.T.)		

(2) AT ROATH PARK, CARDIFF

W. NELMES

In South Wales the summer of 1966 was disappointing. Although rainfall was only 2 in. above average for the six months May–October the weather was predominantly dull and moist. Sunshine over this period was well below average, though July with 1½ in. of rain was comparatively dry. Showers in August were so frequent that sprays were washed away as soon as they were applied! In Roath Park Black Spot was more, and Rust less, prevalent than usual.

The effect of climate on the growth of plants is, as everyone knows, very great and in a summer like 1966 strong-growing varieties were exceptionally vigorous. We really had to look up to 'Uncle Walter'; pruned down to 7 in. the previous March, it had more than 7 ft of growth before the end of the summer. To emphasise the inclement weather a few varieties (including the excellent 'Gavotte') were inclined to ball and many of the single-flowered floribundas were discoloured.

As in previous years Group A consists of those varieties that have done very well, Group B well and Group C fairly well.

Mr R. V. Cheek has been responsible for cultivation and he, with Mr F. Whitney and Mr A. R. Treseder, carried out the periodic judging.

CERTIFICATED VARIETIES

Group A	Group B	Group C
'Gavotte' (H.T.)	'Bel Ange' (H.T.)	'Wisbech Gold' (H.T.)
'Pink Supreme' (H.T.)	'Uncle Walter' (H.T. shrub)	'Blue Diamond' (flori.
'Fragrant Cloud' (H.T.)	'Numéro Un' (H.T.)	H.T. type)
'Elizabeth of Glamis'	'Violet Carson' (flori. H.T.	'Vienna Charm' (H.T.)
(flori.)	type)	'Pascali' (H.T.)
'Europeana' (flori.)	'Alamein' (flori.)	'Heure Mauve' (H.T.)
'Marielle' (flori.)	'Manx Queen' (flori.)	
	'Scarlet Queen Elizabeth'	
	(flori.)	
	'Rose of Tralee' (flori.)	
	'Joyfulness' (flori. H.T. type)	
	'Charleston' (flori.)	
	'Joseph's Coat' (semi-climber)	
	'Copenhagen' (clg. H.T.)	

The Display Garden at Saughton Park, Edinburgh

ALEX COCKER *Regional Representative for Scotland*

About two years ago the Council of The Royal National Rose Society decided to establish a display garden in Scotland. As Scottish Representative for the Society I was asked to find a suitable site and immediately I thought of Edinburgh. So, I made contact with Alfred T. Harrison, Director of Parks and Recreation for Edinburgh Corporation and his deputy, James V. Strachan, who both thought that this was a wonderful scheme and suggested Saughton Park as the most suitable site.

The history of Saughton Park is as follows. An area of 98 acres was purchased from Sir William James Gardner Baird, Bart., with entry at Martinmas 1900. The occupier, Sir John Batty Luke, continued in occupation of the mansion house until 1907, when the whole area was leased to the Scottish Industrial Exhibition for two years. The Gardens were redesigned and planted at that time. The Rose garden of 15,000 roses was the most extensive of its time. Other constructions at that time were a Rock, an American and a Sweet Pea garden. Some modifications were carried out over the years, but all the garden area, with the exception of the Rose garden, was remodelled in 1952 and 1953 to give nine distinct gardens and larger borders. The main area is now the flower garden with spring, summer and autumn bedding, approximately 20,000 subjects being planted twice annually. There are also 5,000 hybrid tea roses in the surrounding border. Other gardens are the Italian, the Scented, the Dahlia and the Heaths, while extensive borders include the Iris, Bulb, Herbaceous and Shrubs.

After visiting Saughton Park with Mr Harrison and Mr Strachan, we decided on an area of land situated to the east of the Dahlia garden on which to develop The Royal National Rose Society's Display Garden. It is readily accessible from the main roads and well signposted within the Park.

Two huge elm trees had to be removed and fresh soil carted into the whole area. After the beds had carefully been prepared the roses were planted in the same manner as at Bone Hill, hybrid teas and floribundas in sixes and climbers in twos. The growth made was ex-

150

ceptionally good and the official opening took place on Friday, 29 July 1966, when members of the Council were given a civic reception and attended a luncheon by kind invitation of the Lord Provost, Magistrates and Council of the City of Edinburgh.

Out at the Display Garden the official hand-over was performed by F. A. Gibson, President of The Royal National Rose Society and senior Bailie Craig H. Richards accepted on behalf of the City of Edinburgh.

It was very gratifying indeed that so many members of The Royal National Rose Society Council undertook the long journey north to honour us with their presence at this important event. Many members of the Council remarked on the wonderful growth all the trees had made for the short time they had been planted.

The Supervisor in charge of Saughton Park is James R. Paterson. He has been successively Gardener, Leading Man, Foreman, Nursery Manager, Deputy Supervisor, and is now Supervisor of the Western District of the City.

The gardener directly in charge of the Display Garden is Jack Sombers, a born rosarian. His father and brothers before him were with Dickson & Co., Castle Nurseries, Edinburgh, rose growers for at least two generations. In such hands the welfare of the Display Garden is assured.

Soon Mr Harrison will be retiring from his position as Director of Parks for Edinburgh and Mr Strachan will take his place. I would like to take this opportunity of thanking both these gentlemen, on behalf of the members and Council of The Royal National Rose Society, for the tremendous effort and enthusiasm which they have put into this project. I sincerely hope that all members, both from home and abroad, when in Edinburgh will take the opportunity of visiting Saughton Park.

The Decorative Classes

JULIA CLEMENTS

No one can deny that the sight of the interior of Alexandra Palace filled with banks of roses is so awe-inspiring that as a visitor you wonder, almost bewilderingly, where to start. I usually stand and stare in silence, then, knowing my place, I make for the decorative section, making mental notes on the way about varieties, colours and new introductions which I intend to investigate later in the day.

Nowhere else in the world do you see so many roses gathered together under one roof, vying with each other for attention, and I might add that nowhere else in the world do you meet such discriminating visitors or members, all able to argue the finer points of the rose under discussion as expertly as those on a professional T.V. Forum. I love the R.N.R.S. Show and would not miss it for the proverbial world, though like all good things I might have to one of these days.

However, on to the decorative classes, which this year I think were the best I have ever seen. Beautifully staged against green nylon backgrounds, the entries were more numerous than ever. The coveted Queen Alexandra Memorial Trophy for a dinner table decoration of roses for a special occasion to be named, went to Mrs B. Green of Chelmsford, who made a lovely pink and white Engagement Party table decoration, using 'First Love' and 'Iceberg', an incongruous assortment of names, perhaps, for an engagement. However, it was beautifully staged, pink baby ribbon running across the table to link two cherub-like candle-sticks.

Mrs B. Green also won first prize in Class 81, which called for a frontal arrangement of roses with rose foliage. She made a really lovely triangular arrangement in a silver vase which stood on a blue velvet covered base, using 'Queen Elizabeth' roses and carmine 'Rosemary Rose', a colour scheme which in my opinion was particularly lovely. Mrs J. A. Rush of Rayleigh was second in this class, with a tall triangular design of scarlet and crimson roses in bronze, on a grey velvet base. Mrs M. Brooker of Swindon came third using 'Queen Elizabeth' and 'Sterling Silver' roses, and 'Raubritter' (old rose) in an opaline vase on purple velvet. I liked also Mrs K.Wells' design of "shocking" and pale pink.

There was a class for "A picture formed with roses within an upright frame", which allowed an accessory and any other foliage. The fact that "any other foliage" could be used greatly enhanced the exhibits, but in some cases the effect of a picture was lost, as a number of the frames were taller than the background provided. I feel the frames should either be backed or boxed in by the Committee, or the exhibitor encouraged to do so, also that the exhibit should appear casual as a free-flowing design in a picture, and not as a studied flower arrangement. Nevertheless, there were some interesting pictures. Mrs Brooker came first, using 'Super Star' roses in a swerved design on a bronze plinth. Grapes were added low in the picture.

Mrs W. Thomas of Ealing, always a talented exhibitor, won a well-deserved first prize with her "small arrangement of miniature roses with any rose foliage in the form of a greeting card, the card not to exceed 8 in. overall". The greeting card frame with central opening was expertly made by Mr Thomas (so useful, these husbands!) and she staged an exquisite pink and white triangular arrangement in a bottle cap which was fixed to the top of a toy candle-stick standing on a further bottle cap as a base. Had this exhibit been blown up ten times in size, there would not have been a fault in it—and this is the true test of a miniature arrangement.

In contrast, she also made a lovely pedestal group of roses and rose foliage standing on a pedestal 4 ft high. The roses flowed out in a loose yet rhythmic manner, whereas some other prizewinners' designs were packed too precisely and too tight. A pedestal group is mainly to be seen from a distance, and judging is better assessed if these exhibits are looked at from afar. The competitor also should stand back frequently when composing it, for if you are too close, you are apt to make it too packed, with the result that from a distance the roses appear as a large blob. Allow the stems to flow loosely, and do not worry if there are some spaces, for each flower head should be clearly seen on its own.

Another interesting class at the Summer Show and one which I feel should be repeated, was "For men exhibitors only" (Class 85). F. M. Bowen of Petts Wood, Kent, staged an excellently designed exhibit here to win first prize. He made a left to right curved arrangement in a shallow black dish, using 'Uncle Walter' and 'Josephine Bruce' roses, visitors all enjoying the fact that the roses were named for their information. B. W. W. Sampson of Brookmans Park came second with a curved design of 'Rubaiyat' roses in a tall lead container standing on a slate base.

The Affiliated Societies Class always appeals to me, yet is not always fully supported. I am sure this is because it is demanded by the schedule that all the roses used must be grown and staged by members of the group. Could not the "grown" part of this condition be dropped? If they were allowed to use roses not necessarily grown by their members, I am certain a greater number of societies would enter for this class.

I love to see a basketful of roses, so particularly enjoyed the class which stipulated an arrangement of roses in a basket using shades and tints of yellow. Some used handled baskets, others were with lids, but Mrs E. Skinner won with a loosely flowing basketful of 'Geheimrat Duisberg' and 'Dr A. J. Verhage', both yellow roses.

At the Autumn Show in Westminster there was again an increase in the number of entries, the "Best in Show" award being won, most deservedly, by Mrs E. M. Woodcock, of Westcliff-on-Sea. To illustrate her song title "Red roses for a blue lady", she made a right to left-hand swerve of red 'Baccara' roses in a dish on an upturned plate looking like a base. Both were painted a pale turquoise blue, as also was a figurine of a lady with swirling skirts, which moved into the crux of the swerved design of roses, all backed with a blue drape. Mrs W. Crabb, of Croydon, used seven 'Super Star' roses with Diervilla variegated foliage in a crescent shape, with a pale yellow half moon accessory, on a blue drape, to illustrate "Moonlight and roses". She came second.

The Christmas buffet class drew excellent entries, many introducing variegated holly and berries between the roses. In judging tables, the cloth is also taken into consideration, so competitors should bear this in mind. One competitor used a cloth that was so strongly patterned it gave a confused appearance; another used pale pink tulle and silver, and whilst many use this colour scheme, it does not typify Christmas, at a show—it seemed more like a wedding or engagement table effect. First prize here went to Mrs E. M. Woodcock, who made a tall central arrangement in a green bottle standing on a green cloth with a grouping of fruit on one side, and glasses on the other. In the bottle she used

swirls of broom with red 'Baccara' roses and variegated holly, centra-
lised with green grapes. Mrs K. Wells of Westcliffe, Dover, took
second prize with a beautifully designed swerved arrangement on one
side which included tall candles, variegated holly, white snowberries
and yellow and green cupressus, balanced by a lower grouping of red
roses and fruit on the other side of the table, all set on a red cloth.

Mrs W. Thomas came first in the class for an arrangement of roses
and heps in a lidded basket or box. She made a swerved design of dark
red and cream roses in a gilded basket on a gold satin base. Second
prize went to Mrs W. Crabb, who used flame-coloured roses and heps
in a mahogany box. I liked also Mrs K. Wells' design in lime green and
yellow. Other interesting classes at the Autumn Show were those for
an all-round design of floribundas, an arrangement using not more than
five roses and one for rose foliage and heps, the last-named being won by
Mrs W. Crabb, who used a twisted wooden base on lime green woollen
material as a background for her colourful heps.

I think most of you know that roses are among the most tricky of
flowers for show competition. Whereas they are a delight at home,
whether fully blown, in bud or only half opened, a particular show
arrangement can be ruined if the rose that was placed at the side has
opened more fully than those which were so carefully placed in the
centre.

So, one of the first considerations if you wish to be a successful
exhibitor, is to get to know your roses, and of course this knowledge
comes from experience, and better still from growing them. There is
plenty of room for gaining show experience in the artistic classes at the
Royal National Rose Society Shows, and there is nothing quite as
satisfying as show work. Added to this, you have the enjoyment of
meeting old and making new friends with an absorbing interest in
common.

Bristol Group Summer Show 1966

L. A. ANSTISS

I must again report on the excellence of the show of the Bristol Group of the Royal National Rose Society, which was held on 6 July 1966.

The President of the R.N.R.S., F. A. Gibson, Maj.-Gen. R. F. B. Naylor, C.B., C.B.E., and other prominent members of the Society made their annual visit and were made most welcome.

Heavy rain on the eve of show day must have made things difficult for some exhibitors, but the general quality of the blooms belied the weather. The exhibit of John Sanday (Roses) Ltd has never been of such high quality and featured several varieties of their own raising which will be popular when they become better known. A Gold Medal card for a non-competitive group was just recognition. The Silver Medal card went to E. & H. Beckett of Bath, whose roses improve yearly.

In the Artistic Section the Flora Perpetual Challenge Cup was deservedly won by Mrs R. Williams and the *Western Daily Press* Challenge Bowl by Miss J. Tramlett. The standard of exhibits in this section improves every year and must surely encourage others to display their prowess. Congratulations, ladies.

F. Wiltshire, although a regular exhibitor, has never shown better roses and firsts in seven classes won for him the R.N.R.S. Challenge Cup, the Victor Osmond Challenge Bowl and the R.N.R.S. Bronze Medal. What a day, even for a regular exhibitor and enthusiast! J. H. Shotter won four firsts in the Open Section with some very good flowers.

In the Restricted Classes W. G. Hinkley was successful in gaining most points to win the Ethel Sanday Challenge Cup and for growers of not more than 150 trees K. E. Jones won most points and the Davey Challenge Bowl.

A perfect bloom of 'Wendy Cussons' won for L. Bird a Bronze Medal for the best bloom in the show and it *had* to be perfect, for the quality throughout was very high, as usual.

The Secretary, Committee and many helpers are to be congratulated on a well organised show.

Cardiff Group Summer Show 1966

MRS L. M. PHILLIPS

The Lord Mayor and Lady Mayoress were amongst the first visitors to our increasingly popular Summer Show, held on 9 July on the Castle Green. In the Open Amateur Classes Mr C. D. Owens of Leominster had outstanding success in winning five first prizes, together with a Bronze Medal and the Alan Gibbs Challenge Trophy. His superb group of 'Montezuma', 'Isabel de Ortiz' and 'Silver Lining' was adjudged best in the show. W. G. Pierce and R. V. Bryan, both of Hereford, and Ken Jones, Cardiff, were the other first prize winners in this section.

In the Under 250 Classes, Mr Jones, repeating his Bristol success, was a notable winner of three first awards, including the Stephen Treseder Challenge Bowl. T. J. Parr and V. Bailey-Wood were other prize winners. Mrs Flora Macadam, R. F. Tree, S. Lewis and F. Hill took awards in the other restricted classes.

An impeccable group exhibited by Stephen Treseder & Sons won them a Gold Medal. A bowl of 'Frau Karl Druschki', introduced in 1900, made a brave showing amid a magnificent display of moderns including 'Grandpa Dickson', 'Europeana' and 'Chinatown'. A novel and charming exhibit by the Cardiff Parks Department also gained a Gold Medal. It consisted of a raised rose garden of fine blooms of hybrid teas and floribundas, backed with trellised climbers, and the whole feature attracted considerable interest and admiration.

The Group's Stand displayed varieties of hybrid teas and brilliant floribundas, staged by L. Poole and F. Whitney, and claimed attention and praise.

The Nine Decorative Classes were of very high standard and gave much pleasure. A new class depicting a Song or Book Title won favour and appreciation, the first prize being awarded to Mrs E. Greer for her composition—"The Age of Elegance", with roses appropriate to the period. Other first prize winners were Mrs L. Phillips and Mrs G. Jones, while Mrs Joan Morgan won the Alan Gibbs Memorial Rose Bowl in the Novice Section.

The Spring Competition

L. G. TURNER

There is little doubt that gardeners and non-gardeners alike greet the first daffodils, rhododendrons and azaleas with the thought that the rigours of winter have passed and summer is around the corner. But to the true rosarian the sight of those few roses on the show bench at Westminster during the first week of May heralds far more. What rose pleasures are soon to come? What new and captivating varieties will the growers be showing? Will the new season surpass that of last year? Perhaps I am a particularly biased gardener but, to me, those first roses come as a breath of fresh air to an over-heated room.

Before the war a successful Spring Show was held annually, and when this small competition was revived in 1956 with only eight exhibitors, it was hoped that in time it would be possible to stage a full show once again. Alas, more than a decade later, with a mere fifty per cent increase in the exhibitors, the hopes of such a show seem to be diminishing. Why should this be? There are far more people growing roses, and this summer when visiting the garden centre of a well-known rose grower, it was interesting to learn that the sales of small greenhouses are higher than ever. Undoubtedly, there is a great sense of achievement in flowering roses out of season and if some of the many keen exhibitors who regularly attend the Summer Show were to pot up and grow a few trees under glass, I am sure they would soon be fired with real enthusiasm, and a Spring Show would not be quite such a forlorn hope.

The most successful competitor in the 1966 competition was E. F. Allen who won the Spring Challenge Cup. He showed a particularly fine specimen of 'Fortune's Yellow' in a pot and also had a non-competitive pot of a yellow seedling of *R. ecae*. Apparently this experienced rosarian uses the same roses for showing as for hybridising but, although he undoubtedly does so with some success, it is not a practice to be advocated for the novice. Mr Allen also gained first prize with his three pots of miniature roses, 'Cinderella', 'Opal Jewel' and 'Scarlet Gem'. B. W. W. Sampson came second using 'Rosina', 'Baby Gold Star' and 'Coralin'.

Mrs Tetley Jones took first prize with a box of six blooms including 'Show Girl', 'Anne Letts', 'Royal Highness', 'Dorothy Anderson' and 'Emily'. I know she would be the first to admit that they were not up to the standard we have come to expect, but her first prize vase of five floribundas, including 'Sweet Repose', 'Pinnochio' and 'Anna Wheatcroft', was excellent.

Mrs Baker Carter showed good blooms in several classes and was unlucky not to win a first prize. R. L. Dillon, who has been exhibiting at the competition only during the last two or three years, produced three magnificent blooms of 'Lal' which earned him a first and the Silver Gilt medal for the best bloom.

Ivan Mayhew travelled from Newton Abbot to receive a first and two seconds. His vase of 'Baccara' was perfect, while F. Fairbrother, living in the same county, and undoubtedly the doyen of this band of exhibitors, received a first prize ticket for his three specimen blooms in the section for growers of fewer than thirty rose trees under glass. The first prize for a box of six specimens in this restricted section went to H. F. Skinner of Harrow, with W. D. Gobbee of Balham a close second.

Not to be outshone by the opposite sex the ladies produced some enchanting arrangements with a maximum of seven blooms. Mrs Sampson came first with a line arrangement in a basket, using a mixture of 'Super Star', 'Silver Lining' and 'Wendy Cussons', and she was closely followed by Miss Aldous from Oxford.

So, to this small band of stalwart exhibitors, a word of thanks for bringing along such a delightful breath of fresh air.

The Summer Show

A. G. L. HELLYER

Once again the Summer Rose Show filled the Alexandra Palace with a blaze of colour and proved beyond doubt that, despite all the rival attractions that exist today, the rose is as popular as ever both with exhibitors and as a garden flower. The trade exhibits in the Great Hall were magnificent and amateur rose growers filled the Palm Court with blooms as good as any that could be found anywhere in the world.

There were weaknesses, of course, and not every class was as well filled as one could have wished. One or two exhibitors had either not studied the schedule sufficiently carefully or maybe in the rush of staging had succeeded in getting their exhibits into the wrong classes. But by and large this was a show to remember, a triumphant vindication of all the work that has been put in by rosarians to make the rose an even better flower.

This year the best rose in the amateur classes was not shown by any of the well-known prize winners nor was it even in an exhibit which won a first prize. It was a bloom of 'Pink Favourite' as large and as perfectly formed as any we are likely to see, shown by D. H. Scott of Beaconsfield in a box of six specimen blooms which came third in Class 63. This is in the section confined to amateurs living within 25 miles of Charing Cross and is the class that carries with it the Gardeners Company Challenge Cup, which was won by G. W. Kimpton with some nice flowers, better balanced as a set than Mr Scott's but none of the quality of that outstanding 'Pink Favourite'.

I always find this section of particular interest and it is noteworthy that each of its four classes has some special award. Class 64, which is for a vase of six specimen blooms, is the Kathleen Louise Mahaffy Memorial Class. It was won by H. W. Palmer with very bright and fresh flowers of 'Montezuma', 'Perfecta', 'Gail Borden', 'Isabel de Ortiz' and 'Rose Gaujard'. 'Montezuma' was the best, the rest lacking a little in form.

I have devoted space to these classes now because they are representative of what the town gardener, working without assistance, can achieve. But now I must start at the beginning and take a more orderly look at this fine show.

'TRAVESTI' (floribunda)
'Orange Sensation' × *'Circus'*
Raised by Geo. De Ruiter, Holland
CERTIFICATE OF MERIT 1966
See page 181

'MOLDE' (floribunda)
Raised by M. Tantau, Germany
TRIAL GROUND CERTIFICATE 1966
See page 182

Division A, open to all amateurs irrespective of the number of trees grown or the amount of help employed, has three trophy classes. The Edward Mawley Challenge Cup is for a box of twelve and it was won by F. Wiltshire with some very large blooms, all perfectly fresh and good but every one showing some sign of weather damage—an indication of the difficulties many exhibitors had had to face.

The S. W. Burgess Memorial Cup is offered for six vases of hybrid tea roses, a difficult class to fill really well. It was won by Col. W. B. Wright, whose best varieties were 'Gavotte' and 'Royal Highness'. He also had 'Jean Campbell', a pale pink rose new to me. The remaining three were 'Montezuma', a trifle weak, 'Karl Herbst' and 'Wendy Cussons'.

Finally in this section there is the Lindsell Cup for twenty-four specimen blooms—a tremendous test of cultural skill. There were five entries and the victor was Maurice L. Kemp with a good even box in which, nevertheless, there were frequent signs of weather damage. 'Peaceful' was a splendid flower and so were 'Diana Maxwell', a grand carmine rose, 'Kathleen Kaye', 'Mrs Charles Lamplough' and 'Pink Favourite'.

Division B is limited to amateurs who grow without assistance but there is no limitation on number of trees grown. Here the Nicholson Challenge Cup is offered for a box of twelve specimen blooms. It was won by L. Poole whose flowers were, I thought, as good as any in Division A. His best bloom was 'Ulster Monarch', a huge flower but still well formed; 'Leonore de Marche' was a deep scarlet rose of particularly fine form and other good flowers were 'Peaceful,' 'Peace' and 'Josephine Bruce'.

The slightly less taxing class for six specimen blooms carries the Brayfort Challenge Cup. This was won by F. M. Bowen with some of the best roses in the show, all nice clean blooms of excellent form and size. One of the largest was 'Directeur Guerin'. The red 'Dame de Coeur' had a rather low centre but it would have been difficult to fault the other four—'Memoriam', 'Brilliant', 'Fragrant Cloud' and 'Grandpa Dickson'.

The Alfred Hewlett Memorial Class is for a bowl of hybrid tea roses and the winner, A. W. J. Green, had what may well have been the best bowl in the show. All were lovely flowers and he had well over the specified minimum of six varieties—actually ten, 'Pink Favourite',

'Liberty Bell', 'Gavotte', 'Gail Borden', 'Peace', 'Margaret', 'Super Star', 'Glory of Rome', 'Show Girl' and 'Isabel de Ortiz'.

Then there is the six vase class for the H. R. Darlington Memorial Cup and here again the winning entry, by L. Poole, was quite outstanding. 'Margaret' was his weakest, 'Wendy Cussons' and 'Royal Highness' his best. The others were 'Gavotte', 'Ethel Sanday' and 'Klaus Stortebeker', a big red rose that I do not remember having seen before.

Division C is restricted to amateurs with not more than 500 rose trees and has only two trophy classes, one for a box of twelve, for the Sam McGredy Challenge Cup, the other for three vases of hybrid tea roses, for the Edward J. Holland Memorial Cup. The box class was won by L. E. J. Wood with flowers that were rather uneven in size. He had one very good 'Gail Borden' and a nice 'Show Girl' with an exceptionally high centre. The three best vases were shown by Capt. C. A. E. Stanfield and here again there was unevenness—an excellent vase of 'Silver Lining', big but slightly untidy flowers of 'Isabel de Ortiz' and 'Super Star' not well matched for size.

There were disappointments, too, in Division D, restricted to amateurs who grow no more than 250 trees. This also has two trophy classes, one for a box of six (the Gilbert Burch Memorial Class), the other for three vases of hybrid tea roses for the Slaughter Memorial Cup. P. G. Thompson won the box class with six blooms of 'Gavotte' and of these there could be little criticism for all were clean, of good size and perfectly matched.

In Division E, for amateurs with no more than 150 trees, the only trophy class is that for the Charles Rigg Cup. This is for a box of six specimen blooms and was won by K. G. Clarke. 'Stella' was his best bloom and the box suffered from a lack of variety in colour.

Finally I can hardly overpraise the two glorious bowls, one of hybrid tea roses, the other of floribundas, with which the Worcester Park Horticultural Society won the Franklin Dennison Memorial Cup in the section for affiliated societies. I noticed here some blooms of 'Anne Mette Poulsen', a very old cherry red floribunda that is seldom seen nowadays. But there were plenty of good modern roses too—'My Choice', 'Perfecta', 'Pink Favourite', 'Montezuma', 'Queen Elizabeth', 'Circus', 'Evelyn Fison' and 'Orangeade' among them.

Before turning to the big trade groups I must say something about the smaller classes for nurserymen. There is, for example, the very interesting Class 4 which carries the William E. Harkness Memorial Trophy and is for thirty stems of any variety which received a Trial Ground Certificate between 1 June 1960 and 31 December 1964. This was won by Frank Cant & Co. Ltd with 'Milord', and it certainly looked most attractive.

Then there are the box classes which always bring George Longley & Sons into the fray. I regret that in the crush I missed the forty-eight blooms with which this firm won the John Hart Memorial Cup but there was no mistaking the masterly cultivation in the twenty-four with which Longley & Sons secured the Kilbee Stuart Memorial Cup. There were some interesting varieties here, too, such as 'President Schroeder', a big carmine rose; 'Moonbeam' and 'Fireflash', both good yellows; 'Angel Wings', a lighter yellow; 'Misty Morn', lighter still; 'Mark Ronsen', 'Pink Lustre', 'Crimson Brocade' and 'Americana'. Longley's also won the A. C. Turner Challenge Cup for fifteen distinct varieties. Frank Cant & Co. Ltd won the Lewis Levy Memorial Cup for three baskets of floribunda roses with 'Iceberg', 'Alain' and 'Fata Morgana', a very attractive orange-apricot rose that was new to me.

Once again the Championship Trophy for the best exhibit in the show and the Queen Mary Trophy for the best exhibit against a background were both won by R. Harkness & Co. Ltd. This huge bank of flowers was arranged with all the skill and precision we have come to take almost for granted and all the many varieties shown were well grown. 'Grandpa Dickson' had a place of honour in the centre and looked very impressive, but really it is invidious to single out any varieties for special mention when all were so good.

Equally attractive in its very different way was the big island group with which John Mattock Ltd won the Coronation Trophy. Here one could peer around the great bowls of flowers instead of looking straight at them and some of them made a tremendous impact when seen in this way. The golden yellow floribunda 'Arthur Bell' was in splendid form and so was the hybrid tea 'Princess', almost the colour of 'Super Star' but apparently a much larger and fuller rose.

The China Trophy is also awarded for an exhibit on an island site but there the size is limited to 15 ft by 10 ft. Warley Rose Gardens Ltd won the trophy and made the maximum use of their space by having, in addition to the usual bowls and vases of flowers, two alcoves devoted to specimen hybrid tea blooms and floribunda sprays in tubes. The purple and gold 'Kronenbourg' was well shown here and so was 'Wisbech Gold'.

Then there is the Norman Rogers Cup for an exhibit against a background, also with a size limitation, 12 ft by 6 ft. F. Carter & Sons produced a nice tight bank of bloom in the Harkness manner and walked away with the Cup.

There was an air of modernity with restraint which I found particularly pleasing in the large exhibit staged by Sam McGredy & Sons Ltd. Here 'Pernille Poulsen' was outstanding, a glowing salmon-pink which attracted from afar. At closer quarters I greatly admired 'Silver Star', one of the latest "blue" roses. It has much the same colour as 'Cologne Carnival', to which I believe it is a sister seedling, but it appears to carry a much more powerful perfume.

Another very good island group was that staged by C. Gregory & Son Ltd. Many of the bowls stood on hexagonal stands with simple white wooden screens to show them off—a display scheme which got the best out of such fine varieties as 'Percy Thrower', 'My Girl' and 'Apricot Silk'. The yellow floribunda 'Goldgleam' looked very good in this exhibit.

The best rose in the nurserymen's section was a fine bloom of 'Gold Crown' included in a large bowl of that variety shown by Frank Cant & Co. Ltd in a large, pleasingly arranged exhibit which made a lovely bank of colour against a light blue background.

Alex Dickson & Sons Ltd included a number of their own novelties with, of course, a place of honour for 'Grandpa Dickson', a rose which everyone likes for its clear colour, size and reliability. 'Trio,' the new scarlet and yellow floribunda, was also well shown and 'Apricot Nectar', a rose of amber-apricot colour, looked delightful.

There was a great deal of variety, too, in the exhibit of Ben. R. Cant & Sons Ltd, though I thought that the combination of maroon coloured stands on a white and black plastic base was rather overpowering and detracted from, rather than helped, the roses. 'Arthur Bell' and 'Apricot Silk' were good also in this exhibit and so were 'Elizabeth of Glamis' and the new bright red hybrid tea 'Ernest H. Morse'.

PRIZE WINNERS, SUMMER SHOW 1966

NURSERYMEN'S CLASSES

Class
1 *A display of roses at the entire discretion of the exhibitor.* THE CHAMPIONSHIP TROPHY, QUEEN MARY TROPHY AND LARGE GOLD MEDAL, R. Harkness & Co. Ltd; CORONATION TROPHY AND LARGE GOLD MEDAL, John Mattock Ltd; LARGE GOLD MEDALS, C. Gregory & Son Ltd; S. McGredy & Son Ltd; GOLD MEDALS, Blaby Rose Gardens Ltd; B. R. Cant & Sons Ltd; Frank Cant & Co. Ltd; Alex Dickson & Sons Ltd; North Hill Nurseries; John Waterer, Sons & Crisp Ltd; SILVER GILT MEDALS, Cramphorn's Nurseries Ltd; Chaplin Bros. (Waltham Cross) Ltd; Wm Lowe & Son (Nurseries) Ltd; Harry Wheatcroft & Sons Ltd; SILVER MEDALS, Gandy's (Roses) Ltd; Watkins Roses Ltd; Wheatcroft Bros Ltd.
2 THE CHINA TROPHY. *Island display of roses 15 ft by 10 ft.* 1. Warley Rose Gardens Ltd; 2. E. B. Le Grice (Roses) Ltd.
3 THE NORMAN ROGERS CUP. *Display of roses 12 ft by 6 ft with background.* 1. F. Carter & Sons; 2. R. Murrell.
4 THE WILLIAM E. HARKNESS MEMORIAL TROPHY. *Bowl of roses, thirty stems.* 1. Frank Cant & Co. Ltd; 2. R. Murrell; 3. Mark Court.
5 THE JOHN HART MEMORIAL CUP. *Box of forty-eight specimen blooms.* 1. George Longley & Sons; 2. Mark Court.
6 THE KILBEE STUART MEMORIAL CUP. *Box of twenty-four specimen blooms.* 1. George Longley & Sons; 2. Mark Court.
7 *Box of twelve specimen blooms, distinct varieties.* 1. Mark Court; 2. George Longley & Sons.
8 THE LEWIS LEVY MEMORIAL CUP. *Three baskets of floribunda roses.* 1. Frank Cant & Co. Ltd.
9 *Three baskets of H.T. roses.* No entry.
10 THE A.C. TURNER CHALLENGE CUP. *Fifteen vases of roses.* 1. George Longley & Sons. 2. Fairmead Nurseries.

AMATEUR CLASSES

Open

13 *Bowl of old garden roses.* 1. E. F. Allen; 2. Mrs B. Tetley-Jones; 3. Mrs R. Langdon.
14 *Vase of old garden roses.* 1. A. B. Rabagliati; 2. E. F. Allen.
15 THE EDWARD MAWLEY CHALLENGE CUP. *Box of twelve specimen blooms, distinct varieties.* 1. F. Wiltshire; 2. Maj.-Gen. R. F. B. Naylor; 3. W. Pearl.
16 *Box of six specimen blooms, distinct varieties.* 1. Col W. B. Wright; 2. F. Wiltshire.
17 *Box of six specimen blooms, one variety.* 1. W. L. Heath; 2. Col W. B. Wright; 3. F. Wiltshire.
18 *Vase of six specimen blooms, two varieties.* 1. Col W. B. Wright; 2. Maj.-Gen. R. F. B. Naylor; 3. E. F. Allen.
19 *Bowl of H.T. roses, eighteen stems.* 1. Maj.-Gen. R. F. B. Naylor; 2. Col W. B. Wright; 3. Dr S. W. Drinkwater.
20 *Bowl of H.T. roses, twelve stems.* 1. Col W. B. Wright; 2. Maj.-Gen. R. F. B. Naylor; 3. J. F. Harkness.
21 THE S.W. BURGESS MEMORIAL CUP. *Six vases of H.T. roses, distinct varieties.* 1. Col W. B. Wright; 2. F. Wiltshire; 3. E. F. Allen.
22 *Three vases of floribunda roses, distinct varieties.* 1. E. F. Allen; 2. Maj.-Gen. R. F. B. Naylor; 3. Dr S. W. Drinkwater.
23 *Bowl of floribunda roses, twelve stems, one variety.* 1. E. F. Allen; 2. J. L. Workman.
24 *Bowl of floribunda roses, twelve stems, four varieties.* 1. E. F. Allen; 2. J. F. Harkness; 3. Maj.-Gen. R. F. B. Naylor.
25 THE LINDSELL CUP. *Box of twenty-four specimen blooms, distinct varieties.* 1. M. L. Kemp; 2. W. Pearl; 3. Dr R. P. Rumsey.
26 *Bowl of H.T. roses, twelve stems, one variety.* 1. L. Poole; 2. M. L. Kemp; 3. Dr R. P. Rumsey.

Amateurs who, without assistance, grow and stage their own roses, irrespective of number of trees grown

27 THE NICHOLSON CHALLENGE CUP. *Box of twelve specimen blooms, distinct varieties.* 1. L. Poole; 2. M. L. Kemp; 3. L. A. Anstiss.
28 THE BRAYFORT CHALLENGE CUP. *Box of six specimen blooms, distinct varieties.* 1. F. M. Bowen; 2. L. Poole; 3. W. L. Heath and C. M. Lister.
29 *Box of six specimen blooms, one variety.* 1. L. Poole; 2. Dr R. P. Rumsey; 3. J. Roscoe; 4. M. L. Kemp.
30 *Vase of six specimen blooms, two varieties.* 1. L. Poole; 2. F. Fairbrother; 3. J. H. Shotter.
31 *Bowl of H.T. roses, eighteen stems.* 1. L. Poole; 2. A. W. J. Green; 3. Dr R. P. Rumsey.
32 THE ALFRED HEWLETT MEMORIAL CLASS. *Bowl of H.T. roses, twelve stems.* 1. A. W. J. Green; 2. F. Fairbrother; 3. F. C. R. Dell; 4. C. C. Hart.
33 THE H.R. DARLINGTON MEMORIAL CUP. *Six vases of H.T. roses, distinct varieties.* 1. L. Poole; 2. W. H. Brooks; 3. Dr R. P. Rumsey.
34 *Three vases of floribunda roses, distinct varieties.* 1. L. A. Anstiss; 2. F. Fairbrother; 3. J. H. Shotter; 4. C. C. Hart.
35 *Bowl of floribunda roses, twelve stems.* 1. C. C. Hart; 2. E. C. Stallman; 3. F. Fairbrother.
36 *Bowl of floribunda roses, twelve stems, four varieties.* 1. F. M. Bowen; 2. W. N. Dolley; 3. F. Fairbrother; 4. Dr R. P. Rumsey.

Amateurs with not more than 500 rose trees, who grow and stage without assistance

37 THE SAM MCGREDY CHALLENGE CUP. *Box of twelve specimen blooms, eight varieties.* 1. L. E. J. Wood; 2. H. V. Mitchell; 3. J. Jamieson.
38 *Box of six specimen blooms, four varieties.* 1. L. E. J. Wood; 2. F. J. Houghton; 3. E. E. Gatward; 4. A. B. Rabagliati.
39 *Vase of six specimen blooms, distinct varieties.* 1. J. E. G. Heritage; 2. T. F. Pearson; 3. L. E. J. Wood; 4. F. J. Quinn.
40 *Bowl of H.T. roses, twelve stems.* 1. J. E. G. Heritage; 2. J. H. Shotter; 3. Capt. C. A. E. Stanfield, R.N.; 4. L. E. J. Wood.
41 *Vase of H.T. roses, six stems.* 1. J. E. G. Heritage; 2. S. J. Williams; 3. L. E. J. Wood; 4. F. J. Houghton.
42 THE EDWARD J. HOLLAND MEMORIAL CUP. *Three vases of H.T. roses, distinct varieties.* 1. Capt. C. A. E. Stanfield, R.N.; 2. D. H. Scott; 3. L. E. J. Wood.
43 *Bowl of floribunda roses, twelve stems.* 1. Capt. C. A. E. Stanfield, R.N.; 2. W. N. Dolley; 3. Miss I. R. Sharland; 4. R. O. Samuel.
44 *Bowl of floribunda roses, nine stems.* 1. Capt. C. A. E. Stanfield, R.N.; 2. C. A. Norrington; 3. F. J. Houghton.

Amateurs with not more than 250 rose trees, who grow and stage without assistance

45 THE GILBERT BURCH MEMORIAL CLASS. *Box of six specimen blooms.* 1. P. G. Thompson; 2. S. J. Williams; 3. E. Jarman; 4. P. N. Wesson.
46 *Vase of three specimen blooms.* 1. P. N. Wesson; 2. J. E. B. Horrell; 3. E. H. Hill; 4. F. J. Quinn.
47 *Bowl of H.T. roses, twelve stems.* 1. S. J. Williams; 2. H. J. Preston; 3. W. G. Hinkley; 4. J. E. B. Horrell.
48 THE SLAUGHTER MEMORIAL CUP. *Three vases of H.T. roses.* 1. M. Cranton; 2. W. G. Hinkley; 3. E. W. J. Wonnacott.
49 *Bowl of floribunda roses, six stems, two or more varieties.* 1. H. V. Mitchell; 2. Miss M. Bairstow; 3. G. Stewart; 4. J. K. Stephens.
50 *Bowl of floribunda roses, six stems, one variety.* 1. E. Jarman; 2. F. C. R. Picton; 3. J. K. Stephens.

Amateurs with not more than 150 rose trees, who grow and stage without assistance

51 THE CHARLES RIGG CUP. *Box of six specimen blooms, four varieties.* 1. K. G. Clarke; 2. F. C. H. Witchell; 3. C. C. Harris; 4. L. A. Lawrence.
52 *Vase of six specimen blooms.* 1. J. B. Martin; 2. I. T. Mayhew; 3. F. C. H. Witchell; 4. W. D. Roberts.
53 *Vase of three specimen blooms.* 1. R. L. Dillon; 2. D. Ball; 3. W. W. N. Hobbs; 4. L. H. Aylard.
54 *Vase of H.T. roses, six stems.* 1. W. D. Roberts; 2. Lt-Col E. W. Busk; 3. E. A. Brown.
55 *Vase of H.T. roses, three stems.* 1. Mrs Mercy Short; 2. K. G. Clarke; 3. R. West; 4. A. E. Sheppard.
56 *Vase of floribunda roses, four stems.* 1. F. Longhurst; 2. C. C. Harris; 3. W. W. N. Hobbs.
57 *Bowl of floribunda roses, six stems.* 1. J. B. Martin; 2. D. M. Porteus; 3. R. L. Dillon; 4. Mrs D. Whittle.

Amateurs with not more than 100 rose trees, who grow and stage without assistance

58 *Box of six specimen blooms, one or more varieties.* 1. D. H. Cowderoy; 2. E. W. A. Perry; 3. W G. Henderson.
59 *Vase of three specimen blooms.* 1. D. F. Tranter; 2. Mrs M. R. Stewart; 3. W. G. Henderson; 4. M. R. Bailey.
60 *Vase of H.T. roses, six stems.* 1. Mrs M. R. Stewart; 2. D. F. Tranter; 3. S. C. Godding; 4. Lt-Col E. B. MacCarthy.
61 *Vase of H.T. roses, three stems.* 1. Mrs M. R. Stewart; 2. E. W. A. Perry; 3. J. V. Jarvis; 4. Mrs E. H. Day.
62 *Vase of floribunda roses, four stems.* 1. F. L. Mayer; 2. M. Johnson; 3. M. R. Bailey; 4. B. T. King.

Metropolitan Classes

63 THE GARDENERS' COMPANY CHALLENGE CUP. *Box of six specimen blooms, distinct varieties.* 1. G. W. Kimpton; 2. F. M. Bowen; 3. D. H. Scott; 4. B. Dennis.
64 THE KATHLEEN LOUISE MAHAFFY MEMORIAL CLASS. *Vase of six specimen blooms.* 1. H. W. Palmer; 2. B. Dennis; 3. G. W. Kimpton; 4. A. C. Stevens.
65 THE ALBERT E. GRIFFITH MEMORIAL CLASS. *Bowl of H.T. roses, twelve stems.* 1. H. W. Palmer; 2. F. M. Bowen; 3. R. G. Conisbee; 4. L. Willingale.
66 THE FRANKLIN DENNISON MEMORIAL BOWL. *Bowl of floribunda roses, twelve stems.* 1. F. C. R. Dell; 2. D. H. Scott; 3. W. Birkbeck; 4. B. Dennis.

Amateurs who have never won a first prize at any Show of the Society

67 *Box of six specimen blooms, four varieties.* 1. T. J. Vale; 2. K. J. D. Barnes; 3. P. N. Wesson; 4. J. S. Jellyman.
68 *Vase of six specimen blooms.* 1. T. R. Parker; 2. M. Cranton; 3. Mrs R. Langdon; 4. K. J. D. Barnes.
69 *Vase of three specimen blooms, distinct varieties.* 1. T. J. Vale; 2. L. J. Morrell; 3. P. G. Thompson; 4. T. R. Parker.
70 *Vase of three specimen blooms, one or more varieties.* 1. C. W. Juniper; 2. P. N. Wesson; 3. P. Coy; 4. T. J. Vale.
71 *Vase of H.T. roses, six stems.* 1. D. F. Tranter; 2. G. Morrison; 3. P. N. Wesson.
72 *Vase of H.T. roses, three stems.* 1. P. Coy; 2. P. N. Wesson; 3. D. F. Tranter.

73 *Vase of floribunda roses, four stems.* I. Mrs M. G. Santer; 2. F. C. R. Dell; 3. R. G. Paines; 4. F. H. Blackburn.

Amateurs who have never previously exhibited at any Show of the Society

74 *Vase of three specimen blooms.* I. C. A. Norrington; 2. J. L. Waterman; 3. S. J. Hadlow; 4. A. E. Hills.
75 *Vase of H.T. roses, six stems, distinct varieties.* I. C. A. Norrington; 2. K. J. D. Barnes; 3. P. L. Lockton.
76 *Vase of H.T. roses, six stems, one or more varieties.* I. Mrs A. M. Royston; 2. J. S. Jellyman; 3. P. Robson.
77 *Vase of floribunda roses, four stems.* I. C. A. Norrington; 2. R. A. Beckwith; 3. P. L. Lockton; 4. Mrs M. R. Stewart.

Affiliated Societies Composite exhibit

78 THE FRANKLIN DENNISON MEMORIAL CUP. *Bowl of floribunda roses and bowl of H.T. roses.* I. Worcester Park Horticultural Society; 2. East Kent Rose Society; 3. Ickenham & Swakeleys Horticultural Society.
79 *Three vases of floribunda roses, distinct varieties.* I. Radlett & Aldenham Horticultural Society; 2. East Kent Rose Society; 3. Eastcote Horticultural Society.

FLORAL ARRANGEMENT SECTION

Amateurs who grow and stage their own roses

80 THE QUEEN ALEXANDRA MEMORIAL TROPHY. *Arrangement of roses for a dinner table.* I. Mrs B. Green; 2. Mrs E. M. Woodcock; 3. Mrs M. Brooker.
81 *A frontal arrangement of cut roses.* I. Mrs B. Green; 2. Mrs J. A. Rush; 3. Mrs M. Brooker; 4. Mrs E. I. Sampson.
82 *An all-round arrangement of floribunda roses.* I. Mrs E. M. Woodcock; 2. Mrs W. Thomas.
83 *An arrangement of Old Garden Roses.* I. Mrs W. Thomas; 2. Mrs M. J. Parfitt; 3. Mrs D. Thorn.
84 *A picture formed by roses.* I. Mrs M. Brooker; 2. Mrs W. Thomas; 3. Mrs B. Green.
85 *For men exhibitors only. A frontal arrangement of roses.* I. F. M. Bowen; 2. B. W. W. Sampson; 3. B. Green.
86 *A composition of 'Super Star' roses.* I. Mrs J. A. Rush; 2. Mrs W. Thomas; 3. A. W. Woodcock.

Amateurs staging roses obtained from any source

87 *An arrangement of roses on a pedestal.* I. Mrs E. M. Woodcock; 2. Mrs K. Wells; 3. Mrs W. Thomas.
88 *A composition of roses with any natural plant material.* I. Mrs E. M. Woodcock; 2. Mrs B. Green; 3. Mrs T. A. Wade; 4. Mrs J. A. Rush.
89 *An arrangement of roses on a natural base.* I. Mrs M. Brooker; 2. Mrs M. J. Aitchison; 3. Mrs W. Thomas; 4. Mrs K. Wells.
90 *A basket arrangement of roses in shades, tints and tones of yellow.* I. Mrs E. K. Skinner; 2. Mrs W. Thomas; 3. Mrs K. Wells.
91 *A "greeting card" arrangement of miniature roses.* I. Mrs W. Thomas; 2. Mrs H. Goodall; 3. Mrs E. M. Woodcock.

Amateurs who have never previously exhibited in the Floral Arrangement Section at any Show of the Society

92 *An arrangement of roses to face front.* I. Mrs K. Pitman; 2. Mrs M. Jones-Fuller; 3. Mrs H. Goodall.

Affiliated Society Class

93 *A group of rose arrangements.* I. East Kent Rose Society.

SPECIAL AWARDS

BEST BLOOM (A) 'PINK FAVOURITE', D. H. Scott.
BEST BLOOM (N) 'GOLD CROWN', Frank Cant & Co. Ltd.
AMATEUR CHAMPION, L. Poole.
EDWARD MAWLEY MEMORIAL MEDAL, Capt. C. A. E. Stanfield, R.N.
THE REV. H. HONEYWOOD D'OMBRAIN MEMORIAL CUP, Capt. C. A. E. Stanfield, R.N.

The Northern Rose Show

R. C. BALFOUR

In the delightful setting of Roundhay Park, Leeds, the Northern Rose Show was again held last July in conjunction with the Roundhay (Leeds) Horticultural Society. This had been enhanced by the new rose garden where the mass planting of the new salmon floribunda 'City of Leeds', awarded a Gold Medal in 1965, caught the eye.

Visitors to the Leeds Flower Show come mainly from the West Riding, but exhibitors travel not only from the rest of Yorkshire and neighbouring counties, but from even farther afield. For rose lovers the attraction of the show was that they could see not only the colourful displays of some of the leading rose growers, but also many of the newest varieties. For those gardeners whose interest is not confined to roses there was the added pleasure of seeing other plants, brilliantly coloured dahlias, dwarf shrubs for ground cover, foliage plants for the house, cacti and succulents for the greenhouse and the delightful rock garden designed by Rowley and Sons of Leeds, which earned them the premier award in the show for the second successive year. They could also admire the centre-piece of the show, the garden with pool and terrace amid silver birch trees, designed and laid out by Mr Knight and the Leeds Parks Department.

The competition for the premier award among the roses, the Brotherton Trophy, was very close and the judges spent a long time before they finally awarded it to Fryer's Nurseries of Knutsford, who also gained a Large Gold Medal, as well as the medal for the best bloom among the trade exhibits, a fine specimen of the apricot yellow hybrid tea 'Diorama'. Their display, with a garden seat and wooden tables, was beautifully arranged so that you could see all the blooms, often with two bowls of the same variety, one raised above the other. Outstanding among their roses were 'Ideal Home', with fine foliage and full blooms of rich pink inside and ivory reverse; the yellow 'Golden Giant'; the full-petalled orange salmon 'Colour Wonder' and the small pink blooms, rather like a phlox, of the shrub rose 'Ballerina,' which adds so much to a herbaceous border. The huge blooms of 'Gail Borden' were also outstanding.

McGredy's Large Gold Medal exhibit, arranged in bowls on plain wooden platforms on tall metal stands, featured appropriately, among others of their new roses, 'City of Leeds', the deep salmon-red floribunda contrasting with two yellow floribundas, 'Jan Spek' and 'Arthur Bell', with its rich green foliage. Notable also on their stand were the well-budded trusses of that lovely salmon-pink floribunda, 'Pernille Poulsen', the bright blooms of 'Rose of Tralee' and that strange bi-coloured sport from 'Peace', 'Kronenbourg', a rose which people seem either to love or hate. Of his novelties the full pinky-red blooms of 'Reg Willis' were attracting the ladies especially, and a bright red hybrid tea, 'Tradition', bred by Reimer Kordes, looked promising. Among the floribundas was 'Ice White', with its profusion of white blooms against deep green foliage. Two new light vermilion floribundas shown were 'Irish Mist' and 'Bobbie Lucas'.

Gregory's of Nottingham, also winners of a Large Gold Medal, had a large display at one end of one of the three adjoining marquees, with full bowls of roses on stands with white nylon at the back, giving the display an impression of much greater depth. Their floribundas were outstanding, probably the best in the show, so much better than their hybrid teas. There were huge bowls of the lovely salmon 'Elizabeth of Glamis' at one end contrasting with the scarlet of 'Evelyn Fison' at the other; at one corner 'Coral Queen Elizabeth' was alongside its scarlet namesake and the red 'Dorothy Wheatcroft'; at another was the lovely deep orange-salmon floribunda 'My Girl'; others to attract were 'Strawberry Fair' with its deep red flat blooms and 'Spanish Orange'.

The Gold Medal earned by Lowe's of Beeston was well deserved. Not a large exhibit, it was well arranged in bowls on wooden tables, featuring the vivid orange of 'Princess Michiko', the vermilion 'Super Star' and 'Tradition' with its deep red buds opening so attractively; it should be a great rose for cutting.

E. B. Le Grice's Silver Gilt display set against a blue background included many curious colours, the browny-yellow of 'Amberlight' and the lavender-mauve of 'Overture' contrasting with the fresh pink of 'Dainty Maid', the orange-tinged buds and the single cream blooms of 'Dairy Maid' and deep red 'Europeana'. Among his new varieties he was showing the canary yellow floribunda 'Goldgleam', with its strong scent and attractive foliage, and 'Tom Brown', two shades of brown which will appeal to flower arrangers looking for unusual colour blendings. But to me his most fascinating new rose was 'Dimples', a fragrant yellowy-cream floribunda whose blooms are said to be unaffected by wet weather and to fall cleanly when over. It earned its name because everyone who saw it bent down to smell and always came up with a smile.

Geo. De-Ruiter were showing many new roses delightfully arranged, against a setting of wooden fencing, with the rich yellow of 'Golden Treasure' contrasting with the deep red of 'Europeana', the deep orange salmon of 'My Girl', the small tight buds and orange yellow flowers of 'Travesti' and the blood red of 'Scania'.

Among the 'Garnette' roses 'Carol', with its beautiful pink flowers was shown off well in baskets and 'Golden Garnette' looked most attractive. I hope their admirers realised that, while long lasting as cut flowers, they are not suitable as bedding roses.

David Lister of Leeds won a Silver Medal for a representative group of cut roses in bowls set on black cloth, among which 'Eden Rose', 'Peace' and 'Mischief' were outstanding. Another local nurseryman to do well was Charles Kershaw, who earned a Silver Gilt Medal with an interesting display, including a bowl of very bright and fresh blooms of that striking floribunda 'Charleston' and another of the delicate pink and amber hybrid tea 'Polly'.

Prominent among the successful amateur exhibitors was J. M. Robinson of Kendal, whose 'Christian Dior', in a box in which 'Stella' and 'Isabel de Ortiz' were also outstanding, was adjudged the best bloom shown by an amateur. J. Hardaker, a regular exhibitor from Leeds, won the Roundhay (Leeds) Rose Cup and showed blooms of 'Memoriam' and 'Dorothy Peach' of high quality. The winner of the Jubilee Trophy with the highest number of points in the classes for those who grow and stage their own roses was A. J. Brindley of Knypersley. He had fine blooms of 'Fragrant Cloud' and 'Perfecta' in his winning boxes and of 'Europeana' among his floribundas. Three 'Perfecta' and three 'Stella' shown by Mr Birkby of Halifax were outstanding, but they would have looked even better if they had not been so bunched in the vase.

Other winners included S. C. Thomson, the Chairman of the Roundhay Society, Mrs R. C. Moorhouse of Leeds, W. Tazzyman of Stockbridge and G. Greenwood of Huddersfield. The Congleton and

District Horticultural Society won both the classes for affiliated societies.

In a tent shared with the other rose classes and the floral arrangements of the Leeds Flower Show, which as usual were of a very high standard, the rose floral arrangement classes were somewhat disappointing in the number of entries—in at least two classes there was only one entry—and to some extent in quality. Perhaps this is partly due to the restriction of nearly all the classes to rose foliage only; so few gardeners seem to grow such shrub roses as *R. rubrifolia*, which are not only lovely in the garden but also provide such useful material for flower arrangements. However, there were many attractive exhibits and among them was a delightful composition by Mrs S. Bain of Tingley, with 'Pink Garnette' roses in a tall china stemmed cherub vase; second in the same class, Mrs Paley of Leeds used 'Masquerade' and 'Peace' with a miner's lamp to celebrate the opening of a mine. Mrs E. A. Shephard of Barnsley won many prizes, including one for a clever blending of five varieties of red roses in a brass candle-stick. Mrs M. A. Chambers' winning arrangement of floribunda roses was light and fresh and Mrs J. A. Crowther's red roses set off by a polished wooden stand were attractive.

Among the other exhibits in the amateur tent was an especially interesting one by the Yorkshire Flower Club showing flowers of the genus ROSA, which besides various species of rose included such plants as potentilla and geum.

Finally I am sure all visiting members of this Society must have been impressed, not only by the superb organisation but also by the pleasant friendly atmosphere, both so characteristic of Leeds Flower Show. Our thanks are due to the Officers and Committee of the Roundhay Society and their helpers.

The Autumn Rose Show

GORDON FORSYTH

During over forty years of active gardening, combined with horticultural journalism, I do not think I have missed one of the Society's
London exhibitions, but I cannot remember any Autumn Show better
than that which filled both R.H.S. halls at Westminster on 9 and 10
September, nor one supported so magnificently by the trade growers.
Although, in numbers, entries in the competitive sections for amateurs
may have been slightly below average, due to the bad weather that
immediately preceded the show, there was no lack of top quality
blooms or keen competition, and the floral section again proved a
major attraction.

Only the parade of award-winning new roses, which we have come
to look upon as one of the major attractions of this show, was disappointing. Comparatively few of those that had received Certificates of
Merit and Trial Ground Certificates—with, alas, no Gold Medals—
were on display, and, candidly, they did not look a very impressive
lot. The one I liked best, for its large semi-double flowers, which in
colour I noted as a vivid salmon-vermilion, was the new shrub rose
'Fred Loads'. Raised by R. Holmes, and shown by Fryer's Nurseries, I
was pleased to discover that in addition to its Certificate of Merit, it
was also the first winner of the Torridge Silver Salver for the best
new seedling rose raised by an amateur.

Champion exhibitor of the show—and how often does this
happen—was Jack Harkness, or rather R. Harkness and Co. Ltd of
Hitchin, Herts. How I wish I possessed only half of Jack's knowledge
of roses, and how to grow them. I just do not know how many times
I have reported that the Autumn Roses Challenge Cup, plus a Large
Gold Medal, was won by the Harkness firm, but they did it again with
blooms that outclassed all others in quality and selection of varieties,
both old and new. Eye-catchers among their hybrid teas, for instance,
were light yellow 'Burnaby', dating back to 1954; rich pink 'Ballet';
'Memoriam'; last year's Gold Medal winner 'Ernest H. Morse', surely
the most brilliant red of all; rich yellow 'Summer Sunshine' from
America, and, of their own raising, with medium-size blooms of

exquisite form, bright pink 'Guinevere'. And in support a grand selection of floribundas, including their Certificate of Merit-winning salmon-pink 'King Arthur', and mid-pink 'Dandy Dick', both of hybrid tea type, which surely must be the roses of the future.

For artistic arrangement, combined with quality of blooms, I gave top marks to C. Gregory and Son, and so was not surprised at their award of a Large Gold Medal. When inspecting exhibits, I do my own personal judging, putting "X's" against the varieties of outstanding quality. In this case I gave three each to hybrid teas 'Grandpa Dickson', one of the outstanding roses of the show, 'Fragrant Cloud', pink 'Percy Thrower', 'Blue Moon', surely the best of the lavender shades; golden 'King's Ransom', 'Wendy Cussons' and 'Chicago Peace', and likewise to their floribundas salmon 'City of Leeds', 'Scarlet Queen Elizabeth' and its coral counterpart, and, for profusion of bloom so late in the season, their repeat-flowering climber 'Pink Perpétue'.

Bees Ltd likewise fully deserved their Large Gold Medal for a beautifully arranged group of varieties suitable for general garden planting, and particularly reliable for autumn display. Outstanding among their hybrid teas were 'Mischief' in superb form, 'Piccadilly' at its most brilliant, 'Blue Moon', 'King's Ransom', 'Grandpa Dickson', 'Wendy Cussons' and rich pink-flushed 'Ideal Home', and for a glorious trio of floribundas their bowls of 'Orangeade', 'Sea Pearl' and 'Pink Parfait' would have been hard to beat.

Superb quality, combined with skilful arrangement to display each variety at its best, not surprisingly again put S. McGredy and Son in the Large Gold Medal class. In my personal judgment, I gave full marks for their hybrid teas rich pink 'Shannon', 'Grandpa Dickson', light red 'Reg Willis', and, with blooms of ideal size for cutting, rick pink 'Lady Seton' and crimson-red 'Tradition'. Needless to say, they showed their new floribundas, 'Ice White', salmon-pink 'Pernille Poulsen', light yellow 'Jan Spek' and 'City of Leeds', in grand condition, together with their new large pink climbing rose 'Galway Bay', which looks most promising.

No fewer than seven Gold Medals were awarded to trade exhibits, sure testimony to the magnificence of the show. Floribundas were outstanding in Benjamin R. Cant's display, especially such grand all-rounders as 'Orangeade', really superb 'Elizabeth of Glamis', 'Scarlet Queen Elizabeth', 'Dearest' at its best, 'Iceberg' and 'Highlight'.

Their 1965 President's Trophy winner, 'Grandpa Dickson', was shown in superb form by Alex. Dickson and Sons, also hybrid teas 'Colour Wonder', ivory 'Pascali' and 'Mischief', with floribundas of outstanding autumn quality in 'Pink Parfait', bicolour 'Innisfree' of their own raising, and the large-flowered, fully double, fragrant 'Honeymoon'.

For beautiful arrangement, with each variety artistically and spaciously displayed, Wm. Lowe and Son without question deserved their Gold Medal. Their bowls of hybrid teas 'Rose Gaujard', 'Lady Seton', coral-salmon and buff 'Miss Ireland', 'Summer Sunshine', 'Fragrant Cloud' and 'Super Star' were as good as any to be seen in the trade section, and they had as fine a bowl of floribunda 'Dearest' as one would wish to see, with 'Scarlet Queen Elizabeth', 'Pink Parfait' and 'Iceberg' again in strong support.

We can always rely on an interesting collection of top quality roses from John Mattock and he did not let us down, his stand including as it did the best bloom shown by a nurseryman, a very fine specimen of hybrid tea 'Brandenburg'. I must say I was impressed by his Trial Ground Certificate-winner 'Shepherdess', a sturdy and upright growing floribunda, again of the hybrid tea type, red in the young bud, opening cream, flushed pink, very colourful and with all the hallmarks of a first class garden rose. Fragrant yellow 'Arthur Bell' and 'Sea Pearl' were eye-catchers among his floribundas, with that grand shrub rose 'Chinatown'.

The bright double lilac-pink shrub rose 'Lavender Lassie', shown well in the Gold Medal collections of both H. Robinson and the Waterhouse Nurseries, immediately made me decide to give it a trial; likewise the new hybrid tea rose, rich velvety vermilion 'Elida' in the Wheatcroft Bros. exhibit for, although it has received no R.N.R.S. awards to date, it certainly has "class". I also noted specially their floribundas pink 'My Fair Lady', and light vermilion 'Fireworks', and hybrid teas 'Cherry Brandy' and large, full-petalled red 'Greetings', as certainly worth more than passing attention.

In Geo. De Ruiter's collection I must confess I liked the look of his new floribundas, gold and cherry-red 'Travesti', and large double 'Tombola', orange-gold in the bud, opening golden salmon, two varieties of the future, I feel sure. And in the very artistically arranged display of Harry Wheatcroft and Sons, their hybrid teas 'Pascali' and 'Youki San' both appealed to me as very welcome additions to the whites, with the equally promising floribunda cerise-salmon 'W. I. Jubilee', though loveliest of all was their bowl of pink 'Ballerina'.

Congratulations to Sir Harry Pilkington, St. Helens, on winning the Society's Challenge Cup against very keen competition in the amateurs' open class for a box of twelve specimen blooms. His beautifully matched set included a really superb 'Perfecta', and for the record his other varieties were pale flesh 'Royal Highness', 'Fragrant Cloud', 'Super Star', a really perfect 'Mischief', the yellowest 'Peace' in the show, soft pink 'Princess Grace of Monaco', 'Paris-Match', 'Karl Herbst', 'Margaret', 'Uncle Walter' and light pink 'Tiffany'.

Col W. B. Wright, Instow, was a champion exhibitor in this section, scoring firsts with a box of six blooms, three varieties, with glorious pairs each of 'Memoriam', 'Pink Favourite' and large white, pink-flushed 'Royal Highness'; a vase of six blooms, two varieties, 'Royal Highness' and 'Peace'; and a bowl of eighteen hybrid tea blooms, with really glorious specimens of 'Gavotte', 'Pink Favourite', 'Chicago Peace', 'Anne Letts', 'Silver Lining', 'Montezuma' and 'Perfecta'. Another first prize exhibit worthy of special mention in this section was Maj.-General R. F. B. Naylor's bowl of floribunda roses, a grand selection embracing the varieties 'Queen Elizabeth', scarlet 'Marlena', yellow 'Jan Spek', 'Pink Parfait', orange-salmon 'Flamenco', 'Red Favourite' and flame-red 'Charlotte Wheatcroft'.

In Division B, limited to amateurs who grow their roses without assistance, A. J. Brindley, Knypersley, achieved a remarkable triumph, not only by winning the Challenge Cup for a box of twelve specimen blooms, distinct, but seven other prizes. I particularly admired his first prize box of six blooms, especially the two specimens of 'Brilliant'.

Two of the most attractive and keenly contested classes in the show were those for three vases of hybrid teas, in the divisions for growers of not more than 500 trees, and 250, respectively, and each carrying the award of a Challenge Cup. The judges certainly had a difficult task in judging the many fine entries, and it is worth recording that the winning set staged by L. E. J. Wood, Waddesdon, embraced magnificent blooms of 'Brilliant', 'Montezuma' and 'Anne Letts', and in Division D, S. J. Williams, Aylesbury, triumphed with varieties 'Montezuma', 'Paris-Match' and 'Rose Gaujard'. It was in this class, by the way, that Capt. C. A. E. Stanfield, Walmer, won the Silver Gilt Medal for the best bloom shown by an amateur—'Pink Favourite' in perfect form.

PRIZE WINNERS, AUTUMN SHOW 1966

NURSERYMEN'S CLASSES

Class
1 THE AUTUMN ROSES CHALLENGE CUP. *A representative group of Cut Roses, space 20 ft by 5 ft.* CHALLENGE CUP AND LARGE GOLD MEDAL, R. Harkness & Co. Ltd; GOLD MEDAL, North Hill Nurseries.
2 *A display of Cut Roses.* LARGE GOLD MEDALS, Bees Ltd; C. Gregory & Son Ltd; S. McGredy & Son Ltd; GOLD MEDALS, B. R. Cant & Sons Ltd; Alex. Dickson & Sons Ltd;Wm Lowe & Son (Nurseries) Ltd; John Mattock Ltd; Herbert Robinson; Waterhouse Nurseries Ltd; Wheatcroft Bros Ltd; SILVER GILT MEDALS, Frank Cant & Co. Ltd; Chaplin Bros Ltd; Fryer's Nurseries Ltd; Harry Wheatcroft & Sons Ltd; SILVER MEDALS, Geo. De Ruiter; Hillier & Sons; E. B. Le Grice (Roses) Ltd; John Waterer, Sons & Crisp Ltd.
3 THE DE ESCOFET MEMORIAL CUP. *A display of Roses with Rose foliage only. Island table 15 ft by 10 ft.* 1. Warley Rose Gardens Ltd.
4 R.N.R.S. CHALLENGE CUP, 1. Henry Drew.
5 THE A.C. TURNER CHALLENGE CUP. *Fifteen distinct varieties.* 1. Mark Court; 2. George Longley & Sons.
6 NO ENTRY.
7 NO ENTRY.
8 *Box of twenty-four specimen blooms.* 1. Mark Court; 2. George Longley & Sons; 3. Northfield's Roses.
9 *Box of twelve specimen blooms, distinct varieties.* 1. Mark Court; 2. George Longley & Sons; 3. Northfield's Roses.

AMATEUR CLASSES

Open

12 R.N.R.S. CHALLENGE CUP. *Box of twelve specimen blooms, distinct varieties.* 1. Sir Harry Pilkington; 2. J. M. Robinson; 3. M. L. Kemp.
13 *Box of six specimen blooms, three distinct varieties.* 1. Col W. B. Wright; 2. M. L. Kemp; 3. Sir Harry Pilkington.
14 *Vase of six specimen blooms.* 1. Col W. B. Wright; 2. M. L. Kemp; 3. Maj.-Gen. R. F. B. Naylor.
15 *Bowl of H.T. roses, eighteen stems.* 1. Col W. B. Wright; 2. Sir Harry Pilkington; 3. Maj.-Gen. R. F. B. Naylor.
16 *Six vases of H.T. roses, distinct variety in each.* 1. No award. 2. Sir Harry Pilkington.
17 *Bowl of floribunda roses, twelve stems.* 1. Maj.-Gen. R. F. B. Naylor; 2. E. F. Allen.
18 *Bowl of floribunda roses, nine stems.* 1. Maj.-Gen. R. F. B. Naylor; 2. E. F. Allen.

Amateurs who without assistance grow and stage their own roses, irrespective of number of trees grown

19 R.N.R.S. CHALLENGE CUP. *Box of twelve specimen blooms, distinct varieties.* 1. A. J. Brindley; 2. M. L. Kemp; 3. F. M. Bowen; 4. G. E. Hunt.
20 *Box of six specimen blooms, three distinct varieties.* 1. A. J. Brindley; 2. L. A. Anstiss; 3. G. E. Hunt; 4. W. Pearl.
21 *Box of six specimen blooms.* 1. A. J. Brindley; 2. M. L. Kemp; 3. L. A. Anstiss; 4. W. Pearl.
22 *Vase of six specimen blooms.* 1. A. J. Brindley; 2. C. H. Parker; 3. J. H. Shotter; 4. M. L. Kemp.
23 *Bowl of H.T. roses, eighteen stems.* 1. A. J. Brindley; 2. T. Thornley.
24 *Bowl of H.T. roses, twelve stems.* 1. A. J. Brindley; 2. F. V. Parkin; 3. F. Fairbrother.
25 *Vase of H.T. roses, six stems.* 1. F. M. Bowen; 2. A. J. Brindley; 3. W. H. Brooks.
26 NO ENTRY.
27 *Bowl of floribunda roses, twelve stems.* 1. A. J. Brindley; 2. F. M. Bowen; 3. B. Dennis; 4. F. Fairbrother.
28 *Bowl of floribunda roses, nine stems.* 1. E. W. J. Wonnacott.

Amateurs with not more than 500 trees who grow and stage without assistance

29 *Box of six specimen blooms.* 1. C. D. Owens; 2. L. E. J. Wood; 3. G. E. Hunt.
30 *Vase of three specimen blooms, distinct varieties.* 1. C. D. Owens; 2. C. H. Parker; 3. L. R. Lane; 4. C. A. Norrington.
31 *Vase of six specimen blooms.* 1. D. A. Sproat; 2. C. H. Parker; 3. L. E. J. Wood.
32 *Bowl of H.T. roses, twelve stems.* 1. C. D. Owens; 2. L. E. J. Wood; 3. Capt. C. A. E. Stanfield, R.N.
33 *Vase of H.T. roses, six stems.* 1. C. D. Owens; 2. L. E. J. Wood; 3. L. R. Lane; 4. E. C. Still.
34 R.N.R.S. CHALLENGE CUP. *Three vases of H.T. roses, distinct variety in each.* 1. L. E. J. Wood; 2. D. H. Scott; 3. C. H. Parker.
35 *Bowl of floribunda roses, nine stems.* 1. E. H. Lockton; 2. E. H. Buckingham; 3. J. H. Shotter.
36 *Bowl of floribunda roses, six stems.* 1. C. A. Norrington; 2. C. M. Lister; 3. J. H. Shotter.

Amateurs with not more than 250 trees who grow and stage without assistance

37 *Box of six specimen blooms.* 1. S. J. Williams; 2. F. W. Marston; 3. H. J. Preston.

'TOMBOLA' (floribunda)
'Amor' × (*'Ena Harkness'* × *'Peace'*)
Raised by Geo. De Ruiter, Holland
TRIAL GROUND CERTIFICATE 1966
See page 182

'SHEPHERDESS' (floribunda—H.T. type)
'Allgold' × *'Peace'*
Raised by John Mattock Ltd
TRIAL GROUND CERTIFICATE 1966
See page 182

38 *Vase of three specimen blooms, distinct varieties.* 1. A. A. H. Campbell; 2. S. J. Williams; 3. E. W. J. Wonnacott; 4. F. W. Marston.
39 *Vase of three specimen blooms.* 1. A. A. H. Campbell; 2. F. W. Marston; 3. S. J. Williams; 4. C. C. Harris.
40 R.N.R.S. CHALLENGE CUP. *Three vases of H.T. roses, distinct variety in each.* 1. S. J. Williams; 2. F. W. Marston; 3. E. W. J. Wonnacott.
41 *Vase of H.T. roses, three stems.* 1. S. J. Williams; 2. F. W. Marston; 3. Mrs Mercy Short; 4. K. E. Chattenton.
42 *Bowl of floribunda roses, six stems.* 1. E. Stanhope; 2. E. W. J. Wonnacott; 3. G. Stewart.
43 *Bowl of floribunda roses, six stems, one variety.* 1. F. Longhurst; 2. E. W. J. Wonnacott; 3. F. R. Willis.

Amateurs with not more than 150 trees who grow and stage without assistance

44 *Box of six specimen blooms.* 1. K. G. Clarke; 2. W. D. Roberts; 3. G. W. Kimpton.
45 *Vase of six specimen blooms, distinct varieties.* 1. M. L. Watts; 2. G. W. Kimpton; 3. Lt-Col E. B. MacCarthy.
46 *Vase of H.T. roses, six stems.* 1. W. D. Roberts; 2. W. E. Cattell; 3. K. G. Clarke.
47 *Vase of H.T. roses, three stems.* 1. G. W. Kimpton; 2. Mrs M. J. Parfitt; 3. Lt-Col E. B. MacCarthy; 4. K. G. Clarke.
48 *Vase of floribunda roses, four stems.* 1. F. M. Bowen; 2. Lt-Col E. B. MacCarthy; 3. F. H. Blackburn.

Amateurs living within twenty-five miles of Charing Cross, who grow and stage without assistance

49 *Box of six specimen blooms, distinct varieties.* 1. B. Dennis; 2. W. D. Gobbee; 3. A. C. Stevens.
50 *Vase of six specimen blooms.* 1. B. Dennis; 2. A. C. Stevens; 3. C. M. Lister.
51 *Bowl of H.T. roses, twelve stems.* 1. D. H. Scott; 2. B. Dennis; 3. F. R. Willis.
52 *Vase of floribunda roses, four stems.* 1. E. L. W. Lenihan; 2. C. M. Lister; 3. F. H. Blackburn.

Amateurs who have never won a first prize at any Show of the Society

53 *Box of six specimen blooms.* 1. J. E. Bullough; 2. L. K. Raven; 3. R. P. Court.
54 *Vase of six specimen blooms.* 1. J. E. Bullough; 2. K. J. D. Barnes; 3. V. L. Natusch.
55 *Vase of three specimen blooms, distinct varieties.* 1. V. L. Natusch; 2. J. E. Bullough; 3. L. J. Morrell.
56 *Vase of H.T. roses, six stems.* 1. G. Morrison; 2. K. J. D. Barnes; 3. V. L. Natusch.
57 *Vase of H.T. roses, three stems.* 1. J. E. Bullough; 2. V. L. Natusch; 3. G. Morrison.
58 *Vase of floribunda roses, four stems.* 1. K. J. D. Barnes; 2. J. Hatfield; 3. F. H. Blackburn.

Amateurs who have never previously exhibited at a Show of the Society

59 *Vase of H.T. roses, six stems.* 1. J. E. Bullough; 2. V. L. Natusch; 3. Mrs A. Ginbey.
60 *Vase of floribunda roses, four stems.* 1. V. L. Natusch.

AFFILIATED SOCIETIES
A composite exhibit from not fewer than five members of each society competing
61 Congleton Horticultural Society.

FLORAL ARRANGEMENT SECTION
(All stems must reach the water)
Amateurs who grow and stage their own roses

62 *An arrangement of roses in a box or basket.* 1. Mrs W. Thomas; 2. Mrs W. M. Crabb; 3. Mrs E. Godfrey; 4. Mrs M. J. Parfitt.
63 *A composition of rose foliage and heps.* 1. Mrs W. M. Crabb; 2. Mrs E. M. Woodcock; 3. Mrs W. Thomas.
64 *An arrangement of not more than five or less than three roses with any rose foliage and/or heps.* 1. Mrs R. Tallack; 2. Mrs W. Thomas; 3. Mrs W. M. Crabb; 4. Mrs C. M. Bowen.
65 *An all-round arrangement of floribunda roses.* 1. Mrs W. M. Crabb; 2. Mrs W. Thomas; 3. Mrs E. F. Homewood.
66 *A small frontal arrangement of roses.* 1. Mrs K. Wells; 2. Mrs W. M. Crabb; 3. Mrs W. Thomas; 4. Mrs M. J. Parfitt.

Open

67 *An arrangement of roses on a pedestal.* 1. Mrs W. Thomas; 2. Mrs W. M. Crabb; 3. Mrs E. M. Woodcock.
68 *A decoration of roses for a Christmas buffet table.* 1. Mrs E. M. Woodcock; 2. Mrs K. Wells; 3. Mrs J. Edwards.
69 *A composition of roses depicting a song, play or book title concerned with roses.* 1. Mrs E. M. Woodcock; 2. Mrs W. M. Crabb; 3. Mrs W. Thomas; 4. Mrs K. Wells.

Amateurs who have never exhibited in the Floral Arrangement Section of the Royal National Rose Society Shows

70 *A frontal arrangement of roses with any rose foliage and/or heps.* 1. Mrs R. Tallack

SPECIAL AWARDS

BEST BLOOM (A) 'PINK FAVOURITE'. Capt. C. A. E. Stanfield, R.N.
BEST BLOOM (N) 'BRANDENBURG'. John Mattock Ltd.
R.N.R.S. CHALLENGE TROPHY, FLORAL ARRANGEMENT SECTION. Mrs E. M. Woodcock.

The Trial Ground and Display Garden 1966

L. G. TURNER

Looking back over the reports for several years past there is little doubt that a fine summer is the exception rather than the rule. Instead of going into details of the vagaries of our climate I will dismiss the usual weather report by describing it as "normal"! But there is one feature that must be mentioned as, judging from the numerous letters received on the subject, the problem was not confined to Bone Hill. I refer to the extensive damage caused by the frost early in November 1965. Although all the wood that appeared to have been affected was cut away at pruning time, there was still evidence of it in the following June. In several cases stems that had produced a good crop of blooms suddenly wilted and died and an examination proved that the cause was frost damage.

It is inevitable that with varieties of unknown merit being sent for trial, these gardens are more prone to disease than those of the ordinary members. Nevertheless, until mid-September, Black Spot and Rust were kept under control. Later in the autumn there were signs of the former disease, but Rust, fortunately, was almost negligible. Mildew was evident for most of the season, but this may have been due in large measure to the prevailing weather. All trees were sprayed with Bordeaux mixture during the dormant season and maneb immediately after pruning. This early treatment undoubtedly proved of great benefit.

The most important innovation during the last year was the introduction of the Henry Edland Memorial Medal for the most fragrant rose on trial. For many years it had been felt that the Clay Challenge Vase for the most fragrant British-raised rose was not sufficient. One can think of many roses raised overseas that merited an award for fragrance but, until now, the judges were powerless to make it. My predecessor was particularly keen on fragrant roses, especially hybrid teas, and I am sure no better memorial could have been instituted. The medal is struck in 9-ct gold and depicts the Tudor Rose. Congratulations to Herr Tantau on being the first winner with 'Charm of Paris', a full pink floribunda-H.T. type. Regretfully, the Clay Vase has been withdrawn as it was felt that two awards so closely associated would cause confusion to the public.

Another important event was the winning of the Torridge Silver Salver and Torridge Silver Spoons for the first time. These were presented to the Society by Edgar M. Allen in 1960 for award to the best and second best amateur-raised seedlings of Trial Ground Certificate standard. That there should have been two roses for consideration in the same year as Mr Allen was awarded the Dean Hole Medal for his work in connection with the rose, is indeed a happy coincidence and must have given him much pleasure. Congratulations to R. A. Holmes, raiser of 'Fred Loads', a tall-growing vermilion floribunda shrub and to G. W. C. Vincent, raiser of 'Herself', a pale pink floribunda of medium height. I am sure these awards will serve as an incentive to other amateurs to try their hand at hybridising, although, at the same time, it must be emphasised that a new rose is not enough—it must be different and meritorious for it to make the grade.

At this point it might be pertinent to mention the standards of the basic awards. The lowest is the Trial Ground Certificate (T.G.C.) which is a fair indication that the variety has reached a standard when it may be relied upon to do well in the average garden. The next higher category is the Certificate of Merit (C. of M.). Such a rose is outstanding, although not quite up to the highest standard of the Gold Medal (G.M.). A variety in this last group must be of a very high quality and have some exceptional characteristic.

Thus we come to this season's seedlings and the fact that the judges considered no variety to be worthy of a Gold Medal award. The trials are intended as a serious adjudication of the quality of the roses sent and are not meant to be a means of publicity for particular varieties. They are judged only on their performance at St Albans. I am sure that the judges are correct in not lowering their sights just to ensure that a Gold Medal award is made. Perhaps next year there will be a number of Gold Medal award winners—I hope so.

Last year I mentioned that plans were afoot for development of the area where the apple walk had stood. This, however, has been deferred for the time being, as with the purchase of the additional land, the lay-out of the whole of the eastern side of the gardens is to be re-designed. At present the plans are on the drawing board, but it is expected that these will be approved by the spring and that work will commence next autumn.

One cannot envy Mr Clacy and his small sub-committee their task of attempting to incorporate the numerous suggestions submitted. But I am sure that the design ultimately adopted will become a garden of lasting beauty that will prove a great attraction to visitors from both home and overseas.

With the closure of the John Innes Institute at Bayfordbury, it appears that the National Rose Collection established there is in jeopardy. The Council feels that the Society should be responsible for the collection, and although it will not be possible to transfer it in its entirety, it is envisaged that the new plans will include a basic collection of the species and their hybrids.

The Council is aware that car parking during the height of the season is a problem and, in view of this, it has agreed to allocate a portion of the new land as additional parking space. This will certainly ease the congestion, and coupled with the extension of opening times as explained on page 13, I am sure members and their friends will enjoy their visits even more. Last season there were over 11,000 visitors and, with the foregoing arrangements, there should be many more in the coming season. I would like to congratulate and thank all visitors for being so conscious of the "Keep Britain Tidy" campaign. It is indeed a pleasure to walk around the garden when the last of seven or eight hundred visitors have left and not to be able to find even the occasional toffee paper—thank you.

The Awards to New Roses in 1966

* Denotes varieties for which it is understood protection is being sought under the Plant Varieties and Seeds Act 1964.

The Henry Edland Memorial Medal awarded to the most fragrant rose on trial, irrespective of country of origin, and Certificate of Merit:
*CHARM OF PARIS (Flori.-H.T. type). 'Prima Ballerina' × 'Montezuma'. Trial Ground No. 738. Reg. No. 952. *Raiser:* M. Tantau, Germany. *Distributor:* Harry Wheatcroft & Sons Ltd, Nottingham. Bloom: Clear pink, double, 3½ in.; fragrant. Growth: Medium, branching. Foliage: Semi-glossy, medium green, large, abundant.

The Rose of Torridge Silver Salver for the best new seedling rose raised by an amateur and Certificate of Merit were awarded to:
FRED LOADS (Shrub). 'Orange Sensation' × 'Dorothy Wheatcroft'. Trial Ground No. 933. Reg. No. 1089. *Raiser:* R. Holmes, Stockport. *Distributor:* Fryer's Nurseries Ltd, Knutsford. Bloom: Vermilion-orange, single, 4 in.; fragrant. Growth: Vigorous, tall, upright. Foliage: Semi-glossy, light green, large.

Certificates of Merit were awarded to:
*★BON SOIR (H.T.). Seedling × Seedling. Trial Ground No. 864. Reg. No. 1080. *Raiser and Distributor:* Alex Dickson & Sons Ltd, N. Ireland. Bloom: Peach pink, very full, well shaped; fragrant. Growth: Vigorous, medium, upright. Foliage: Glossy, dark green, large.
★KING ARTHUR (Flori.-H.T. type). 'Pink Parfait' × 'Highlight'. Trial Ground No. 820. Reg. No. 1067. *Raiser and Distributor:* R. Harkness & Co. Ltd, Hitchin. Bloom: Salmon pink, double, 4 in. Growth: Medium, branching. Foliage: Matt, medium green, large.
★REDGOLD (Flori.-H.T. type). ('Karl Herbst' × 'Masquerade') × ('Faust' × 'Piccadilly'). Trial Ground No. 648. Reg. No. 996. *Raiser and Distributor:* Alex Dickson & Sons Ltd, N. Ireland. Bloom: Golden yellow, edged cherry red, 3 in. Growth: Vigorous, medium, upright. Foliage: Semi-glossy, medium green, small.
★TRAVESTI (Flori.). 'Orange Sensation' × 'Circus'. Trial Ground No. 710. Reg. No. 971. *Raiser:* Geo. De-Ruiter, Holland. *Distributor:* Geo. De-Ruiter, Chilwell. Bloom: Yellow, flushed cherry red with yellow reverse, 2½ in.; slightly fragrant. Growth: Vigorous, medium, branching, uniform. Foliage: Semi-glossy, dark green, small.

The Rose of Torridge Silver Spoons and Trial Ground Certificate:
*★HERSELF (Flori.). 'Sweet Repose' × 'Moulin Rouge'. Trial Ground No. A18. Reg. No. 909. *Raiser:* G. W. C. Vincent, Hemingford Grey. *Distributor:* R. Harkness & Co. Ltd, Hitchin. Bloom: Pale pink, semi-double, 4 in.; slightly fragrant. Growth: Medium, upright. Foliage: Semi-glossy, dark green, large.

Trial Ground Certificates were awarded to:
GUINEVERE (H.T.). 'Red Dandy' × 'Peace'. Trial Ground No. 816. Reg. No. 1066. *Raiser and Distributor:* R. Harkness & Co. Ltd, Hitchin. Bloom: Pink, full, well shaped. Growth: Medium, branching. Foliage: Matt, light green, small.
★IRISH MIST (Flori.-H.T. type). 'Orangeade' × 'Mischief'. Trial Ground No. 877. Reg. No. 1018. *Raiser:* S. McGredy IV. *Distributor:* S. McGredy &

Son Ltd, N. Ireland. Bloom: Orange-salmon, moderately full, well shaped; slightly fragrant. Growth: Medium, branching. Foliage: semi-glossy, dark green, small.

*MOLDE (Flori.). Parentage unknown. Trial Ground No. 739. Reg. No. 956. *Raiser:* M. Tantau, Germany. *Distributor:* Harry Wheatcroft & Sons Ltd, Nottingham. Bloom: Brilliant scarlet. Growth: Low, branching. Foliage: Glossy, dark green, large.

*SANTA FE (H.T.). 'Mischief' × 'Super Star'. Trial Ground No. 872. Reg. No. 1105. *Raiser:* S. McGredy IV. *Distributor:* S. McGredy & Son Ltd, N. Ireland. Bloom: Pink, lighter reverse, full, large. Growth: Vigorous, upright. Foliage: Matt, dark green, small.

SHEPHERDESS (Flori.-H.T. type). 'Allgold' × 'Peace'. Trial Ground No. 954. Reg. No. 1090. *Raiser and Distributor:* J. Mattock Ltd, Nuneham Courtenay. Bloom: Yellow flushed pale salmon, semi-double, 3 in.; slightly fragrant. Growth: Vigorous, medium, branching. Foliage: Glossy, dark green, bronze tinted.

*SIR LANCELOT (Flori.). 'Vera Dalton' × 'Woburn Abbey'. Trial Ground No. 817. Reg. No. 1064. *Raiser and Distributor:* R. Harkness & Co. Ltd, Hitchin. Bloom: Apricot yellow, semi-double, 4 in. Growth: Vigorous, medium, branching. Foliage: Matt, light green, small.

*TOMBOLA (Flori.). 'Amor' × seedling. Trial Ground No. 715. Reg. No. 1046. *Raiser:* Geo. De-Ruiter, Holland. *Distributor:* Geo. De-Ruiter, Chilwell. Bloom: Deep salmon, to carmine pink, shaded gold, 4 in. Growth: Vigorous, medium, upright. Foliage: Glossy, dark green, large.

International Awards 1966

ROME

LARGE FLOWERS		
Gold Medal	Unnamed	Meilland, France
First Certificate	'Lemon Spice'	Armstrong Nurseries, U.S.A.
Certificates	'Sphinx'	J. Gaujard, France
	'Versailles'	Georges Delbard, France
FLORIBUNDA		
Gold Medal	Unnamed	M. Tantau, Germany
First Certificate	'Bobino'	Dorieux, France
Certificates	'Sangria'	Louisette Meilland, France
	'Pink Perpétue' (climber)	C. Gregory & Son Ltd, Great Britain

MADRID

LARGE FLOWERS		
Gold Medal	'Samurai'	Louisette Meilland, France
First Certificates	'Versailles'	Georges Delbard, France
	'Lady X'	Louisette Meilland, France

FLORIBUNDA

Certificate	'Bobino'	F. Dorieux, France
Second Certificate	'Elan'	Paul Croix, France

A Certificate was awarded to an unnamed variety raised by A. Meilland, France

PARIS—BAGATELLE

Gold Medal	'Majorette' (H.T.)	Louisette Meilland, France
First Certificate	'Agéna' (H.T.)	Georges Delbard, France
Certificates	'Princess Michiko' (Flori.)	Alex Dickson & Sons Ltd, N. Ireland
	'Versailles' (H.T.)	Georges Delbard, France

GENEVA

LARGE FLOWERS
Gold Medal and Prize of the City of Geneva

	'Versailles'	Georges Delbard, France
Silver Medal	'Agéna'	Georges Delbard, France
Certificates	'Apogée'	Georges Delbard, France
	'Summer Rainbow'	Conard-Pyle Co., U.S.A.

FLORIBUNDA

Gold Medal and Prize	'Sangria'	Louisette Meilland, France
Silver Medal	'Suzanne Dolard'	J. Gaujard, France
Certificate	'Ice White'	S. McGredy IV, N. Ireland

4 other award winners were unnamed

THE HAGUE

FLORIBUNDA

Gold Medal	'Sangria'	Louisette Meilland, France
First Certificate	'John Dijkstra'	G. A. H. Buisman, Holland

HYBRID TEA
Certificate for the most fragrant variety

	'Versailles'	Georges Delbard, France

CLIMBERS

First Certificate	'Altissimo'	Delbard–Chabert, France

In the beds of roses planted out in the Westbroekpark the International Jury awarded the *Golden Rose of The Hague* to 'Lilli Marlene' (Flori.) raised by W. Kordes, Germany, and a *First Class Certificate* to 'Fervid' (Flori.) raised by E. B. Le Grice, Great Britain. The *Crystal Trophy* for fragrance was awarded to 'Frosty' (miniature) raised by R. Moore, U.S.A.

LYON

HYBRID TEA

Gold Medal	'Apogée'	Georges Delbard, France
Silver–Gilt Medal	'Versailles'	Georges Delbard, France
Certificates	'Tendresse'	Dorieux, France
	'Agéna'	Georges Delbard, France

FLORIBUNDA

Certificate	'Sangria'	Louisette Meilland, France

CLIMBERS

Certificates	'Bienvenue'	Meilland, France
	'Iseran'	M. Combe, France

ORLÉANS

FLORIBUNDA
Golden Rose of the City of Orléans

	'Fidélio'	A. Meilland, France
First Certificate	'Lacre'	Moreira da Silva, Portugal

U.S.A.

ALL AMERICA ROSE SELECTIONS
'Roman Holiday' (Flori.) raised by R. V. Lindquist; 'Gay Princess' (Flori.) raised by E. S. Boerner; 'Bewitched' (H.T.) raised by Dr W. E. Lammerts; 'Lucky Lady' (H.T.) raised by H. C. Swim, all U.S.A.

BELFAST

HYBRID TEA
Gold Medal of the City of Belfast

	'Colour Wonder'	Reimer Kordes, Germany

FLORIBUNDA
The "Golden Thorn" Award

	'Marlena'	Reimer Kordes, Germany
The "Uladh" Award	'Sea Pearl'	Pat Dickson, N. Ireland
Certificates	'Elizabeth of Glamis'	Sam McGredy, N. Ireland
	'Rose of Tralee'	Sam McGredy, N. Ireland
	'My Girl'	Geo. De-Ruiter, Holland

JAPAN

HYBRID TEA

Silver Medal	Unnamed	Georges Delbard, France
Certificates	'Apogée'	Georges Delbard, France
	'Grandpa Dickson'	Alex Dickson & Sons Ltd, N. Ireland
	'Versailles'	Georges Delbard, France
	Unnamed	M. Tantau, Germany

MASS EFFECT

Silver Medal	'Altissimo'	Georges Delbard, France
Certificates	'Princess Michiko'	Alex Dickson & Sons Ltd. N. Ireland
	Unnamed	Laperrière, France
	Unnamed	Sam McGredy, N. Ireland
	Unnamed	S. Onodera, Japan

Book Review

The Charm of Old Roses, by Nancy Steen, 264 pp.
Published by A. H. and A. W. Reed, of Wellington, Auckland
and Sydney, 47s. 6d. (N.Z.)

There is a newly awakened interest in old roses as Mr Graham S. Thomas (the greatest authority on these varieties) will confirm.

I welcome this well produced and informative work by a lady rosarian from New Zealand, although it is confined to a record of roses which have bloomed in that country since it became a colony of Great Britain in 1840.

There have been numerous works on the old roses even before Dean Hole's *A Book about Roses* (1874) and since *Old Roses for Modern Gardens* by Richard Thompson (1959). The book contains many acknowledgments to well-known writers on old roses, and a mass of copyrighted material from Ellen Willmott onwards is reproduced with permission and is of considerable interest (though I miss Redouté or any reference to Leroy of Bagatelle).

Mrs Steen and her husband have spent twenty-one years collecting and cultivating old roses, and she is a fine descriptive writer well qualified to produce a book which must freshen our interest and enhance our appreciation of the high decorative value, the hardiness, the colour, the natural beauty and the fragrance of old roses.

The work describes the origin, the historic association, the characteristics and the cultivation of hundreds of varieties of the Gallicas, the Damasks, the Albas, the China roses, the Rugosas, the Centifolias and the Portland roses (which became the parents of the hybrid perpetuals) and some early hybrid teas. In these chapters she gives a living background to the pre-modern varieties. Other interesting chapters include the "Hybrid Musks", shrub roses, climbers and ramblers.

The book has 264 pages and included in the index are the names of 860 varieties mentioned in the text. The Bibliography contains 82 works on roses dating from 1799 to 1962 of which 80 are in the author's library. The book is liberally illustrated with 48 coloured and 17 black and white plates, all taken in the author's garden by her husband.

The work is a valuable guide, both for the beginners and the specialists, and I have nothing but praise for the way Mrs Steen has assembled material of considerable extent and of unfailing interest.

Harry Wheatcroft has visited Mrs Steen's garden in Auckland and writes a eulogistic foreword to her book.

E. ROYALTON KISCH

The Rose Analysis

L. G. TURNER

The tables have been prepared and presented in a similar manner to last year, but the voting has been undertaken by a panel some eleven per cent larger this time. There are few sensational changes, with perhaps the exception of 'Peace' being relegated from first place in both North and South tables for General Garden Cultivation. Thus, the fears expressed last year that this rose was on the decline appear to be correct. At that time I thought 'Super Star' would be the variety to supersede it in both tables, but in some areas this suffered badly from frost damage and die back, which may well be the reason that 'Wendy Cussons' has taken over the lead in the North.

The usual changes owing to dates of introduction have taken place in the audit of newer hybrid teas, with 'Mischief', 'King's Ransom', 'Miss Ireland' and 'Golden Giant' giving way to 'Ernest H. Morse', 'Grandpa Dickson', 'Pascali' and 'Princess'. With the exception of 'Miss Ireland' all have found places in other tables.

In the audit of newer floribundas, 'Orange Sensation', 'Dorothy Wheatcroft', 'Zambra', 'Vera Dalton' and 'Celebration' have been replaced by 'City of Leeds', 'Pink Parfait', 'Pernille Poulsen', 'Scented Air' and 'Charlotte Elizabeth'. During the five years when 'Orange Sensation' appeared in the audit, it earned one of the first three places on four occasions, and it has now entered the general floribunda list in fourth place. This is indeed an outstanding achievement for a fine variety that will possibly go even higher.

'Queen Elizabeth' has been displaced by 'Iceberg', mainly, I suspect, because in many gardens it is allowed to get out of hand and grow too tall. Visitors to Bone Hill may remember the hedge of this variety growing alongside the entrance and I am sure they will agree that it can be kept at a reasonable height by suitable pruning. However, 'Iceberg' is a worthy leader and I do not wish to give the impression of "damning it with faint praise". It blooms throughout the season and even at the end of November there are still plenty of flowers to be seen.

There have been a few changes in the lower positions in the tables, but these are mainly in respect of older varieties, fluctuating in and out of the tables year by year—'McGredy's Yellow' and 'Sam McGredy' are two in particular.

To avoid any misunderstanding, I should emphasise that these tables are prepared from the returns submitted by the voting panel and do not necessarily reflect the official opinion of the Society. There are several varieties at Bone Hill, particularly climbers, that are growing exceptionally well and on their performance deserve a place in the tables, but they are perhaps not sufficiently well known. In one or two instances a footnote has been added to the table mentioning such varieties.

Once again the thanks of the Editorial Board are extended to all the members of the panel who devote so much time to observing the performance of rose varieties throughout the season.

The voters this year were:

C. J. Abrahams (Yorks.), Miss A. M. Aldous (Oxon.), E. F. Allen (Suffolk), L. A. Anstiss (Hants.), D. M. Arnot (Angus), E. F. Bailey (Glam.), W. K. Bentley (Leics.), A. D. Bide (Surrey), F. M. Bowen (Kent), G. F. Bradford (Berks.), A. J. Brindley (Staffs.), C. Broadhurst (Devon), W. H. Brooks (Sussex), S. Carson (Northumberland), W. G. H. Cates (Sussex), G. W. Chadwick (Yorks.), Mr & Mrs H. G. Clacy (Surrey), A. M. Cocker (Aberdeens.), R. G. Conisbee (Surrey), Dr T. M. Cullingworth (Warwicks.), Dr A. Dick (Lanarks.), A. P. C. Dickson (Co. Down), C. J. Dillon (Northumberland), Dr S. W. Drinkwater (Norfolk), G. Edwards (Sussex), A. Eling (Essex), W. H. Ellerker (Co. Durham), E. V. Elwes (Kent), Mrs T. Evans (Brecons.), F. Fairbrother (Devon), F. Fryer (Cheshire), Miss J. Fulford (N. Devon), J. A. K. Garratt (Middx.), S. M. Gault (London), C. R. Gregory (Notts.), Mrs A. E. Griffith (Suffolk), J. Hardaker (Yorks.), A. N. Harding (Kent), J. L. Harkness (Herts.), W. L. Heath (Berks.), J. E. G. Heritage (Dorset), H. Hillier (Hants.), C. S. Hilton (Berks.), F. J. Houghton (Salop), G. Hunt (Lancs.), E. W. Hurst (Yorks.), W. A. James (Wilts.), J. H. Jess (Co. Antrim), Mrs B. Tetley-Jones (Essex), H. Jones (Cheshire), M. L. Kemp (Essex), C. M. Land (Yorks.), E. B. Le Grice (Norfolk), Mr & Mrs T. Leishman (Stirlings.), C. M. Lister (Bucks.), E. H. Lockton (Bucks.), Messrs. George Longley & Sons (Kent), A. W. Lowe (Notts.), Rev A. Macara (Ayrshire), J. W. Mattock (Oxon.), S. McGredy (Co. Armagh), W. J. Mead (Herts.), E. Mooney (Lancs.), Mrs R. C. Moorhouse (Yorks.), W. A. Morse (Norfolk), Miss H. Murrell (Salop), Maj.-Gen. R. F. B. Naylor (Herts.), A. E. Nevard (Essex), G. H. Northfield (Cambs.), R. L.

Pallett (Surrey), W. Pearl (Kent), S. Peat (Suffolk), Sir Harry Pilkington (Lancs.), L. Poole (Glam.), H. N. Raban (Bristol), Mrs M. E. Robbins (Cornwall), J. M. Robinson (Westmorland), J. Roscoe (Lancs.), B. W. W. Sampson (Herts.), R. O. Samuel (Middx.), W. J. W. Sanday (Bristol), J. Scammell (Pembs.), K. W. Seaman (Herts.), Miss I. R. Sharland (Glos.), T. H. Shaw (Yorks.), Mrs Mercy Short (Hants.), J. H. Shotter (Glos.), E. Shreeves (E. Yorks.), L. C. Smith (London), Mrs S. Sowerby (Herts.), R. D. Squires (Lancs.), Capt. C. A. E. Stanfield, R.N. (Kent), Graham S. Thomas (Surrey), J. W. Thompson (Notts.), S. C. Thomson (Yorks.), Mr & Mrs W. C. Thorn (Essex), T. Thornley (Yorks.), Mrs W. T. Toogood (Surrey), W. E. Tysterman (Cambs.), A. N. Urquhart (Renfrews.), B. S. T. Wallace (Hants.), Dr E. McP. Watts (Kent), M. G. Watts (Hants.), C. Wheatcroft (Notts.), P. Wheatcroft (Notts.), F. Wiltshire (Bristol), E. W. J. Wonnacott (Herts.), L. E. J. Wood (Bucks.), H. Woods (Lancs.), R. S. Woolley (Northumberland), Col W. B. Wright (N. Devon).

AUDIT OF NEWER ROSES—HYBRID TEAS

This table includes only varieties introduced in this country since 1 January 1962

Position	Number of points	NAME	Introduced	COLOUR
1	902	*Fragrant Cloud	1964	Geranium lake
2	544	Gavotte	1963	Light pink with silvery reverse
3	499	Isabel de Ortiz	1962	Deep pink with silvery reverse
4	483	*Ernest H. Morse	1965	Rich turkey red
5	461	Grandpa Dickson	1966	Yellow fading to creamy yellow
6	413	*Blue Moon	1964	Silvery lilac
7	408	Royal Highness	1962	Soft light pink
8	402	Chicago Peace	1962	Phlox pink, base canary yellow
9	371	Uncle Walter	1963	Scarlet with crimson shadings
10	362	Vienna Charm	1963	Coppery orange
11	361	Summer Sunshine	1962	Rich yellow
12	306	*Papa Meilland	1963	Dark crimson
13	236	Norman Hartnell	1964	Deep cerise
14	203	Pascali	1963	White
15	135	Princess	1964	Intense vermilion

* Most fragrant

AUDIT OF NEWER ROSES—FLORIBUNDAS

This table includes only varieties introduced in this country since 1 January 1962

Posi-tion	Number of points	NAME	Intro-duced	COLOUR
1	838	*Elizabeth of Glamis	1964	Light salmon
2	751	Evelyn Fison	1962	Vivid red with scarlet shading
3	611	Europeana	1963	Deep crimson
4	604	Paddy McGredy	1962	Carmine, lighter reverse
5	499	Sea Pearl	1964	Soft pink with yellow
6	474	Violet Carson	1963	Soft peach pink, silvery reverse
7	363	Woburn Abbey	1962	Orange with yellow
8	354	Scarlet Queen Elizabeth	1963	Orange scarlet
9	235	City of Leeds	1966	Rich salmon
10	222	Manx Queen	1963	Gold, orange tipped
11	190	Charleston	1963	Yellow and crimson, flushed cherry
12	174	Pink Parfait	1962	Medium to light pink, yellow at base
13	173	*Pernille Poulsen	1965	Salmon pink fading lighter
14	146	*Scented Air	1965	Salmon pink
15	135	Charlotte Elizabeth	1965	Deep rose pink tinged red

FLORIBUNDA ROSES

This table includes only varieties introduced in this country before 1 January 1962

Posi-tion	Number of points	NAME	Intro-duced	COLOUR
1	1401	Iceberg	1958	Pure white
2	1285	Queen Elizabeth	1955	Clear self pink
3	1041	Allgold	1956	Unfading golden yellow
4	1037	*Orange Sensation	1961	Orange vermilion
5	1022	Orangeade	1959	Bright orange vermilion
6	915	Lilli Marlene	1959	Scarlet red
7	863	*Dearest	1960	Rosy salmon
8	749	Anna Wheatcroft	1959	Light vermilion
9	723	Circus	1955	Yellow, pink and red
10	711	Korona	1953	Bright orange scarlet
11	627	Frensham	1946	Deep scarlet crimson
12	572	Masquerade	1950	Yellow, pink and red
13	513	Highlight	1956	Orange scarlet
14	470	Paprika	1958	Bright turkey red
15	450	Dorothy Wheatcroft	1961	Bright orient red
16	435	Sarabande	1957	Dazzling scarlet
17	433	Vera Dalton	1961	Pale camellia rose
18	381	Zambra	1961	Orange shading to yellow
19	371	Faust	1956	Golden yellow with pink
20	367	*Sweet Repose	1956	Light yellow, amber and pink
21	338	Shepherd's Delight	1958	Flame, orange and yellow
22	309	*Fashion	1947	Orange salmon
23	303	Chanelle	1958	Buff, overlaid peach pink
24	289	Dickson's Flame	1958	Scarlet flame

* Most fragrant

HYBRID TEA ROSES PRODUCING LARGE SPECIMEN BLOOMS SUITABLE FOR EXHIBITION

This table includes only varieties introduced in this country before 1 January 1962

Northern Counties

Posi-tion	Number of points	NAME	Intro-duced	COLOUR
1	229	Peace	1942	Light yellow edged pink
2	210	Perfecta	1957	Cream, shaded rose red
3	189	Brilliant	1952	Rich scarlet
4	181	Stella	1958	Carmine shading to cream
5	179	*Wendy Cussons	1960	Deep cerise
6	175	*Super Star	1960	Light vermilion without shading
7	174	Pink Favourite	1956	Deep rose pink
8	170	Memoriam	1960	White tinted pale pink
9	165	Gail Borden	1956	Pale gold with peach, inside salmon rose
10	145	Christian Dior	1959	Velvety scarlet
11	124	*Ena Harkness	1946	Bright crimson scarlet
12	119	*Silver Lining	1958	Pale rose with silver reverse
13	109	Margaret	1954	Pink with lighter reverse
14	94	Rose Gaujard	1958	White, flushed rich pink
15	91	*My Choice	1958	Pink, reverse pale yellow
16	74	Gold Crown	1960	Deep golden yellow
17	72	Piccadilly	1960	Scarlet, yellow reverse
18	68	Montezuma	1956	Deep salmon red
19	66	Paris Match	1956	Deep carmine pink
20	61	*Eden Rose	1950	Deep pink, lighter reverse
21	49	Anne Letts	1953	Pale pink with paler reverse
22	40	Karl Herbst	1950	Deep red with lighter reverse
23	36	Dorothy Peach	1956	Yellow edged buff
24	34	McGredy's Yellow	1933	Buttercup yellow

* Most fragrant

MINIATURE ROSES

Mostly of about 6 to 9 in. in height, rarely more

Position	NAME	COLOUR
1	Baby Masquerade	Yellow and red
2	Rosina	Sunflower yellow
3	Pour Toi	White tinted yellow at base
4	Coralin	Coral red to orange red
5	Baby Gold Star	Golden yellow
6	Cinderella	White tinted carmine
7	Perla de Montserrat	Clear pink with deeper shadings
8	Colibri	Apricot shaded orange
9	Sweet Fairy	Lilac pink

HYBRID TEA ROSES PRODUCING LARGE SPECIMEN BLOOMS SUITABLE FOR EXHIBITION

This table includes only varieties introduced in this country before 1 January 1962

Southern Counties

Position	Number of points	NAME	Introduced	COLOUR
1	517	Pink Favourite	1956	Deep rose pink
2	497	Perfecta	1957	Cream shaded rose red
3	444	Stella	1958	Carmine shading to cream
4	435	*Wendy Cussons	1960	Deep cerise
5	419	Memoriam	1960	White tinted pale pink
6	372	Peace	1942	Light yellow edged pink
7	359	Brilliant	1952	Rich scarlet
8	329	Gail Borden	1956	Pale gold with peach, inside salmon rose
9	306	*My Choice	1958	Pink, reverse pale yellow
10	303	Montezuma	1956	Deep salmon red
11	302	*Super Star	1960	Light vermilion without shading
12	291	*Silver Lining	1958	Pale rose with silver reverse
13	288	Margaret	1954	Pink with lighter reverse
14	268	Anne Letts	1953	Pale pink with paler reverse
15	244	Rose Gaujard	1958	White flushed rich pink
16	199	Karl Herbst	1950	Deep red with lighter reverse
17	192	Gold Crown	1960	Deep golden yellow
18	142	Christian Dior	1959	Velvety scarlet
19	127	Dorothy Peach	1956	Yellow edged buff
20	124	*Josephine Bruce	1952	Deep velvety crimson scarlet
21	106	Golden Giant	1961	Golden yellow
22	103	Peaceful	1956	Deep coral rose pink, reverse lighter
23	86	*Ena Harkness	1946	Bright crimson scarlet
24	83	Sam McGredy	1937	Deep chamois to cream

SOME HYBRID TEA ROSES FOR INDOOR DECORATION

NAME	Introduced	COLOUR
*Super Star	1960	Light vermilion without shading
*Sutter's Gold	1950	Light orange shaded red
Queen Elizabeth	1955	Clear self pink
*Wendy Cussons	1960	Deep cerise
Peace	1942	Light yellow edged pink
Mischief	1961	Coral salmon
Virgo	1947	White flushed pale pink
*Lady Sylvia	1927	Light pink with yellow base
Montezuma	1956	Deep salmon red
Mojave	1954	Deep orange and reddish flame
*Sterling Silver	1959	Silvery lilac
Spek's Yellow	1947	Bright rich yellow

* Most fragrant

HYBRID TEA ROSES FOR GENERAL GARDEN CULTIVATION

This table includes only varieties introduced in this country before 1 January 1962

Northern Counties

Position	Number of points	NAME	Introduced	COLOUR
1	500	*Wendy Cussons	1960	Deep cerise
2	497	*Super Star	1960	Light vermilion without shading
3	490	Peace	1942	Light yellow edged pink
4	410	Stella	1958	Carmine shading to cream
5	380	Piccadilly	1960	Scarlet, yellow reverse
6	378	Pink Favourite	1956	Deep rose pink
7	324	Rose Gaujard	1958	White flushed rich pink
8	313	*Ena Harkness	1946	Bright crimson scarlet
9	265	*Josephine Bruce	1952	Deep velvety crimson scarlet
10	265	Mischief	1961	Coral salmon
11	241	*Prima Ballerina	1958	Deep pink
12	239	Gail Borden	1956	Pale gold with peach, inside salmon rose
13	231	Perfecta	1957	Cream shaded rose red
14	221	*Silver Lining	1958	Pale rose with silver reverse
15	207	*My Choice	1958	Pink, reverse pale yellow
16	191	King's Ransom	1961	Rich pure yellow
17	190	Margaret	1954	Pink with lighter reverse
18	182	Beauté	1954	Orange yellow and apricot
19	161	Gold Crown	1960	Deep golden yellow
20	131	*Sutter's Gold	1950	Light orange shaded red
21	125	*Eden Rose	1950	Deep pink, lighter reverse
22	124	Ballet	1958	Deep pink
23	122	Mojave	1954	Deep orange and flame
24	107	Memoriam	1960	White tinted pale pink

REPEAT FLOWERING CLIMBERS

Position	Number of points	NAME	Introduced	COLOUR
1	672	Danse du Feu	1954	Orange scarlet
2	616	Golden Showers	1957	Golden yellow
3	573	*Zéphirine Drouhin	1868	Bright carmine pink
4	528	Mermaid	1917	Primrose yellow
5	482	*New Dawn	1930	Pale pink
6	427	Parkdirektor Riggers	1957	Blood red
7	400	Royal Gold	1957	Deep yellow
8	305	Casino	1963	Soft yellow
9	299	Meg	1954	Apricot yellow shaded pink
10	242	Maigold	1953	Bronze yellow
11	212	Pink Perpetue	1965	Clear pink with carmine pink reverse
12	195	Elegance	1937	Pale yellow

The following varieties may also be recommended: 'Aloha', 'Dortmund', 'Hamburger Phoenix', 'Handel', 'Parade' and 'Soldier Boy'.

★ Most fragrant

HYBRID TEA ROSES FOR GENERAL GARDEN CULTIVATION

This table includes only varieties introduced in this country before 1 January 1962

Southern Counties

Position	Number of points	NAME	Introduced	COLOUR
1	980	*Super Star	1960	Light vermilion without shading
2	892	Peace	1942	Light yellow edged pink
3	842	*Wendy Cussons	1960	Deep cerise
4	745	Stella	1958	Carmine shading to cream
5	696	Piccadilly	1960	Scarlet, yellow reverse
6	631	Rose Gaujard	1958	White flushed rich pink
7	626	Pink Favourite	1956	Deep rose pink
8	588	*Josephine Bruce	1952	Deep velvety crimson scarlet
9	578	Mischief	1961	Coral salmon
10	547	*Silver Lining	1958	Pale rose with silver reverse
11	516	*Ena Harkness	1946	Bright crimson scarlet
12	483	Gail Borden	1956	Pale gold with peach, inside salmon rose
13	468	*My Choice	1958	Pink, reverse pale yellow
14	420	Perfecta	1957	Cream shaded rose red
15	405	*Prima Ballerina	1958	Deep pink
16	344	Margaret	1954	Pink with lighter reverse
17	324	King's Ransom	1961	Rich pure yellow
18	306	*Sutter's Gold	1950	Light orange shaded red
19	300	*Eden Rose	1950	Deep pink, lighter reverse
20	232	Grand'mère Jenny	1950	Light yellow flushed pink
21	217	Montezuma	1956	Deep salmon red
22	185	Gold Crown	1960	Deep golden yellow
23	169	Karl Herbst	1950	Deep red with lighter reverse
24	166	Ballet	1958	Deep pink

WICHURAIANA CLIMBING AND RAMBLING ROSES— SUMMER FLOWERING

Suitable for pergolas and fences

Position	Number of points	NAME	Introduced	COLOUR
1	703	*Albertine	1921	Reddish salmon to copper pink
2	600	Paul's Scarlet Climber	1915	Bright scarlet crimson
3	523	Emily Gray	1916	Rich golden buff
4	471	American Pillar	1902	Bright rose with white eye
5	406	Excelsa	1909	Bright rosy crimson
6	397	*Dr W. van Fleet	1910	Pale flesh pink
7	369	*Albéric Barbier	1900	Yellow to creamy white
8	366	Dorothy Perkins	1901	Rose pink
9	364	Crimson Shower	1951	Crimson
10	363	Chaplin's Pink Climber	1928	Bright pink
11	280	Sanders' White	1915	White
12	208	Crimson Conquest	1931	Deep scarlet, white base

* Most fragrant

CLIMBING AND RAMBLING ROSES FOR SPECIAL PURPOSES

Position	NAME	Introduced	COLOUR
	Suitable for walls or closeboard fencing		
1	Danse du Feu	1954	Orange scarlet
2	Cl. Mrs Sam McGredy	1929	Bright orange copper
3	Mermaid	1917	Primrose yellow
4	*Albertine	1921	Reddish salmon to pink
5	Royal Gold	1957	Deep yellow
6	*Cl. Shot Silk	1937	Light carmine shaded orange
7	*Cl. Etoile de Hollande	1931	Deep red
8	*Cl. Ena Harkness	1954	Bright crimson scarlet
9	Maigold	1953	Bronze yellow
	Suitable for open fences		
1	*Albertine	1921	Reddish salmon to pink
2	Danse du Feu	1954	Orange scarlet
3	*New Dawn	1930	Pale pink
4	Paul's Scarlet Climber	1915	Bright scarlet crimson
5	Emily Gray	1916	Rich golden buff
6	American Pillar	1902	Bright rose with white eye
7	Chaplin's Pink Climber	1928	Bright pink
8	*Albéric Barbier	1900	Yellow to creamy white
9	Excelsa	1909	Bright rosy crimson
	Suitable for pillars		
1	Golden Showers	1957	Golden yellow
2	Danse du Feu	1954	Orange scarlet
3	*Zéphirine Drouhin	1868	Bright carmine pink
4	Royal Gold	1957	Deep yellow
5	Casino	1963	Soft yellow
6	Paul's Scarlet Climber	1915	Bright scarlet crimson
7	*Albertine	1921	Reddish salmon to pink
8	*Aloha	1955	Deep rose pink
9	Hamburger Phoenix	1955	Crimson

SHRUB ROSES—REPEAT FLOWERING

NAME	COLOUR	Height in feet
*Penelope	Creamy salmon	5
*Chinatown	Yellow with cherry at edge of petals	6
Bonn	Orange scarlet	6
Nevada	Pale creamy white	6
Kassel	Scarlet red	6
*Cornelia	Pink with yellow base	5–6
Heidelberg	Bright red	5–6
Elmshorn	Light crimson	5
*Felicia	Rose pink, shaded yellow	6
*Blanc Double de Coubert	Pure white	6
Prosperity	White	6
Vanity	Deep pink	8

* Most fragrant

SHRUB ROSES—SUMMER FLOWERING ONLY

NAME	COLOUR	Height in feet
R. moyesii	Deep red	8–10
Frühlingsgold	Clear light yellow	6
Canary Bird	Rich yellow	6
R. hugonis	Yellow	5
Frühlingsmorgen	Deep pink to yellow, maroon stamens	6
R. gallica versicolor	Crimson striped pink and white	4
R. rubrifolia	Clear pink, with purplish foliage	6
*Mme Hardy	White tinged flesh pink	6
*Celestial (Alba)	Blush pink	5
R. cantabrigiensis	Yellow	8
*Maiden's Blush (Alba)	Warm pink shading to cream pink	5
R. highdownensis	Light velvety crimson	8–10

REPEAT FLOWERING ROSES FOR HEDGES
Up to 5 ft

Position	NAME	Introduced	COLOUR
1	Queen Elizabeth	1955	Clear self pink
2	Iceberg	1958	Pure white
3	Frensham	1946	Deep scarlet crimson
4	Peace	1942	Light yellow edged pink
5	Masquerade	1950	Yellow, pink and red
6	*Chinatown	1963	Yellow with cherry at edges
7	*Super Star	1960	Light vermilion
8	Dorothy Wheatcroft	1961	Orient red with deeper shades
9	*Penelope	1924	Creamy salmon
10	Korona	1953	Bright orange scarlet
11	Shepherd's Delight	1958	Flame, orange and yellow
12	Scarlet Queen Elizabeth	1963	Orange scarlet

REPEAT FLOWERING ROSES FOR HEDGES
Over 5 ft

Position	NAME	Introduced	COLOUR
1	Queen Elizabeth	1955	Clear self pink
2	Bonn	1949	Orange scarlet
3	*Chinatown	1963	Yellow with cherry at edges
4	Nevada	1927	Pale creamy white
5	Golden Showers	1957	Golden yellow
6	*Zéphirine Drouhin	1868	Bright carmine pink
7	Joseph's Coat	1963	Yellow, orange and red
8	Heidelberg	1958	Bright red
9	Kassel	1958	Scarlet red
10	Frensham	1946	Deep scarlet crimson
11	*Cornelia	1925	Pink with yellow base
12	Uncle Walter	1963	Scarlet with crimson shadings

* Most fragrant

WEATHER RESISTANT ROSES—HYBRID TEAS

NAME	Intro-duced	COLOUR
Peace	1942	Light yellow, edged pink
*Super Star	1960	Light vermilion without shading
*Wendy Cussons	1960	Deep cerise
Stella	1958	Carmine shading to cream
Mischief	1961	Coral salmon
Rose Gaujard	1958	White flushed rich pink
Piccadilly	1960	Scarlet, yellow reverse
*Fragrant Cloud	1964	Geranium lake
Pink Favourite	1956	Deep rose pink
Gail Borden	1956	Pale gold with peach, inside salmon rose
*Ena Harkness	1946	Bright crimson scarlet
McGredy's Yellow	1933	Buttercup yellow

WEATHER RESISTANT ROSES—FLORIBUNDAS

NAME	Intro-duced	COLOUR
Iceberg	1958	Pure white
Evelyn Fison	1962	Vivid red with scarlet shading
Queen Elizabeth	1955	Clear self pink
Allgold	1956	Unfading golden yellow
Orangeade	1959	Bright orange vermilion
Lilli Marlene	1959	Scarlet red
Korona	1953	Bright orange scarlet
*Orange Sensation	1961	Orange vermilion
Frensham	1946	Deep scarlet crimson
Sarabande	1957	Dazzling scarlet
Paprika	1958	Bright turkey red
*Elizabeth of Glamis	1964	Light salmon

* Most fragrant

Articles for *The Rose Annual* should be submitted to the Hon. Editor by the end of August, addressed to him at The Royal National Rose Society's Offices, Bone Hill, Chiswell Green Lane, St Albans, Herts. They should be the author's own work, should not have been accepted by any other publication and should be typed in double spacing or, if handwritten, the lines should be well spaced. Black and white photographs of good definition, featuring items of general interest to members, are also welcomed.

1968

THE FOURTH INTERNATIONAL

ROSE CONFERENCE

WILL BE HELD

AT

The Park Lane Hotel, London

ON

3rd, 4th and 5th July 1968

●

Brochure will be available in June 1967
Please write for copy

●

BOOK THESE 1968 DATES NOW

SUMMER SHOW 28TH AND 29TH JUNE

CONFERENCE 3RD, 4TH AND 5TH JULY

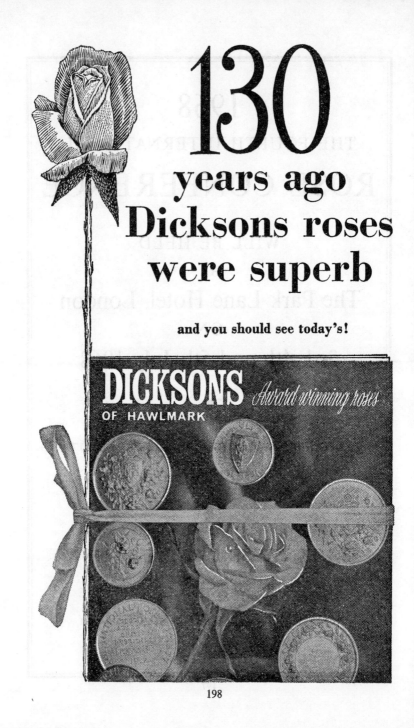

130

years ago
Dicksons roses
were superb

and you should see today's!

DICKSONS
OF HAWLMARK

Award winning roses

The world's oldest rose breeders present six new roses

Antique. Flor.

(Kordes 1967)

A novel floribunda with a unique colour. The scarlet and gold flowers give a bright and warming effect. A bushy, free-growing plant of medium height. A new colour which will be much in demand.

Jubilant. Flor.

(Dickson 1967)

Resembles 'Dearest', its mother parent, in many important respects. The flower colour, a soft flesh pink, is consistent from bud to petal fall. The perfectly formed fragrant blooms are continuous all summer. Strong, bushy growth. Highly disease-resistant. Cert. of Merit, R.N.R.S.

Kerry Gold. Flor.

(Dickson 1967)

Deep canary yellow from bud to old flower. A red vein colours the young bud but disappears quickly as the petals unfold. A reliable low growing and strong little bush with a profusion of flowers.

Red Devil. H.T.

(Dickson 1967)

Already acclaimed by three Continents as a really great, new red rose. Everything about this variety lives up to its name; tough stems, big plant, disease-resistant, leathery foliage. Intensely perfumed very beautiful flowers with up to seventy-five petals. Cert. of Merit, R.N.R.S.

Redgold. Flor.

(Dickson 1967)

There is nothing like Redgold. It is original in its merging of red into gold and each perfectly formed bloom, on a large truss, holds its attractiveness until the petals fall. Compact growing habit; well balanced and of medium height; red and dark freen foliage. Cert. of Merit, R.N.R.S.

Vision. H.T.

(Dickson 1967)

Shapely, medium sized blooms of gold shaded pink are borne freely on a strong, healthy plant. Gloriously fresh and clean, the dark leather-like foliage completes its charm. A fine bedding rose with great resistance to weather.

BY APPOINTMENT
NURSERYMEN
AND SEEDSMEN
TO THE LATE
KING GEORGE VI

DICKSONS
OF HAWLMARK
Incorporated by Alex. Dickson & Sons Ltd

ROSE FAMOUS SINCE 1836
NEWTOWNARDS, CO. DOWN
N.IRELAND

IN THE SERVICE OF THE ROSE

Dear Rose Lovers,

During 1966 I travelled far and wide in the service of the rose. I visited several West European countries in May and June to serve as a judge at International Rose Competitions, a pleasant task that I have been doing for many years.

In July I was invited to take part in a symposium on roses in Erfurt, East Germany. Erfurt, a town noted for its horticultural interests, is the centre of a seed-growing area. This was new ground to me and the invitation was readily accepted. An International Horticultural Show was being held and most East European countries had exhibits there. The symposium devoted most of its time to greenhouse roses which are being grown on an ever increasing scale to try and keep pace with the demand for cut flowers. I thought this a very healthy sign.

From East Germany, I went to Hungary and met a group of people who were breeding and testing roses, notably Dr Gergely Mark of the Budapest Horticultural Institute, who gave me his book on roses. When I was registering at the hotel, an elderly Hungarian who had emigrated to America some 50 years ago, came up to me and asked if he could shake me by the hand. I said certainly, but I couldn't think why. He replied: "You remind me so much of my beloved Emperor, Franz Joseph."

Next, on to Rumania for a few days, where I was amazed to see the quantities of roses grown along the main roads near the towns.

I visited Professor Polocsay, in charge of the Horticultural Experimental Station at Cluy, who has done a lot of work on roses and many other plants—a most interesting character.

September saw me off to America to attend the American Rose Society's Convention and Show at Omaha, Nebraska, where I was the Guest of Honour. Over 500 rose lovers were there from all over America and I had an interesting three days talking roses to them. From the Gateway to the West back to New Jersey to address another Convention and Rose Show.

On then to Chicago, Florida, Atlanta, Tulsa and California, where for several days I visited some famous hybridists and saw millions of roses in bloom.

My final call was at Tyler, Texas, a centre of rose growing, as an honoured guest at the Rose Festival, where a Queen is crowned and the procession through the town to the Sports Stadium includes decorated floats and all the school bands. My wife and I travelled in a large open car with "HARRY WHEATCROFT, ENGLISH ROSARIAN" painted on the side. I heard many pleasant and humorous remarks as we wended our way through a crowd of 100,000 onlookers.

On my return home I found that things had gone on well without me and that the demand for our roses was greater than ever.

Thanks to my sons who have shouldered so much of my responsibility here, I am able to accept some of the very kind invitations I get from all over the world. I feel my task now is to spread the love of roses and the understanding that comes with them, particularly amongst our friends beyond the seas. In a world of roses, peace reigns, and we all need that blessing.

Rosily yours,

Harry Wheatcroft

TWELVE OF THE MOST OUTSTANDING ROSES GROWN TODAY

It's unusual to offer a collection in The Rose Annual but I'm anxious that all members should get to know about our extra selected roses. Hence this bargain offer of the 12 most outstanding roses of recent introduction—all guaranteed to bloom, they are illustrated in colour in our catalogue—which is free for the asking.

Bettina—*A sun-kissed shapely blonde all bronze with a golden base and petals veined in deeper hue—a real laster when cut.*

Chicago Peace—*A colourful sport of Peace with all its virtues—size, habit, health plus shimmering pink with canary yellow and occasional copper tones adding glamour.*

Cologne Carnival—*There must be a bluish rose in an up-to-date collection and Cologne Carnival's my choice; it's a good grower and has form.*

Ernest H. Morse—*The Gold Medal crimson rose of 1965. So good that all enthusiasts must have it—it's fragrant too!*

Fragrant Cloud—*A warm coral red. We are proud to have introduced this rose—I rate it No. 1 and use it as my yardstick to judge the others.*

King's Ransom—*Tops amongst the yellows—shapely, full and free growing with deep glossy green foliage. All-America Award Winner.*

Papa Meilland—*Chosen by the raiser to bear his name and like its namesake it has great character. Deep, deep velvety red with large and fragrant blooms—adorable.*

Pascali—*The best white we have—Elizabeth blood, which accounts for the healthy growth. I've seen it world over—all the specialists agree, none better.*

Piccadilly—*My favourite bi-colour. Red and yellow; a startling and gay bedder with shapely blooms freely flowering against a background of dense dark bronzy green foliage.*

Prima Ballerina—*Warm rose pink with a most delightful fragrance. I have a great love for this—it has made me so many friends.*

Super Star—*I saw the first 3 trees of Super Star 12 years ago and predicted its greatness. I still marvel at its brilliant and glowing colour and wonder if it can ever be surpassed.*

Wendy Cussons—*rosy red—pink. A rose with many charms—fragrant, full, free, rudely healthy, with deep green glossy foliage.*

THE 12 ROSES ABOVE ARE OFFERED AS MY ENTHUSIAST'S COLLECTION

59/6 + 4/- c. & p.

Catalogue value 85/6

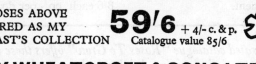

HARRY WHEATCROFT & SONS LTD

EDWALTON, NOTTINGHAM *Telephone: 211231*

NEW ROSES FOR 1967

Three Roses of Great Merit and Distinction

CITY OF HEREFORD (H.T.) A clear two-toned pink with *intensely sweet perfume*. Well formed blossoms of good shape and substance borne very free on strong erect healthy growths.

12/6 each, 136/- per doz.

DIMPLES (Fl.) Fully double, sweetly scented, creamy white flowers with unique golden centre. Glossy foliage with large flower heads unaffected by rain. A delightful and restful foil for brilliant colours. 10/6 each, 115/- per doz.

VESPER (Fl.) A new shade known as "Mars Orange". Ideal for flower arrangers. The clear pastel shade offers a new and effective colour for bedding. 10/6 each, 115/- per doz.

E. B. Le GRICE (Roses) Ltd.
NORTH WALSHAM   NORFOLK
(TEL. 3124)

GOLDGLEAM (Fl.) This variety has more than fulfilled its early promise. It retains its clear yellow, has proved very healthy and flowers freely over a very long period. *The unfading yellow which grows.* 8/6 each, 90/- per doz.

TOM BROWN (Fl.) We were sorry to disappoint so many customers last season but can offer better supplies of this two-toned brown, which offers new material for flower arrangement. 8/6 each, 90/- per doz.

Our Illustrated catalogue "Roses To Grow" offers these and many other varieties, giving heights, colours and perfume ratings. Free on request.

Frank Cant & Co. Ltd.

BRAISWICK ROSE GARDEN
STANWAY
COLCHESTER

THE WORLD-FAMED SPECIALISTS

Growers of over 600 varieties of roses, including some of the newest varieties, and older varieties not found in all Catalogues

Over 100 roses are shown in colour in our Catalogue, which is also full of advice

Our experience and advice are always with pleasure at your service

Telephone: MARKS TEY 360

Winners of over 5,000 Prizes

PLEASE STATE CATALOGUE NO. 12 - POST 6d

203

Cocker & Harkness announce NEW VENTURE

*Breeding new roses
500 miles apart . . .*

**JAMES COCKER & SONS (Rose Specialists) LTD. of ABERDEEN, and
R. HARKNESS & CO. LTD., of HITCHIN**

wish to announce that our two firms are breeding new Roses under the direction in Aberdeen of Mr Alex Cocker, and in Hitchin of Mr Jack Harkness.

The combining of new ideas from two rosarians, each with over 30 years experience, is probably unique in the history of Rose breeding. We are exchanging ideas, breeding stock and information. The varieties we obtain are immediately tested in both nurseries—an ideal arrangement, for we are 500 miles apart with radically different soil, climate and conditions.

As Harkness started hybridising a year sooner, it follows that the first introductions are from Hitchin. But the Aberdeen varieties are going through their tests with flying colours too.

Cockers were founded in 1841 and Harkness in 1879. For three generations the families have successively formed friendships; a strong basis for our present co-operation.

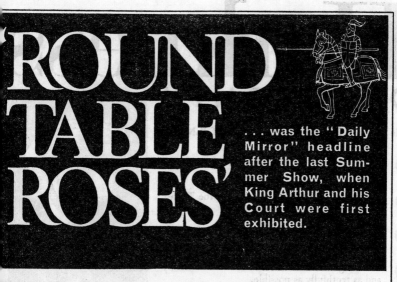

'ROUND TABLE ROSES'

... was the "Daily Mirror" headline after the last Summer Show, when King Arthur and his Court were first exhibited.

HERE ARE THE FIRST INTRODUCTIONS FOR 1967

All raised by Harkness, and selected by Mr Alex Cocker and Mr Jack Harkness

KING ARTHUR	Flor. (H.T. type) Salmon pink Awarded Certificate of Merit	10/6
GUINEVERE	H.T. Clear pink Awarded Trial Ground Certificate	12/6
SIR LANCELOT	Flor. Apricot yellow Awarded Trial Ground Certificate	10/6
MERLIN	Flor. Red, pink and yellow	10/6
SIR GALAHAD	Flor. Red, attractive form	10/6
EXCALIBUR	Flor. Scarlet to orange red	10/6
ADELINE GENEE	Flor. Yellow, large flowers	15/-
GLORY OF CEYLON	Flor. Orange yellow, scented	12/6
DANDY DICK	Flor. (H.T. type) Pink, spicy scent	10/6
ESCAPADE	Flor. Rosy magenta, very appealing	10/6
LITTLE LADY	Poly. Short, blush to ice	10/6

Available for Autumn 1967 delivery from leading Nurseries. Please order early.

COCKER

JAMES COCKER & SONS
(Rose Specialists) LTD. (Dept. RA),
Whitemyres, Lang Stracht,
ABERDEEN

HARKNESS

R. HARKNESS & CO. LTD.
The Rose Gardens (Dept. RA),
HITCHIN,
Hertfordshire

Harkness
OF HITCHIN

This is what we offer to Members of R.N.R.S.

Plants famed for high quality due to hard ripe wood and strong fibrous roots.

The largest selection of varieties in the Trade: we grow one thousand varieties.

New Roses of our own raising including the famous KING ARTHUR series.

A catalogue which describes the Roses factually and as truthfully as possible.

Harkness Rose Tokens, making an ideal gift administered in a pleasant way.

FREE admission to our Rose Trials, ten acres of them, where over 500 varieties are tested under tough garden conditions. A wonderful day out when the sun is shining.

**NEW ROSE AWARDS
1966**

*Certificate of Merit for
King Arthur;
Trial Ground Certificate for
Guinevere and Sir Lancelot*

**R.N.R.S. SHOW AWARDS
1966**

*Championship Trophy,
Queen Mary's Cup,
Autumn Roses Cup,
2 Large Gold Medals*

*Write for our
Catalogue and come
and see our gardens*

Phone Hitchin 4027 & 4171

R. HARKNESS & CO, LIMITED
THE ROSE GARDENS, HITCHIN, HERTFORDSHIRE

Cocker
OF ABERDEEN

NEW SUPERB ROSES

•

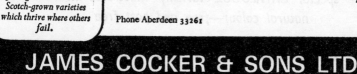

FREE COLOUR CATALOGUE

Send now for your copy, containing full details of the best varieties. Fill your garden with our Scotch-grown varieties which thrive where others fail.

KING ARTHUR Floribunda/H.T. Type   Salmon
Large flowers for a Floribunda, very full petalled, clear salmon pink. Vigorous plant with large and ample foliage. A very fast grower; when King Arthur is in full bloom, the young shoots bearing the next crop are well advanced. Certificate of Merit. Parentage: Pink Parfait × Highlight.
10/6 each

MERLIN Floribunda   Multicolour
This gay variety is yellow, with flushes of red and pink in varying shades. The flower form is attractive, and the colour remains pleasing at all stages. An upright, bushy plant, very free in flower, the colour effect particularly clean and fresh. Parentage: Pink Parfait × Circus.
10/6 each

GUINEVERE Hybrid Tea   Pink
Light rose pink, a clear colour, holding very well. The flowers are large, of quite individual form, fully double, long lasting. They are held on the plant in a most attractive way, giving promise that here is a bedding Rose of much charm and quality. Trial Ground Certificate. Parentage: Red Dandy × Peace.
12/6 each

SIR LANCELOT Floribunda   Apricot yellow
A beautiful, almost unique colour in the young flower; with attractive buds, opening to semi-double flowers of great beauty. Advance bookings are heavy, so please order early for this one. Trial Ground Certificate. Parentage: Vera Dalton × Woburn Abbey.   **10/6 each**

SIR GALAHAD Floribunda   Wine red
Clear red flowers of very pretty form. Very free flowering, producing successive crops of bloom. We think of Sir Galahad as "the Rose that makes you smile back". Parentage: Pink Parfait × Highlight.
10/6 each

DANDY DICK Floribunda/H.T. Type   Pink
Clear bright pink flowers with much of Pink Parfait's elegance of form. A splendid plant habit and spicy scent enable us to say this pink Floribunda will be widely grown for many years. Parentage: Pink Parfait × Red Dandy.
10/6 each

Phone Aberdeen 33261

JAMES COCKER & SONS LTD
WHITEMYRES, LANG STRACHT, ABERDEEN, SCOTLAND

TOP NAME FOR ROSES FOR 200 YEARS

BEN R CANT

We invite you to write for a copy of our special CATALOGUE lavishly illustrated in natural colour—free and post free

BENJAMIN R. CANT AND SONS LTD

The Old Rose Gardens   Mile End   Colchester
Essex

208

'The NAME in Roses'

introduce
the five new roses
that will matter in 1967

CARAMBA Tantau huge pink and silver H.T.
MAJORETTE MEIdad 0500F decorative coppery H.T.
PHARAOH MEIfiga 0467F richest, brightest scarlet H.T.
TAMANGO MEIdaun 0497F very large crimson floribunda.
SAFARI Tantau scented yellow floribunda.

The Wheatcroft Catalogue is a rose grower's must.
If you are not already on our mailing list
write now to be sure you get your copy
as soon as our 1967/8 issue is published.

* And remember—
There's 5 years
of natural goodness
in every Wheatcroft Rose!

To avoid delay please use our full address.
WHEATCROFT BROTHERS LIMITED Ruddington, Nottingham

TAS/WT.55

YOUR GUARANTEE OF QUALITY

GREGORY'S ROSES

16 GOLD MEDALS LAST SUMMER MUST PROVE GREGORY'S ROSES AHEAD OF THE COUNTRY IN QUALITY

Send for new free colour catalogue. 120 varieties in full colour.

INTRODUCING: Wendy Cussons, Orange Sensation, Apricot Silk, Percy Thrower, Lancastrian, Pink Perpetue, Autumn Sunlight.

C. GREGORY & SON LTD., THE ROSE GARDENS, CHILWELL, NOTTINGHAM

GREGORY'S ROSES

Rose Gardens
& ROSE FIELDS

You will be free to walk among millions of roses at your leisure. All are clearly labelled and the varieties have been so arranged that it is possible to see the maximum without having to walk a long way. We believe our rose trials gardens to be the largest in the country. They are always open, including Saturday and Sunday evenings, from July to mid-October, and conveniently near the famous "Grand Farm" where you can obtain an excellent lunch or dinner. If you plan to walk through the rose fields you would be wise to bring along a stout pair of shoes.

HOW TO GET THERE

Our Rose Gardens are at Toton Lane, Stapleford, Notts.

From the M.I you approach our garden by turning off at the A.52 towards Nottingham. One mile along the A.52 turn right at the first traffic island and into the car park about two hundred yards on the left.

The Rose Gardens may also be approached from the A.52 Nottingham–Derby road at the traffic island where it is crossed by the B.6003. The signpost indicating the direction of Long Eaton, points towards the Rose Gardens.

An alternative approach can be made from the A.453 Nottingham–Birmingham road where it is joined by the B.6003 Stapleford Lane and travelling up the lane for about a mile-and-a-half.

A large grass field has been set aside as a car park where you may enjoy a picnic lunch or tea in comfort.

Linwood Roses

One quality, the BEST

New Roses for 1967 include:—

SIR GALAHAD (Harkness 1967)
GUINEVERE (Harkness 1967)
MERLIN (Harkness 1967)
KING ARTHUR (Harkness 1967)
SIR LANCELOT (Harkness 1967)
BOBBY LUCAS (McGredy 1967)
IRISH MIST (McGredy 1967)
RED DEVIL (Dickson 1967)
REDGOLD (Dickson 1967)
KERRY GOLD (Dickson 1967)
PHARAOH (Meilland 1967)

Also

DIORAMA (de Ruiter 1966)
GOLDGLEAM (Le Grice 1966)
ERNEST H. MORSE (Kordes 1966)
GOLDEN TREASURE (Tantau 1966)
GRANDPA DICKSON (Dickson 1966)
CITY OF LEEDS (McGredy 1966)
YOUKI SAN (Meilland 1966)
APRICOT SILK (Gregory 1965)
and many more

Free catalogue on request

LINWOOD ROSES LTD.
SWANLAND   E. YORKS

212

When visiting our Nurseries may we introduce you to:

SHEPHERDESS

Our new floribunda (R.N.R.S. TGC 1966) which inherits the health and vigour of her illustrious parents,

ALLGOLD × PEACE

You will also meet many old friends and favourites among the Old Garden Roses and the best recent introductions such as:

ALTISSIMO	GRANDPA DICKSON	RED DEVIL
APRICOT NECTAR	HANDEL	REDGOLD
ATHOS	IRISH MIST	SCHOOLGIRL
ERNEST H. MORSE	KING ARTHUR	SCENTED AIR
GOLDGLEAM	PRINCESS MICHIKO	SIR LANCELOT

JOHN MATTOCK LTD.
NUNEHAM COURTENAY
OXFORD

Telephone: Nuneham Courtenay 265

Our Rose fields at Nuneham Courtenay are a landmark on the Oxford–Henley Road as are also those at Lodge Hill, Abingdon on the Oxford–Newbury Road. Here during the Summer months you will find amid rural surroundings ample room to park your car, to picnic and to see our Roses.

Full details are in our illustrated catalogue which is available post free in July.

213

NEW ROSES
by HERBERT ROBINSON, M.B.E.

1967 INTRODUCTION
'CORAL STAR' H.T.
This unique rose has blooms of soft Coral Pink, giving a wonderful perfume. Strong, upright growth with disease-resistant foliage.

'FAIRLIGHT' This delightful floribunda produces trusses of coppery-salmon H.T.-type flowers. Of medium height. Attractive copper-bronze foliage.

'REGALIA' H.T. A really outstanding bi-colour, the velvet-like petals are Burgundy Red with Silver reverse. Vigorous and healthy growth, very fragrant.

'WINEFRED CLARKE' H.T. A most attractive yellow rose with high centre and superb form. Large, deep green foliage. Hardy, vigorous, disease resistant.

Victoria Nurseries
Coventry Road, Burbage, Hinckley, Leics.   Tel: Hinckley 2233
Catalogue on request

By
Appointment
Nurserymen
and Seedsmen

To
H.M. Queen
Elizabeth the
Queen Mother

We publish annually the following Catalogues

TREES AND SHRUBS

including Rhododendrons, Conifers, Climbers and Bamboos.
Growers commercially of the greatest number of species and
varieties hardy in the temperate regions

Comprehensive descriptive publication, price 7/6

PRICE LIST FREE

HEDGING PLANTS

Large specimen Trees and Shrubs for immediate effect
Hardy Perennial, Biennial, Alpine and Aquatic Plants (Price 2/6). **Bulbs.**
Rose Trees (including species and old-fashioned types) and **Fruit Trees.**
Please send us your request for those in which you may be interested.

Any not at present available will be sent when published

HILLIER & SONS, WINCHESTER

Fryer's
of Knutsford

TROPHIES at...
Shrewsbury, R.N.R.S., Leeds,
Blackpool, Southport
and many others

1966 Premier Award Winners

for Roses that catch the Eye

Send for our full colour
catalogue showing all
the latest and up-to-date
roses as well as the best
of older varieties.

•

*Two 1967
outstanding new
floribundas*
**KERRY GOLD
SIR LANCELOT**

Throughout 4 generations the name McGredy has been synonymous with fine roses. Sam McGredy's whole life is roses. Always has been. Today he stands among the world's leading specialists in hybridisation.

The men in the McGredy team are equally particular. Roses like Jan Spek and Bobbie Lucas could only be grown by men who knew as much, and cared as deeply.

Year after year Sam McGredy captures the imagination of the rose-growing world by breeding new roses of outstanding beauty and exceptional quality.

Samuel McGredy & Son
Royal Nurseries, Portadown, N.Ireland

THE
POPULAR WAY
TO GARDENING
SUCCESS...

starts when you read a magazine that makes you really at home with every aspect of gardening. From long experience, thousands upon thousands of enthusiasts find *Popular Gardening* a winner all the year round for its useful know-how on flowers, fruit and vegetables.

Week by week Editor Gordon Forsyth and his team of experts make "PG" a step-by-step guide for every season, giving readers practical down-to-earth advice and solutions to every possible gardening problem.

Their experience ensures your success with . . .

POPULAR GARDENING

Britain's Brightest and Best Gardening Weekly

Every Thursday 8d   A Fleetway Publication.

By appointment to Her Majesty The Queen
Garden Contractors and Nurserymen
JOHN WATERER, SONS & CRISP, LTD

WATERER'S ROSES

From the Floral Mile

We have a wonderful stock of well grown Bushes, Standards, Climbers, Shrub Roses, etc., available for supply in the Autumn.
Price list will gladly be sent free on request.

OUR NEW COMPREHENSIVE
FULL COLOUR CATALOGUE

Contains: ROSES, FRUIT TREES, HERBACEOUS PLANTS, IRISES, SHRUBS, ORNAMENTAL TREES, CLIMBERS, HEDGING PLANTS, ETC.

We believe this to be the most comprehensive full colour catalogue of Nursery Stock yet produced in this country.

PRICE 2/- POST PAID

JOHN WATERER, SONS & CRISP LTD, THE FLORAL MILE, TWYFORD, BERKS. Wargrave 551

218

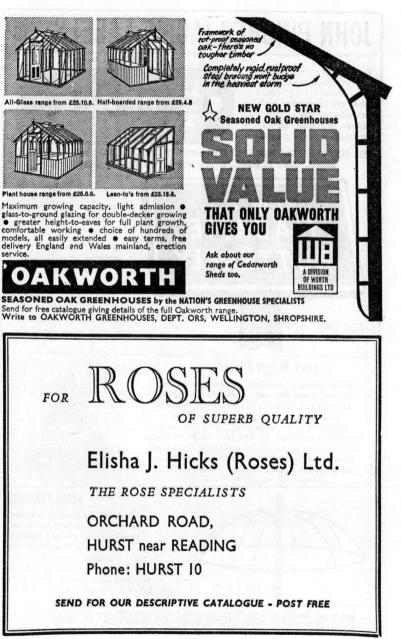

All-Glass range from £25.10.6.   Half-boarded range from £29.4.6

Plant house range from £26.0.6.   Lean-to's from £23.15.6.

Maximum growing capacity, light admission ● glass-to-ground glazing for double-decker growing ● greater height-to-eaves for full plant growth, comfortable working ● choice of hundreds of models, all easily extended ● easy terms, free delivery England and Wales mainland, erection service.

OAKWORTH

Framework of rot-proof seasoned oak—there's no tougher timber

Completely rigid, rustproof steel bracing won't budge in the heaviest storm

☆ **NEW GOLD STAR**
Seasoned Oak Greenhouses

SOLID VALUE

THAT ONLY OAKWORTH GIVES YOU

Ask about our range of Cedarworth Sheds too.

WB
A DIVISION OF WORTH BUILDINGS LTD

SEASONED OAK GREENHOUSES by the NATION'S GREENHOUSE SPECIALISTS
Send for free catalogue giving details of the full Oakworth range.
Write to OAKWORTH GREENHOUSES, DEPT. ORS, WELLINGTON, SHROPSHIRE.

FOR **ROSES**
OF SUPERB QUALITY

Elisha J. Hicks (Roses) Ltd.

THE ROSE SPECIALISTS

ORCHARD ROAD,
HURST near READING
Phone: HURST 10

SEND FOR OUR DESCRIPTIVE CATALOGUE - POST FREE

JOHN PINCHES (ACME LABELS) LTD

ACME LABEL No. 1

For *all* Rose names, including the very latest varieties. Size of label 2½" x ⅞". No. I labels can be supplied with soft wire for attaching to bushes, or special holders for standing in the ground.

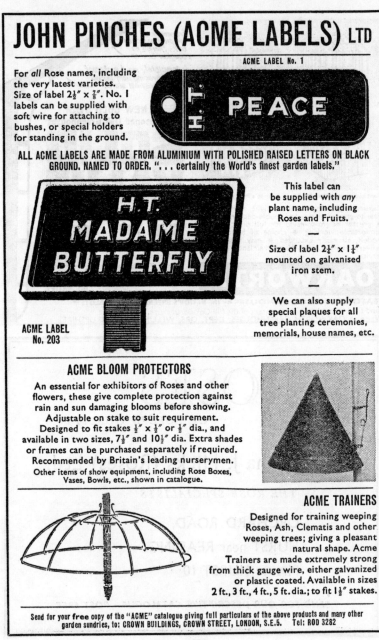

ALL ACME LABELS ARE MADE FROM ALUMINIUM WITH POLISHED RAISED LETTERS ON BLACK GROUND. NAMED TO ORDER. ". . . certainly the World's finest garden labels."

This label can be supplied with *any* plant name, including Roses and Fruits.

—

Size of label 2¼" x 1¼" mounted on galvanised iron stem.

—

We can also supply special plaques for all tree planting ceremonies, memorials, house names, etc.

ACME LABEL No. 203

ACME BLOOM PROTECTORS

An essential for exhibitors of Roses and other flowers, these give complete protection against rain and sun damaging blooms before showing. Adjustable on stake to suit requirement. Designed to fit stakes ½" x ½" or ½" dia., and available in two sizes, 7½" and 10½" dia. Extra shades or frames can be purchased separately if required. Recommended by Britain's leading nurserymen.

Other items of show equipment, including Rose Boxes, Vases, Bowls, etc., shown in catalogue.

ACME TRAINERS

Designed for training weeping Roses, Ash, Clematis and other weeping trees; giving a pleasant natural shape. Acme Trainers are made extremely strong from thick gauge wire, either galvanized or plastic coated. Available in sizes 2 ft., 3 ft., 4 ft., 5 ft. dia.; to fit 1½" stakes.

Send for your **free** copy of the "ACME" catalogue giving full particulars of the above products and many other garden sundries, to: CROWN BUILDINGS, CROWN STREET, LONDON, S.E.5. Tel: ROD 3282

220

Owing to the enormous
demand for our

SHRUB ROSES

we have increased our stock
for sale in Autumn 1967

Orders should be placed early,
however, as we are carrying
forward a large number of
orders from last Season

EDWIN MURRELL

PORTLAND NURSERIES
SHREWSBURY

Tel. 51497

Forget that hoe!

Use Murphy's
Rose Bed Weed Killer
(Printop® in measured·dose sachets)

With Murphy's Rose Bed Weedkiller you apply it to weed-free beds just once in early Spring and then look forward to a hoeless weed-free season. Even summer use is possible if the ground is cleared of weeds and watered to bring it to a moist condition.

Murphy's Rose Bed Weedkiller—watered on—is long lasting, totally effective and safe for roses. In the special measured-dose sachet packs it will give you just the right application rate so there's no wastage.

Ask your local gardening shop for Murphy Rose Bed Weedkiller. Only 3/9d. a pack; sufficient for 50 sq. yds. Specially prepared for those who love roses but hate hoeing.

Send today for the special Murphy Pest Chart for rose-growers—it's packed with useful, readable information.

Murphy

THE MURPHY CHEMICAL CO. LTD., WHEATHAMPSTEAD, ST. ALBANS, HERTS.

SANDAY

ALMONDSBURY ROSES

"Founded on Quality"

Thousands of our rose friends visit us and write to us annually. To them we send our warm greetings and our best thanks. They know from experience our slogan "Founded on Quality" is no idle boast. To be told over and over again of the joy our trees are bringing to gardens throughout the country is a wonderful satisfaction to everyone here from junior staff to Directors, for the growing of good roses is a vocation in the truest sense.

Our 1967 comprehensive catalogue available in May will of course include our recent introductions Eve Allen (Allen 1964), Gavotte, Jean Campbell, Lilac Rose, Miss Delightful, Parasol, etc., etc., and will also bring you these new Almondsbury Roses.

SEVERN VALE, a delightful salmon hybrid tea of perfect decorative form which many have seen growing in our Display Gardens, will, we feel, capture everyone. We doubt if we shall have sufficient plants to carry us through the whole season.   12/6 each.

MINSTREL is a dwarf bedding scarlet floribunda, very compact and full of flower with deep olive green foliage. 10/6 each.

JOHN SANDAY (Roses) LTD.
ALMONDSBURY, BRISTOL
Tel.: ALMONDSBURY 2195

TWICE the POWER

WILKINSON SWORD

Two-Handed Pruner*

THE LENGTH—14½″ handles give you the powerful leverage you need to cut the hardest wood and make it easy to prune in the most inaccessible places.

THE BLADES—'Wilkinson Sword'. Need more be said? Blades forged from the finest sword steel to stay sharp and last and last and last.

THE ACTION—the smooth, effortless action that only precision engineering can give.

■ *Sap groove—cleans off sap and prevents blades sticking.*
■ *Shaped PVC easy-grip handles.*
■ *Light weight lessens wrist fatigue.*

*Available from all Wilkinson Sword stockists, 50/-

Timmermans

GROWERS OF FIRST CLASS ROSES FOR OVER 80 YEARS

A cordial invitation to friends old and new. Why not visit our nursery, which is seen at its best July–September, and join our ever growing list of satisfied customers? If you are unable to come yourself please send for our free coloured catalogue.

Timmermans' Roses
Woodborough, 5
Nottingham.
Tel. Lowdham 2393

Tel. Alsager 2101

Grown on our now famous
root stock

ROSA SAYII

Write for catalogue, available
June

Visit our Rose Fields and
Display Gardens.

WATERHOUSE NURSERIES Ltd.
Radway Green, Nr. Crewe, Cheshire

For Old Roses

New Roses

Shrub Roses

In fact, for all that's best in Roses

LEICESTER ROSE Co. (Dept R.A.)
ARNESBY, Leics.

FIRST AMONGST THE FINEST

Telephone: Fleckney 376

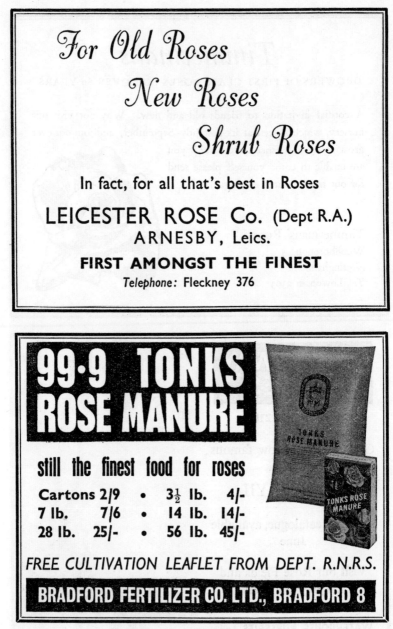

99·9 TONKS ROSE MANURE

still the finest food for roses

Cartons 2/9	•	3½ lb.	4/-
7 lb.	7/6	• 14 lb.	14/-
28 lb.	25/-	• 56 lb.	45/-

FREE CULTIVATION LEAFLET FROM DEPT. R.N.R.S.

BRADFORD FERTILIZER CO. LTD., BRADFORD 8

BASILDON
Rose Gardens
LIMITED

Roses of Quality

ESSEX has always been known for the quality of the Roses grown in its rich, fertile soil. When purchasing Roses from us you can be sure they are everything a top quality ESSEX Rose should be. Such is our confidence in them that we guarantee to replace any supplied by us that fail to grow. During the summer months visit our show grounds and see the Roses we offer in full bloom, including these new and recent introductions:

APRICOT NECTAR Fl.	**MARIA CALLAS H.T.**
BOBBIE LUCAS Fl.	**RED DEVIL Fl.**
ELIDA H.T.	**REDGOLD Fl.**
GRANDPA DICKSON H.T.	**SANTA FE H.T.**
JAN SPEK Fl.	**TRADITION H.T.**
JUBILANT Fl.	**WESTERN SUN H.T.**

Open Seven Days a Week   Large Car Parks Available

If you cannot visit us, send for our beautifully illustrated colour catalogue which will be sent to you *FREE*, as soon as it is published

(Dept. R.A.)
BURNT MILLS ROAD, BASILDON, ESSEX

The ♔APPROVED Sprays

for BLACK SPOT and RUST

BUGGES MANEB 80%

for MILDEW

BUGGES A.M.62
(25% Dinocap)

During last summer, our two fungicides once again proved to be quite outstanding in performance against the Black Spot, Rust and Mildew diseases of Roses; this in spite of a very difficult season. We take this opportunity to express our sincere thanks for the many letters of appreciation and satisfaction we have received from our customers, and are happy to have been of service to them. We hope that you will let us make 1967 a happy Rose year for you too.

AGRICULTURAL CHEMICALS
APPROVAL SCHEME

BUGGES INSECTICIDES LTD.

SITTINGBOURNE   KENT   TEL 3475·6

BUGGES INSECTICIDES LTD
B.I.L.
SITTINGBOURNE

IMMEDIATE DELIVERY – POST PAID
ASK FOR PRICE LIST OF APPROVED GARDEN PRODUCTS
EXPORT ENQUIRIES SOLICITED

TO ALL ROSE LOVERS

A WELCOME AWAITS YOU AT BLABY

WE EXTEND AN INVITATION FOR YOU TO VISIT OUR NURSERY DURING THE SUMMER AND SEE THE WONDERFUL SELECTION OF OVER 400 VARIETIES, BOTH OLD AND NEW, WHICH WILL DELIGHT THE EYE. IF A PERSONAL VISIT IS NOT POSSIBLE, THEN PLEASE ASK FOR OUR FULLY ILLUSTRATED CATALOGUE WHICH WILL BE SENT TO YOU COMPLETELY FREE OF CHARGE.

BLABY *Rose Gardens* LTD.

Visitors are most welcome to our special SHOW GARDENS at BLABY, on the A426 Lutterworth to Leicester Road. Parking Space for 600 cars.

BLABY ROSE GARDENS LTD. (RA) BLABY, LEICS.

229

CLASSIC ROSE BOOKS
Written and illustrated in colour and monochrome by
GRAHAM STUART THOMAS

Climbing Roses Old and New

Here, one of the great rose authorities of the world has produced the only work solely devoted to climbers and ramblers. 45s

The Old Shrub Roses

This 'mine of information' (*The Times*) by 'one of the great gardeners of our time' (*Sunday Telegraph*). Fifth impression. 32s 6d

Shrub Roses of Today

This 'timely and important book' (*Gardeners Chronicle*) 'gives really precise information' (*Ideal Home*). 45s

FROM BOOKSELLERS

Phoenix House Books published by J. M. Dent & Sons Ltd from 10-13 Bedford Street, London WC2

HARLOW PARK NURSERIES LTD.
ROSE GROWERS

LONDON ROAD, POTTER STREET, HARLOW, ESSEX

We grow 250,000 Bush Roses in 150 varieties, and 20,000 Standard, Half Standard and Weepers in the best varieties including many of the following:

APRICOT SILK	HANDEL	ROSE OF TRALEE
ARTHUR BELL	ICE WHITE	SCHOOLGIRL
BOSSA NOVA	JAN SPEK	SHANNON
BRANDENBURG	JOHN CHURCH	SILVER STAR
CITY OF LEEDS	KRONENBOURG	TIKI
COLOUR WONDER	LADY SETON	TRADITION
ELIZ. OF GLAMIS	MARIE ELIZABETH	etc., and many other
EUROPEANA	PERCY THROWER	new varieties
EVELYN ELLICE	PERNILLE POULSEN	
FRAGRANT CLOUD	PINK PERPÊTUE	

Send for our Catalogue or visit us at the above address where you can inspect our large quantities of Shrubs and Plants.   A large Car Park available.

230

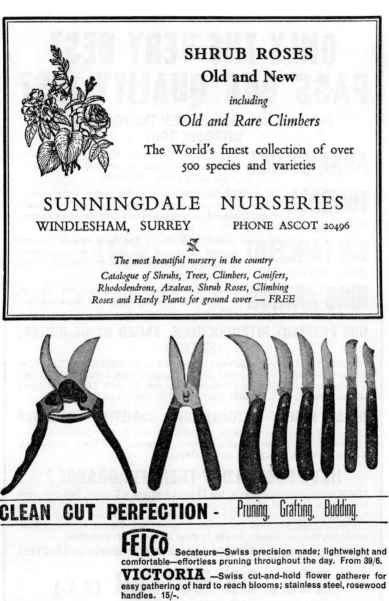

SHRUB ROSES
Old and New

including

Old and Rare Climbers

The World's finest collection of over
500 species and varieties

SUNNINGDALE NURSERIES

WINDLESHAM, SURREY   PHONE ASCOT 20496

The most beautiful nursery in the country

*Catalogue of Shrubs, Trees, Climbers, Conifers,
Rhododendrons, Azaleas, Shrub Roses, Climbing
Roses and Hardy Plants for ground cover — FREE*

CLEAN CUT PERFECTION - Pruning, Grafting, Budding.

FELCO Secateurs—Swiss precision made; lightweight and comfortable—effortless pruning throughout the day. From 39/6.

VICTORIA —Swiss cut-and-hold flower gatherer for easy gathering of hard to reach blooms; stainless steel, rosewood handles. 15/-.

Write for full details to the sole U.K. agents:

TINA —German made budding, pruning and grafting knives. Supreme quality. From 25/-.

BURTON McCALL & CO., 55 Welford Rd. Leicester Tel: Leicester 28515

ONLY THE VERY BEST
PASS OUR QUALITY TEST

FOR 1967 WE HAVE CHOSEN THE FOLLOWING INTRODUCTIONS

 **ANNA LOUISA** DE RUITER (Flor.) Very charming pink flowers, produced freely and continuously on a medium high, bushy plant. 10/6 each.

TOMBOLA DE RUITER (Flor.) This outstanding variety will give satisfaction to everyone, especially the large blooms, which are camellia shaped, of a salmon—to a carmine—pink colour. Very strong scented. 10/6 each.

 **SIR LANCELOT** HARKNESS (Flor.) The light orange flowers change to apricot and later to orange yellow. They are produced freely on healthy strong plants. 10/6 each.

 **KING ARTHUR** HARKNESS (Flor.). A very healthy variety, with salmon blooms, which are large and full. 10/6 each.

OUR PREVIOUS INTRODUCTIONS, RAISED BY DE RUITER, HOLLAND

TRAVESTI (Flor.) Yellow, peach and orange. 8/6 each. **CRITERION** (H.T.) Cerise. 8/6 each. **DIORAMA** (H.T.) Apricot yellow. 8/6 each. **PINK SUPREME** (H.T.) Soft pink. 8/6 each. **SCANIA** (Flor.) Unfading deep red. 7/6 each. **CARLA** (H.T.) Soft salmon pink. 7/6 each. **MY GIRL** (Flor.) Deep salmon. 7/6 each.

OTHER HIGHLY RECOMMENDED VARIETIES AVAILABLE

Charm of Paris, Ernest H. Morse, Grandpa Dickson, Apricot Silk, Blue Moon, Fragrant Cloud, Mister Lincoln, Princess, Elizabeth of Glamis, Europeana, Golden Treasure, Goldgleam, and Tip-Top.

HAVE ROSES LOST THEIR FRAGRANCE ?

Not in our special collection of **the 12 most fragrant H.T. roses.** One tree each of Diorama, Ernest H. Morse, Fragrant Cloud, Pink Supreme, Charm of Paris, Super Star, Blue Moon, Mister Lincoln, Eden Rose, Sutters Gold, My Choice, and Wendy Cussons. 84/- each Collection. C. and P. paid. See our illustrated Rose catalogue, free on request, for **the 12 most fragrant Flor. collection.**

FULL AND HALF STANDARDS AVAILABLE IN NEWEST VARIETIES

GEO. DE RUITER (R.A.)
THE ROSE SPECIALIST
65 School Lane, Chilwell, Beeston, Nottingham

RECOMMENDED NEW AND RECENT INTRODUCTIONS

ANNA LOUISA (Flor.) A new Floribunda in a clean **light pink** colour. Well shaped, double blooms.

TOMBOLA (Flor.) An outstanding novelty with excellent characteristics. Large blooms, **salmon to carmine-pink** colour and a remarkable **strong** fragrance. Trial Ground Cert. R.N.R.S.

TRAVESTI (Flor.) The blooms are well formed and coloured **peach, flushed cherry red**, with a yellow reverse. Trial Ground Cert. and Cert. of Merit, R.N.R.S.; Silver Medal, Intern. Rose Competition, Belgium.

CRITERION (H.T.) Excellent, healthy growth. Large blooms with unfading **deep cerise red** colour. **Fragrant.** Cert. of Merit, Intern. Rose Competition, Italy.

DIORAMA (H.T.) One of the best varieties which will go right to the top. The buds always open into large perfectly formed blooms, even in the wettest weather conditions. **Apricot-yellow** colour with the guard petals flushed pink. **Strong** fragrance. Trial Ground Cert., R.N.R.S.

SCANIA (Flor.-H.T. type) The H.T.-shaped double blooms are 4 inches across and exceptionally long lasting. **Deep velvety red** unfading colour.

PINK SUPREME (H.T.) Exceptionally free-flowering with large well shaped blooms. The colour is a lovely shade of **soft pink. Very strong** fragrance. Trial Ground Cert. and Cert. of Merit, R.N.R.S. Gold Medal and prize of the City of Geneva, Switzerland.

MY GIRL (Flor.) A charming Floribunda with an attractive **salmon** colour. **Camellia-shaped** blooms in large clusters. Cert. of Merit, Intern. Rose Trials, Belfast, N. Ireland. Gold Medal, Intern. Rose Competition, The Hague, Holland.

These varieties have all been raised by G. de Ruiter, Holland, were selected for introduction after various trials on the Continent and in England, and are now grown for you by many rose growers in Great Britain.

ASK YOUR SUPPLIER FOR THESE GLORIOUS ROSES

Applications have been made for Grants of Plant Breeder's Rights or such rights have been granted in respect of all varieties mentioned in this advertisement.

Trade inquiries to:

De Ruiters' New Roses Ltd.
Chilwell, Beeston, Notts.

WORCESTER
ROSES

❖

Famous for Vigour and Quality
All our Roses are grown in
good open country ensuring
Hardy and Vigorous Plants

❖

A visit to our Nurseries between July and September
will be cordially welcomed

❖

Order with Confidence from

JAMES TOWNSEND & SONS
(C. Townsend—Proprietor)

LOWER BROADHEATH, WORCESTER

Established 1860

Telephone: HALLOW 252
WICHENFORD 259

CATALOGUES FREE ON APPLICATION

Everyone enjoys visiting

'HIGH PEAK ROSES'

AND FAMED GARDEN CENTRE

BAMFORD, DERBYSHIRE

ESTABLISHED BY AND CATALOGUES FROM

PROCTOR'S

Specialist Rose Growers since 1825

OF CHESTERFIELD

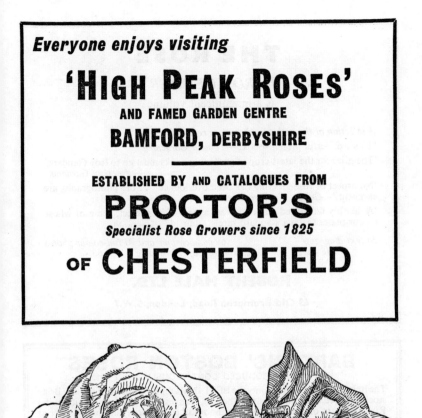

VISIT OUR ROSE GARDENS

and see many thousands of roses in bloom, beautifully displayed in 3½ acres.
If unable to call, write for your free copy of our latest Rose Catalogue showing 16 pages
of life-size plates in full colour, including the following varieties: Red Devil, Red Gold, Jubilant,
Bobby Lucas, Santa Fé, City of Leeds, Jan Spek, Ernest H. Morse, Grandpa Dickson,
Goldgleam, Apricot Nectar, Handel (Climber), Schoolgirl (Climber), etc.

KENILWORTH RD. - HAMPTON-IN-ARDEN - SOLIHULL - WARWICKSHIRE
on main A.452 Stonebridge–Kenilworth Road   Phone: H. in A. 2866 & 2270

WATKINS ROSES LTD

235

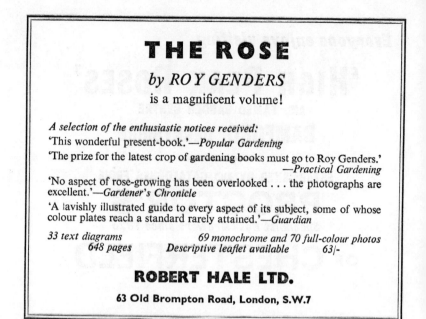

THE ROSE

by *ROY GENDERS*

is a magnificent volume!

A selection of the enthusiastic notices received:

'This wonderful present-book.'—*Popular Gardening*

'The prize for the latest crop of gardening books must go to Roy Genders.'
—*Practical Gardening*

'No aspect of rose-growing has been overlooked . . . the photographs are excellent.'—*Gardener's Chronicle*

'A lavishly illustrated guide to every aspect of its subject, some of whose colour plates reach a standard rarely attained.'—*Guardian*

33 text diagrams   *69 monochrome and 70 full-colour photos*
648 pages   *Descriptive leaflet available*   *63/-*

ROBERT HALE LTD.

63 Old Brompton Road, London, S.W.7

BARTONS' BOSTON ROSES
HAVE BEEN PRODUCED CONTINUOUSLY SINCE 1919

The Barton Nurseries grow only the BEST IN ROSES, budded on Seedling Briar stock (*Rosa canina*). Grown upon the stiff, loamy soils around the Mouth of the River Witham on the Wash, they cannot fail to be hardy and should succeed in your gardens no matter where they may be, anywhere in the British Isles.

Bush Hybrid Teas cultivated in the World's BEST and latest varieties.
Floribundas are grown by the thousand in all the leading colours to make perfect beds for a continuous display right up to the sometimes "mild" December days.
Climbing Hybrid Tea varieties as well as Rambler roses always in stock.
Weeping Standard, Standard Hybrid Tea and Floribunda Standards budded on *Rosa rugosa* stems in the most suitable and scented varieties; Standards soon sell out so early booking is advised.
Seedling Briars (*Rosa canina*) supplied during December for those wishing to bud their own roses.

Visitors are always welcome to come along and see our many thousands of Maiden Roses in older as well as newer varieties.

Members of the Society can receive our catalogue each year by sending their names and addresses for inclusion in our mailing list.

WRITE NOW FOR 1967 CATALOGUE WHICH WILL BE SENT TO YOU FROM JUNE ONWARDS POST FREE

THE BARTON NURSERIES
Rose Tree Specialists
31 Sibsey Road, Boston, Lincolnshire   **Telephone: Boston 2916**

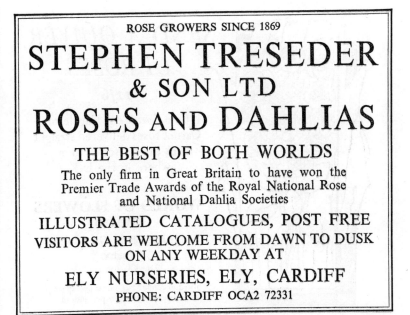

ROSE GROWERS SINCE 1869

STEPHEN TRESEDER
& SON LTD
ROSES AND DAHLIAS

THE BEST OF BOTH WORLDS

The only firm in Great Britain to have won the
Premier Trade Awards of the Royal National Rose
and National Dahlia Societies

ILLUSTRATED CATALOGUES, POST FREE

VISITORS ARE WELCOME FROM DAWN TO DUSK
ON ANY WEEKDAY AT

ELY NURSERIES, ELY, CARDIFF

PHONE: CARDIFF OCA2 72331

ERNEST H. MORSE

*is without doubt the Finest Red Rose in commerce.
Its perfume is unsurpassed, combined with habit of growth,
no weak stems. This variety has come to stay*

PRICE, AUTUMN 1967, 8s. 6d. each, 96s. dozen.

AWARDED: *THE TRIAL GROUND CERTIFICATE
CERTIFICATE OF MERIT
GOLD MEDAL 1965*

*Many more of the choicest varieties in cultivation
are listed in the New Catalogue issued early August 1967.*

APPLY: **HENRY MORSE & SONS,
WESTFIELD NURSERIES,
EATON, NORWICH,**
Phone: 54259   **NOR. 65.F**

237

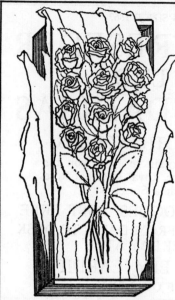

SEND A QUIVER OF ROSES

12/6

One dozen cut Carole or Garnet roses delivered straight from the nurseries to anywhere in the U.K.

Write:

WORLD OF FLOWERS
LIMITED
St. John's Rd., Gt. Clacton, Essex
Tel.: Clacton 21181

also 2 dozen for 24/-, or monthly supply roses/freesias £7 per annum

---

For a Perfect Velvet Carpet

for your ROSES
—YOU NEED D.B.&T's
LAWN SEED

TRIPLE TESTED *for Quality, Purity and Germination.*

ACCURATELY BLENDED *for perfection of Colour and Texture.*

D.B.&T's 'CUMBERLAND' MIXTURE (*Free of Ryegrass and Coarse Grasses*) **Produces a dense, evergreen velvet lawn of permanent beauty.** Composed entirely of the new brilliant green, bred strain of "High-light" Chewings Fescue, together with Certified Brown Top and genuine Cumberland Marsh Fescue—all dwarf fine-leaved grasses. Sow 1½ oz. per sq. yd.

Per lb. 10/-   **14 lb. and over 9/6 lb.**   **28 lb. and over 9/- lb.**

All seed dressed with Non-poisonous Bird-repellent.   **OTHER MIXTURES FROM 3/- lb.**
FULL CATALOGUE OF LAWN AND OTHER SEEDS POST FREE ON REQUEST.

DICKSON, BROWN & TAIT LTD.
Seedsmen for over 140 Years

Dept. R, TIMPERLEY, ALTRINCHAM, CHESHIRE.

CALLERS WELCOME. Showrooms near Timperley Electric Station. **Tel.: SALE 2214**

Willik
roses & shrubs

Our showground and nursery are always open for visitors

FREE CATALOGUE AVAILABLE ON REQUEST

WILLIK BROS. LIMITED
NURSERYMEN, REARSBY, SYSTON, LEICESTER. TEL: REARSBY 206

with ROLCUT to prune... a perfect bloom

ROLCUT

Rolcut Secateurs give a lifetime of satisfaction. Special after-sales servicing includes replacement parts, should they be required.

Rolcut range of efficient pruning tools includes: Secateurs – Bush Pruners – Tree Loppers and Pruning Saws.

ROLCUT SECATEURS, rec. prices from: 15/3d. Model No. 1, illustrated, rec. retail price 17/6d.

ROLCUT LIMITED

239

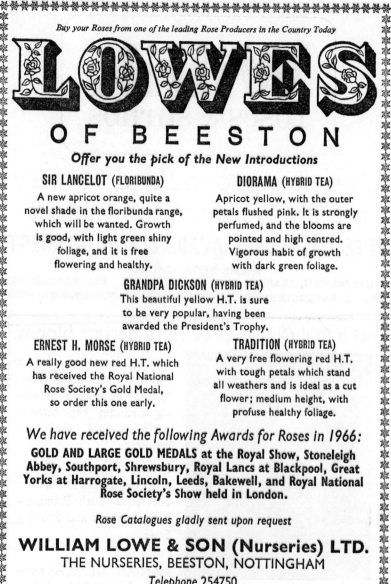

Buy your Roses from one of the leading Rose Producers in the Country Today

LOWES

OF BEESTON

Offer you the pick of the New Introductions

SIR LANCELOT (FLORIBUNDA)

A new apricot orange, quite a
novel shade in the floribunda range,
which will be wanted. Growth
is good, with light green shiny
foliage, and it is free
flowering and healthy.

DIORAMA (HYBRID TEA)

Apricot yellow, with the outer
petals flushed pink. It is strongly
perfumed, and the blooms are
pointed and high centred.
Vigorous habit of growth
with dark green foliage.

GRANDPA DICKSON (HYBRID TEA)

This beautiful yellow H.T. is sure
to be very popular, having been
awarded the President's Trophy.

ERNEST H. MORSE (HYBRID TEA)

A really good new red H.T. which
has received the Royal National
Rose Society's Gold Medal,
so order this one early.

TRADITION (HYBRID TEA)

A very free flowering red H.T.
with tough petals which stand
all weathers and is ideal as a cut
flower; medium height, with
profuse healthy foliage.

We have received the following Awards for Roses in 1966:

**GOLD AND LARGE GOLD MEDALS at the Royal Show, Stoneleigh
Abbey, Southport, Shrewsbury, Royal Lancs at Blackpool, Great
Yorks at Harrogate, Lincoln, Leeds, Bakewell, and Royal National
Rose Society's Show held in London.**

Rose Catalogues gladly sent upon request

WILLIAM LOWE & SON (Nurseries) LTD.

THE NURSERIES, BEESTON, NOTTINGHAM

Telephone 254750

Printed and bound by Hazell Watson & Viney Ltd., Aylesbury, Bucks.
Monochrome and colour gravure plates printed by Clarke & Sherwell Ltd.,
Northampton